ET   3574   2

THE VARIETIES OF
HUMAN PHYSIQUE

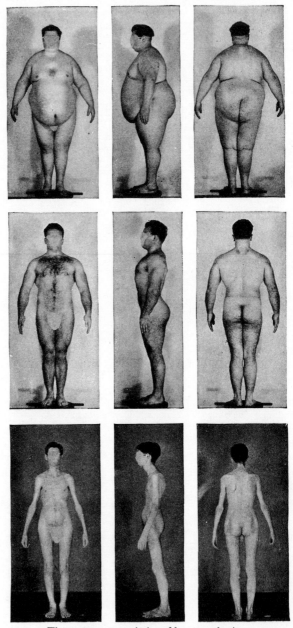

Three extreme varieties of human physique

THE VARIETIES OF
HUMAN PHYSIQUE

AN INTRODUCTION TO
CONSTITUTIONAL PSYCHOLOGY

by

WILLIAM SHELDON, Ph.D., M.D.

With

S. S. STEVENS, Ph.D.
HARVARD UNIVERSITY

and

W. B. TUCKER, M.D.
UNIVERSITY OF CHICAGO

0777 1

HAFNER PUBLISHING COMPANY
DARIEN, CONN.
1970

3574

Copyright© 1940, by Harper & Row, Publishers

Originally Published 1940

Reprinted 1963
2nd Reprint with corrections 1970

Published by Arrangement with William Sheldon

Printed and Published by
Hafner Publishing Company, Inc.
260 Heights Road
Darien, Conn. 06820

Library of Congress Catalog Card Number 63-22610

All Rights Reserved

Printed in the U.S.A.

To

EARNEST A. HOOTON

whose studies in physical anthropology
have vitalized constitutional research

CONTENTS

PREFACE   XI

I. INTRODUCTION AND SUMMARY   I
     A Summary

II. THE MAIN HISTORICAL THREAD   10
     Early Studies, the Italian Anthropometrists
     Viola's Morphological Index
     Kretschmer's Studies of Types
     Review of the Status of the Problem

III. DEVELOPMENT OF THE TECHNIQUE OF SOMATOTYPING   29
     The Photographic Technique
     Identification of the Components
     Morphological Characteristics of the Three Extremes
     Check Lists of Inspectional Criteria (Male)
     Application of the Check List. Anthroposcopy
     The Problem of the Anthropometric Objectification
       of the Anthroposcopic Method
     The Measurements Used
     The Final Construction of the Scales
     The Number of Somatotypes
     The Possibility of Using Other Numbers of Somatotypes
     Note on the Somatotyping of Women
     Secondary Variations

IV. HOW TO PROCEED IN SOMATOTYPING   80
     The Procedure of Somatotyping
     Special Notes and Cautions
     Training of the Investigator
     Somatotyping without Anthroposcopy
     Labor and Cost

V. SOME THEORETICAL CONSIDERATIONS   108
     The Choice of Variables
     Scales for the Measurement of Morphological
       Components
     A Geometrical Representation of the Somatotypes
     The Independence of the Components

vii

0777147

The Surface Approximated by the Somatotypes
A Possible Correction of the Component Scales
Distribution of the Population against the Somatotypes
Summary of the Arguments for and against a
   Correction of the Component Scales

VI. DESCRIPTION OF THE SOMATOTYPES   133
The Sevens in Ectomorphy
The Sixes in Ectomorphy
The Fives in Ectomorphy
The Fours in Ectomorphy
The Threes in Ectomorphy
The Twos in Ectomorphy
The Ones in Ectomorphy

VII. TOWARD A CONSTITUTIONAL PSYCHOLOGY   208
The Problem of Norms
The Question of the Permanence of the Somatotype
The Problem of Constitutional Weight Standards and
   the Prediction of the Individual's Physical Future
The Influence of Heredity
The Influence of Endocrine Function
The Relation of Physical Constitution to Temperament
The Relation of Constitution to Mental Disorder
The Problem of the Relation between Mental Conflict
   and Dysplasia
The Relation of Constitution to Clinical Study and to
   Immunity
The Problem of Differential Food Needs
The Problem of Differential Dress and Differential
   Furniture for Constitutionally Different Personalities
Constitutional Factors in Sexuality and Mating
The Problem of Constitution as Related to Crime and
   Delinquency
The Problem of the Differential Education of Children
The Problem of Early Emotional Entanglements
Conclusion

APPENDIX 1.   TABLES FOR SOMATOTYPING   257

APPENDIX 2.   NINE SOMATOTYPES OF WOMEN   280

BIBLIOGRAPHY   290

INDEX   309

ILLUSTRATIONS

Three extreme varieties of human physique   *Frontispiece*

Fig. 1A. Extreme Endomorphy (a 711)   *Facing p.*   6

Fig. 1B. Extreme Mesomorphy (a 171)   "   6

Fig. 1C. Extreme Ectomorphy (a 117)   "   7

Fig. 2. Showing the locations on the body at which the 17 diameters are measured   *Page* 55

Fig. 3. Showing the percentage of the male population characterized by different amounts of dysplasia   " 69

Fig. 4. Showing the number of cases in 1,000 having various degrees of dysplasia within each of the three components   " 72

Fig. 5A. Two individuals of the same somatotype, 442, showing different degrees of gynandromorphy   *Facing p.* 74

Fig. 5B. Two individuals of different somatotype showing different degrees of gynandromorphy   " 75

Fig. 6A. Case P   " 82

Fig. 6B. Case Q   " 82

Fig. 7. Scatter diagrams showing the correlation between the anthroposcopic estimates of somatotype   *Page* 101

Fig. 8. A machine for determining the somatotype from anthropometric measurements   *Facing p.* 104

Fig. 9. Three perspective views of a cluster of blocks representing the geometrical distribution of 70 of the somatotypes   *Page* 117

Fig. 10. Showing a two-dimensional distribution of the somatotypes   " 118

ix

Fig. 11.   A curve showing the relation of the compo-
            nent scale to a scale which would elimi-
            nate the curvature of the three-dimen-
            sional surface near which the somato-
            types lie   *Page* 125

Fig. 12.   Curve showing the theoretical distribution
            of a "normal" population against one of
            the component scales   "   128

Fig. 13.   The actual distribution of the population
            against the three component scales   "   130

Figs. 14 to 89.   Plates illustrating various of
            the somatotypes as they appear at
            college age   *Following p.* 133

Fig. 90.   Nomograph for handling the anthro-
            pometric data   *Page* 279

Figs. 91 to 99.   Nine somatotypes of women   *Pages* 281 *to* 289

PREFACE

IN THE book *Psychology and the Promethean Will* (Harpers, 1936) the optimistic proposition was put forward that psychology may in the course of time prove useful. It was suggested that to be useful, psychology needs first of all to bring system and order into the description of basic differences among human beings. From such a point of view the first task of psychology seems to be that of standardizing a method for describing quantitatively the varying physical endowments of individuals. In order to systematize the science of human behavior, we must start with some kind of descriptive classification of the behaving structure: the physical constitution. The present volume provides a three-dimensional system for the description of human physique.

But the morphological classification of human beings is merely a means to an end. If this present catalogue of the varieties of human physique provided us with no more than the sizes and shapes of men we should have to confess bankruptcy before the critic who says "So what?" Actually this study opens many new avenues to research—avenues that converge from many directions upon the study of the individual. The work of several investigators in the fields of anthropology, immunology, clinical medicine, personality and temperament comprises what is known as the Constitutional Research Project. The Project's appointed task is that of providing frames of reference for the study of basic individual differences. To the psychologist, the educator, the clinician, the anthropologist, the criminologist and the actuary, a systematic schema for the description and classification of human beings is of obvious importance, and it is hoped that the present study will provide such a schema at the level of human morphology.

In a second volume—*Physique and Temperament*—we propose to present an analogous schema for the description and classification of temperament.

Most of the work described in the present volume was done at the University of Chicago and at Harvard University. So many individuals have contributed to it, in one way or another, that any effort to distribute acknowledgments would be tedious. Yet certain obligations are of such a nature that they need to be mentioned. The later phases of the study, since 1935, have been supported chiefly by the William C. Whitney Foundation. There is a debt of gratitude to the Departments of Student Health at the University of Chicago, Wisconsin, Northwestern, Oberlin and Harvard. The 4000 students upon whom the morphological descriptions have been standardized were recruited from these five institutions of higher learning. Administrative heads at the University of Chicago Clinics, at Wisconsin General Hospital, and at the New York Psychiatric Institute have been generous in making clinical and autopsy material available. Dr. C. W. Dupertuis of the New York Presbyterian Hospital has done a large share of the work of analyzing the data on 1000 of the cases.

Dr. Stevens has collaborated in the general preparation of the manuscript and has contributed especially to the discussion of the mathematical implications of the method. He also contrived the machine for determining somatotypes from anthropometric measurements. Dr. Tucker has worked, during a period of several years, on the task of developing and applying the statistical procedures upon which somatotyping rests.

For critical readings of the manuscript, whole or in part, we are grateful to Drs. E. A. Hooton, Sheldon and E. T. Glueck, E. G. Boring, K. S. Lashley and G. W. Allport of Harvard, and to Drs. O. H. Robertson and M. H. Bro of Chicago. Mr. Robert Waldrop of Chicago has lent valuable assistance at several points.

W. H. S.

Harvard University
March 25, 1940

THE VARIETIES OF
HUMAN PHYSIQUE

CHAPTER I

INTRODUCTION AND SUMMARY

IT IS commonly said that no two human bodies are exactly alike. To this statement it might be added that the ways in which two bodies may differ are endless. Equally obvious is the fact that no two temperaments or personalities are identical—their modes of variation seem infinite. Our friends differ in appearance and in the way they behave. This variety is itself of some interest, but a more important problem is this: Do those who look most alike behave most alike? Does a particular sort of temperament go with a definite physique? Can we predict a man's likes and dislikes by measuring his body?

This is a problem of great antiquity and scarcely a single generation in recorded history has failed to probe some aspect of it. Fervent assertions have been followed by violent denials. Simple rules and elaborate schemas have been proposed for classifying physiques and temperaments. The enthusiasm of one generation has withered under the cold scrutiny of the next, but despite the repeated failure of the schemas of its proponents, the idea of a fundamental connection between physique and temperament has persisted through the ages. That definite personalities attach to definite physiques is implicit in the work of many artists, caricaturists, dramatists, and novelists.

The study of the psychological aspects of human behavior as they are related to the morphology and physiology of the body is a central problem of what may be called *constitutional psychology*.[1]

[1] The term "constitution," as it is used in this book, refers in a general way

1

Constitutional psychology questions the wisdom of study-ing mental function in isolation from morphology, mor-phology apart from physiological processes, and physiological functions as though the body had no shape and could not think. Constitutional psychology shares a growing conviction that the hope and promise of a useful study of personality lies in a program of research which will keep a perspective upon the whole individual. It is this conviction that motivates the study, a part of which is here presented.

Human personality throughout its whole range of manifes-tation presents a complex system of more or less related aspects, of more or less interdependent variables. It is a part of the task of the scientific student of personality—call him psychobiologist, constitutional psychologist or whatever one may prefer—to make sense of these interacting variables. But how is he to proceed? Obviously, his first problem is the selection of the variables he intends to study.

In this volume human personality is broadly conceived as the dynamic organization of the cognitive, affective, conative, physiological, and morphological aspects of the individual. Under this definition the study of personality concerns the structure of the body and the function of its organs, as well as the manner of a person's thinking, feeling, and willing. An

---

to the whole pattern of elemental determinative or individualizing charac-teristics which lie behind personality. Constitution refers to those aspects of the individual which are relatively more fixed and unchanging—morphology, physiology, endocrine function, etc.—and may be contrasted with those aspects which are relatively more labile and susceptible to modification by environ-mental pressures, i.e., habits, social attitudes, education, etc. Further delimi-tation and precision in the definition of constitution would perhaps prove unfruitful at this early stage of investigation. An important product of the scientific process is the continuous revision and clarification of definitions, and it is most likely that sustained research in a field imperfectly defined will eventually operate to crystallize the defining criteria of its subject matter.

Although by constitution we refer to the relatively stable aspects of a person's endowment, we do not mean to insist, and indeed do not believe, that the human constitution is an altogether fixed and unalterable hereditary entity. We mean by constitution the basic, underlying pattern of the living individual, as it is at the time when the individual is studied. That constitu-tion is closely determined by heredity is highly probable, but we do not know that it is entirely so determined.

adequate study of personality requires an integrated attack upon all these aspects of the individual. Admittedly, this definition of personality is inclusive to the point of vagueness, and many will prefer a more restricted usage. Numerous, indeed, are the alternative conceptions among which one can choose.[2] For our own part, we propose no intolerance in the matter of terminology, for it is the conception rather than its name which concerns us most. And the conception basic to the present study is that the adjustments of man to his environment require, for their description and explanation, the selection and functional analysis of "meaningful" variables at all levels of investigation from morphology to cognition.

A study so conceived is clearly too huge for a single volume—perhaps even for a single lifetime. Where, then, should one begin? Actually, almost every phase of the problem has already been probed in some fashion or other, but points of view have been as numerous as investigators and no single conceptual framework has emerged to facilitate coordinated research.

It seems reasonable to suppose that a unifying conceptual schema could most profitably seek anchorage in the solid flesh and bone of the individual. Perhaps if we can discern the *significant* variables at the level of morphology and invent scales to measure them, we can devise a schema for depicting their formal interrelations. This schema may then provide a frame of reference for the analysis of variables at other levels: physiological function, susceptibility to disease, manifestations of temperament, social adjustment, and so on.

This volume, then, presents the results of an effort to lay

[2] For an historical review and a critical evaluation of definitions of personality, see Allport, G. W., *Personality*. (New York: Holt, 1937.) In elaborating his own definition, Allport insists that "personality is neither exclusively mental nor exclusively neural. The organization entails the operation of both body and mind, inextricably fused into a personal unity" (p. 48). Consonant with this conception, the thesis of the present work is that the proper approach to personality is through a study of the body, a study of the "mind," and a study of the functional interdependence of the variables in terms of which each is described.

the foundation, in morphological description, for a systematic study of those aspects of human beings important to personality and to clinical problems. Variables for the classification and description of human physiques have been identified, practical methods for scaling these variables have been devised, and a beginning has been made in the correlation of these variables with other aspects of human behavior.

A SUMMARY

A brief summary of this study is first in order. The problem set was that of discovering first-order criteria for the classification of human physiques. We have obvious criteria for differentiating man from the rest of the animal kingdom and for separating one sex from the other. All members of the same sex are not alike, however. They differ in innumerable ways, and in terms of a host of indices they could be sorted and classified. The challenge lies in finding those aspects for grading human physiques which will produce the most fruitful and "meaningful" schema. These aspects are what we mean by first-order variables. Whether or not, at the level of morphology, we have found these first-order variables must remain the decision of future research.

Three primary aspects of bodily constitution were selected for study, because they appear to provide first-order criteria for differentiation among individuals. These three aspects appear also to behave in bodily morphology as though each were a *component* of structure—something which enters in different amounts into the making of a body.

The identification of these three aspects is simple and straightforward. In order to facilitate the procedure and standardize the technique, the subjects were photographed from three angles. The experimenter could then, on the same print, view the body—front, back, and side. From a series of 4,000 photographs (of men of college age) it was an easy task to select those which appeared to manifest the most extreme variations in physique—those which departed most widely from the "average" male form. Three of these extremes stand out with especial clarity. Their departure from the "average" ·is clearly in terms of a major and not a minor morphological aspect. They seem each to be made of different stuff. Figure 1 shows an example of each of these three variants.

A study of many examples of each extreme variant revealed criteria for identifying the detailed aspects which the members of each extreme group have in common and which set them apart from the other extremes. These criteria serve to identify the components: a component is defined in terms of those aspects of morphological variation which differentiate one of the extreme variants from the others.

The first component, dominant in Fig. 1 A, we call *endomorphy.*

The second component, dominant in Fig. 1 B, we call *mesomorphy.*

The third component, dominant in Fig. 1 C, we call *ectomorphy.*

Endomorphy means relative predominance of soft roundness throughout the various regions of the body. When endomorphy is dominant the digestive viscera are massive and tend relatively to dominate the bodily economy. The digestive viscera are derived principally from the *endodermal* embryonic layer.

Mesomorphy means relative predominance of muscle, bone, and connective tissue. The mesomorphic physique is normally heavy, hard, and rectangular in outline. Bone and muscle are prominent and the skin is made thick by a heavy underlying connective tissue. The entire bodily economy is dominated, relatively, by tissues derived from the *mesodermal* embryonic layer.

Ectomorphy means relative predominance of linearity and fragility. In proportion to his mass, the ectomorph has the greatest surface area and hence relatively the greatest sensory exposure to the outside world. Relative to his mass he also has the largest brain and central nervous system. In a sense, therefore, his bodily economy is relatively dominated by tissues derived from the *ectodermal* embryonic layer.

These three basic components were chosen as first-order variables, and with the aid of extensive check lists of their characteristics, the 4,000 photographs were arranged in rank orders, one order for each component, on the basis of the degree to which each physique exhibited the aspects of the component. Actually the ranking was performed for each of five different regions of the body—a total of fifteen rank orders. In other words, the components were regarded as *continuous* variables of which different physiques can exhibit different amounts. Then, to each ordered series we assigned numerals. The numeral 1 was assigned to the least degree of a component exhibited by any member of the population of 4,000 men of college age. The numeral 7 was assigned to the maximum manifestation, and to the amount which appeared halfway between 1 and 7 the numeral 4 was applied.

In order to objectify the procedure, as well as to facilitate the placement of the intermediate numerals along the scale for each component, we next made anthropometric measurements on the photographs. From 17 measurements of diameters, plus a factor determined by the subject's height and weight, we obtained 18 anthropometric indices. These indices were those retained from a large group tried out for the purpose, because they served best to differentiate the extreme variants, as well as those physiques lying midway along the scales. Using inspectional criteria (anthroposcopy) and aided by the anthropometric indices, we were able to complete the assignment of numerals to the scales for the three components.

This procedure finally made it possible to designate each subject by three numerals, one for his position relative to the scale for each component. Thus, a 711 is a physique extreme in endomorphy and at a minimum in the other two components. The 444 is the individual characterized by being at the mid-point of all three scales. The use of the 18 anthro-

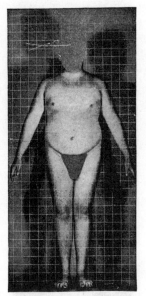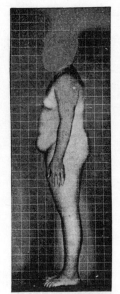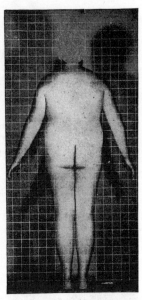

FIG. 1 A. Extreme endomorphy (a 711)

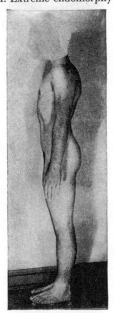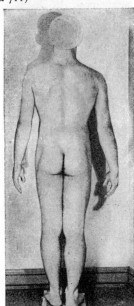

FIG. 1 B. Extreme mesomorphy (a 171)

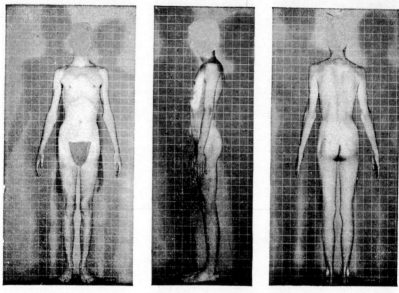

FIG. 1 C. Extreme ectomorphy (a 117)

pometric indices makes the assignment of these numerals a thoroughly objective procedure. (Note: read the somatotype designations as three separate numerals—not as three-digit numbers. Thus 711 should be read as seven-one-one and not as seven hundred and eleven.)

The patterning of the morphological components, as expressed by the three numerals, is called the *somatotype* of the individual. After examining and measuring 4,000 physiques we were able to describe and illustrate 76 different somatotypes. It is possible, however, that other somatotypes will be discovered, because within certain restricted limits the three components behave as independent variables.

In addition to the three basic components, certain second-order variables were isolated and studied:

Dysplasia is the aspect of disharmony between different regions of the same physique. When, for example, a body is of one somatotype in the region of the head and neck and of another somatotype in the legs and trunk, the individual is spoken of as dysplastic. Dysplasia is measured in terms of the differences among the somatotype designations of the five regions of the body.

Gynandromorphy refers to the bisexuality of a physique. Members of each sex exhibit more or less of the secondary characteristics of the opposite sex. The prominence of these secondary indications of bisexuality can be gauged against a 7-point scale.

Texture is a secondary aspect in terms of which physiques obviously vary, but objective defining criteria have not yet been determined for this variable. Nevertheless, photographs can be rank-ordered according to the "fineness" or "coarseness" of the structure displayed.

Hirsutism refers to the hairiness of a physique. Physiques can be scaled according to the abundance of body hair.

There are numerous other secondary aspects which remain to be investigated and which may prove of great importance in the scientific study of man. Some of these other variables have already been rather thoroughly explored by the anthropologists.

The criteria and the procedure for somatotyping, as presented in later chapters, provide a practicable, objective method for segregating and classifying the varieties of human physique. The use of continuous scales for the gradation of aspects of morphological variation establishes a descriptive frame of reference which may prove to be of basic utility in the prosecution of research in physiology, medicine, anthropology and psychology. Chapter VII gives a preview of the kind of clinical and psychological studies in which the theory of somatotypes is relevant.

A more thorough inquiry into these clinical and psychological problems will be undertaken in a second volume. Here it might be pointed out, however, that an analogous component analysis has been made at the level of motivation and temperament. Basic aspects of temperament have been identified, objectified by the method of tests and interviews, and scaled on 7-point scales. These components we refer to as *viscerotonia, somatotonia,* and *cerebrotonia.*[3]

Viscerotonia is roughly identifiable with love of comfort, relaxation, sociability, conviviality, and sometimes with gluttony. It is the motivational organization dominated by the gut and by the function of anabolism. Somatotonia is the motivational pattern dominated by the will to exertion, exercise and vigorous self-expression. It is the drive toward dominance of the functions of the *soma.* Cerebrotonia refers to the attentional and inhibitory aspect of temperament. In the economy of the cerebrotonic individual the sensory and central nervous systems appear to play dominant roles. He is tense, hyperattentional and under strong inhibitory con-

[3] Here as elsewhere the question of terminology has been a difficult one. In place of the terms just listed we have sometimes used *endotonia, mesotonia,* and *ectotonia.* One serious objection to these terms is that they seem to imply a more direct correspondence with the morphological components than appears actually to exist. The suffix -tonia has been quite widely used in such terms as vagotonia, sympatheticotonia, etc., to refer to an overresponsiveness of some aspect or element in a physiological system.

trol. His tendency is toward symbolic expression rather than direct action.

These components of temperament appear to correlate with patterns of somatotypes, and like the morphological components, they combine in various proportions in different individuals. They behave, within limits, as independent variables.

CHAPTER II

THE MAIN HISTORICAL THREAD

A THOROUGH historical summary of a subject whose roots go back as far as there is any record of man's concern with man, and in whose service many thousand pages have been written, lies beyond the ambitions of this book. The story abounds in fascination, but here we shall content ourselves with only a scant outline. We shall here indicate approximately from what ancestry the present study is lineally descended and how the early steps of the investigation were guided by the work of others. We hope also to show why, finally, it was necessary to break with the methods and preconceptions of the past and attack from a fresh point of view.

To those interested in the general background of constitutional research, an annotated bibliography of its major books and monographs is presented in the appendix (p. 300). To those interested in a more thorough coverage of the field a forthcoming bibliography by Tucker and Lessa[1] is recommended.

EARLY STUDIES, THE ITALIAN ANTHROPOMETRISTS

The history of human thought about most matters appears to have begun with the postulation of a polar dichotomy in which two tendencies offset and oppose each other. This is as true of man's notions of human morphology as it is of his belief in good and evil. Hippocrates[2] designated two fundamental physical types, and called them the *phthisic habitus*

[1] Tucker, W. B. and Lessa, W. A. Man: A Constitutional Investigation, *Quart. Rev. Biol.*, 1940, 15, nos. 3 and 4.
[2] Hippocrates. *On Ancient Medicine: the Genuine Works of Hippocrates*, translated into English by F. Adams. New York: Wm. Wood.

and the *apoplectic habitus*. The phthisic had a long, thin body, dominated by the vertical dimension. The apoplectic was the short, thick individual, strong in the horizontal dimension. Hippocrates thought that the phthisic physique was particularly susceptible to tuberculosis (phthisis). He knew that the thick, solid individual carried a predisposition for diseases of the vascular system leading to apoplexy. This dichotomy is the prototype for the well-known modern conception of *asthenic* and *pyknic* types, as described by Kretschmer and others.

In 1828 Rostan[3] published a famous treatise describing three essentially different types of physical constitution. These became known as the *type digestif, type musculaire,* and *type cérébral.* This terminology, however, was not new with Rostan. It had been used at least as early as 1797, by another Frenchman (Halle). Gall and Spurzheim,[4] two French anatomists contemporary with Rostan, and known today chiefly as the founders of the school of phrenology, were themselves strongly influenced by the threefold conception of human constitution then prevalent in France.

After Gall and Spurzheim, many schools of phrenology and character reading flourished far into the middle of the nineteenth century. Nearly all of them fell under the French influence and assumed the existence of three basic types of human temperament, which in general were believed to correlate with physical types. The following quotation from Samuel Wells[5] is a fair sample of the phrenological literature of that period, which, although of questionable scientific validity, is rich in human insight.

There are in the human body three grand classes or systems

[3] Rostan, L. *Cours élémentaire d'hygiène* (2 vols., 2nd ed.). Paris, 1828. Rostan's *type respiratoire* is generally regarded as a mixture of his *type musculaire* and his *type cérébral.*

[4] Gall, Franz Joseph, and Spurzheim, J. G. *Recherches sur le Système nerveux.* Paris, 1809.

[5] Wells, Samuel R. *How to Read Character.* New York: Fowler and Wells, 1869.

of organs, each having its special function in the general economy, namely: the *Motive* or Mechanical system; the *Vital* or Nutritive system; and the *Mental* or Nervous system. On this natural basis rests our doctrine of the temperaments, three classes of organs just mentioned, namely:

1. The Motive Temperament;
2. The Vital Temperament; and
3. The Mental Temperament.

Each of these temperaments is determined by the predominance of the class of organs from which it takes its name. The first is marked by a superior development of the osseous and muscular systems, forming the locomotive apparatus; in the second the vital organs, the principal seat of which is in the trunk, give the tone to the organization; while in the third, the brain and nervous system exert the controlling power.

Clearly the phrenologists and characterologists of seventy years ago had the rudiments of a plan in mind. They were applying the cumulative wisdom of observation in a fairly systematic manner, but their system leaned heavily upon subjective judgment. Nevertheless, within its limits the scheme worked. It is not unlikely that Mr. Wells was able to size up a human being with shrewdness, possibly with rare insight.

The generation which followed felt the impact of a new scientific spirit. Darwin, Huxley, Herbert Spencer, and their followers had prepared the ground, and the idea of applying *measuremental*, statistical methods to the problems of human life was growing lustily. Classification, measurement, and correlation were becoming the order of the day. Phrenology was no match for this new crusade. It had neither calipers nor coefficients of correlation, and so phrenology fell upon evil days.

The new science of anthropometry was a descendant in the third generation from a discredited ancestral phrenology. This new field of anthropometry was first explored by a group of Italian anthropologists. About 1885, di Giovanni founded his school of clinical anthropology at Padua, and

his pupil Viola,[6] taking a lead from the earlier anthropometric studies of Beneke,[7] and di Giovanni himself,[8] carried
out a long series of anthropometric studies. Viola went on to
differentiate three morphological types, which he called the
microsplanchnic, normosplanchnic, and *macrosplanchnic*
types. The names are descriptive. The microsplanchnics are
persons with small trunks and relatively long limbs, while
the macrosplanchnics have large, heavy bodies and relatively
short limbs. As Viola himself points out, the microsplanchnic
is the old *phthisic habitus,* and the macrosplanchnic is the
apoplectic habitus. Viola's normosplanchnic is merely an intermediate variation. Hence the important differentiation
which Rostan had made between the digestive and muscular
types is for the time being lost, although destined soon to
be revived by Kretschmer.

VIOLA'S MORPHOLOGICAL INDEX

To arrive at a measure of trunk volume, Viola took eight
trunk measurements and the length of one arm and one leg.

He obtained a *thoracic index* by multiplying the length of the
sternum by the *transverse thoracic diameter,* and by the *anteroposterior thoracic diameter.* Next he derived the *upper abdominal
index* by multiplying the *xipho-epigastric* measurement by the
transverse epigastric diameter. Then the *lower abdominal index*
was obtained by multiplying the *pubo-epigastric distance* by the
transverse pelvic diameter, and by the *antero-posterior epigastric
diameter* (a measurement which he used twice). These three indices were added together to produce the *trunk value.* Finally
the *value* of the *limbs* was obtained by adding the length of an
arm to the length of a leg. Microsplanchny and macrosplanchny
are then indicated by the *morphological index,* which is simply

---

[6] Viola, G. *Le Legge de Correlazione Morfologica dei Tippi Individuali.*
Padova, 1909.

[7] Beneke, F. W. *Die anatomische Grundlagen der Konstitutionsanomalien
des Menschen.* Marburg, 1878.

[8] di Giovanni, A. *Clinical Commentaries Deduced from the Morphology of
the Human Body,* translated into English from the 2nd Italian edition by
J. J. Eyre. London and New York, 1919.

a fraction in which the *value of the limbs* is the numerator and the *value of the trunk* the denominator. A high morphological index indicates microsplanchny and a low one macrosplanchny.

In Northern Italy Viola found that of a group of 400 subjects 24 per cent were microsplanchnic, 48 per cent normosplanchnic, and 28 per cent were macrosplanchnic.

Sante Naccarati, a brilliant Italian working at Columbia University in 1920, had been a pupil of Viola and had studied the older anthropologists with great diligence. He was convinced that in this elemental morphological approach lay the key to a scientific human typology. Two new and promising devices had been added to the scientific equipment of the psychologist: the correlation coefficient and the mental test. The correlational tide was beginning to run high. Doctoral theses were being written with a calculator, a rating scale, and a mental test. Already scores of studies had been published on the correlation between physical measurements and "intelligence." The correlations were almost invariably low, but persistently there appeared a low positive relation between preponderance of vertical measurements and mental ability, and also a low negative relation between lateral or horizontal preponderance and mental ability. A summary[9] of this literature lists more than thirty studies reporting some variation of this finding.

Naccarati was persuaded that a true relationship existed here, and he felt that the reason for the extremely low correlations might lie in the fact that the anthropometric measurements dealt only with isolated parts of bodily structure, such as height, neck length, face length, head size, nose length, and so on. Every one of these measurements had been reported by some investigator or other as showing a low positive correlation with intelligence. Naccarati believed that the morphological index ought to show a "real" relationship to intelligence. He had fully accepted Viola's thesis that the

[9] Sheldon, W. H. Morphologic Types and Mental Ability (doctoral dissertation). University of Chicago, 1926.

microsplanchnic is a hyperevolute and more intelligent type, whereas the macrosplanchnic is hypoevolute and less intelligent. In support of this idea Naccarati, following Viola, cited the following data[10] (see also[11]):

All the characteristics which differentiate the newborn from the adult are found in the macrosplanchnics; all of the characteristics of the adult are found in the microsplanchnics in an exaggerated form. The microsplanchnics in comparison with normosplanchnics show: thorax flatter *in toto,* narrower at the basis and more predominant in volume over the abdomen; umbilicus more distant from the pubis; ribs more inclined; costovertebral angles smaller; heart more vertical . . . lungs longer; lower extremities more developed in comparison with the upper extremities . . . arch of foot more pronounced.

In macrosplanchnics, as in the newborn, the system of vegetative life prevails. . . . The characteristics which liken the macrosplanchnic to the newborn . . . are: relatively larger size of liver, spleen and other abdominal organs; abdomen predominant in volume over the thorax; thorax larger at the base; anteroposterior thoracic diameter larger and predominant over the transverse diameter; less forward inclination of the ribs; costovertebral angles larger; more forward projection of the sternum; lungs shorter . . . lower extremities are relatively short in comparison with the upper extremities; flat foot; broad hands and feet.

Naccarati calculated the morphological indices of several groups of Columbia students, and correlated these data with intelligence as measured by the psychological tests then in vogue. In one group of 75 male students, he found the remarkably high correlation coefficient $+ 0.36$ between morphological index and intelligence test scores. A correlation coefficient of this degree suggested a definite positive relationship between the two factors correlated, although far from the perfect correspondence which would be indicated

[10] Naccarati, S. The morphologic aspect of intelligence. *Arch. Psychol.,* no. 45 (Aug.) 1921.

[11] Naccarati, Sante, and Garrett, H. E. The relation of morphology to temperament. *J. abnorm. soc. Psychol.,* 1924, 19, no. 3.

by a coefficient of + 1.00. Most of the reported correlations between simple physical measurements and mental abilities had been lower than Naccarati's figure.

If now we pause to imagine the great number of variables in human personality which must lie between so gross a physical measurement as morphological index, and so superficial a measurement of conscious behavior as a mental test, Naccarati's findings appear even more striking. He completely ignored all but these two superficial variables and yet found a significant correlation.

At the University of Chicago we set about to test this lead of Naccarati's with a larger number of cases.[12] We duplicated the technique of Viola and measured 450 presumably Caucasian undergraduate students. Two criteria of mental ability were used. These were (1) intelligence test scores and (2) scholastic grades. With this larger group of cases the correlation between morphological index and psychological test scores was + 0.14; that between morphological index and grades, + 0.12.

This was no such result as Naccarati had found, but it was a positive correlation. Something might be there. It seemed worth while to dig further. We studied the correlation of the morphological index with each separate part of the psychological test, and the correlation of each of the measurements entering into the index, with both scholastic grades and psychological test scores. This work revealed nothing. In no case did any of the individual correlations turn out significantly high. The relationship, then, was not to be accounted for by a high correlation between the morphological index and some isolated factor entering into the test score, or between some single factor entering into the index, and mental ability. The possibility of curvilinear regression was considered, and several of the *eta* coefficients

[12] Sheldon, W. H. Morphological types and mental ability. *J. Person. Res.*, 1927, 5, 447-451.

were calculated, but these did not reveal the presence of nonlinear relationships.

Other similar studies had in the meantime been reported, and the trend in all of them was the same. Persistent low correlations had been found between physical structure and various mental traits. Many other investigators had, like Naccarati, conceived the idea that by deriving an index composed of several specific minutely measured bodily factors some cumulative correlational trend might be discerned and relationships of predictive importance might be established. Scores of indices had been calculated, many of them having to do with different measurements about the head and face. The cephalic index (relation of head breadth to head length) and at least twenty different facial indices had been correlated with every sort of test of mental ability. The results were everywhere the same, and on the whole they were uniformly disappointing.

Rating scales for measuring social characteristics had also come into wide use. At Chicago we developed a method for having a selected group of the older members of fraternities carefully rate the younger members as to *sociability, perseverance, leadership, aggressiveness,* and *emotional excitability*.[13] We gave these older raters training in the use and misuse of rating scales before the ratings were made. The results were correlated with the morphological index and with several other bodily indices which we thought might correlate measurably with social personality. Again some low persistent correlations were found, not high enough to be of any predictive value, but too high and too numerous to be due to chance alone. We made one interesting discovery. In this work it was the breadth, or measurements of transverse diameter that appeared to correlate with the social traits, *aggressiveness, leadership* and *sociability*. The general factor of bigness or heaviness showed a definite, low positive cor-

[13] Sheldon, W. H. Social traits and morphological types. *Person. J.*, 1927, vol. 6, no. 1.

relation with all three of these traits. Again, intercorrelations, partial correlations, and careful analysis of specific factors entering into the bodily indices failed to reveal any specific source of these low positive relationships.

There was an insistent notion in some quarters that the face and head might carry the important physical determinants of personality, even though previous investigations had failed to bring to light any high correlations. It had often been suggested that the reason for this failure might lie in the fact that the measurements were small and delicate, and that the differences were so slight that errors might obscure the correlation. We therefore tried to correct this source of error by a photographic method.[14] A chair was constructed with a head rest which could be adjusted to hold the subject's head in a fixed position by contact at four points. It was thereby possible to photograph the head at a fixed distance from the camera, and with both horizontal and vertical movement controlled. The chair was equipped with a swivel device which made it convenient to take both a frontal and a profile photograph without moving the camera or changing the subject's relation to the chair.

The actual measurements were made with fine dividers from an enlarged image projected upon a ground-glass screen. This method enabled the investigator at his leisure to make three-dimensional measurements of any part of the head or face. We used the photographs of one hundred men whose morphological indices had been calculated, and who had also been rated on the five social traits mentioned above. Many measurements were taken, both from the photographs and from the living subjects, and the following indices or ratios were also used in the study:

Cephalic index (head breadth x 100 over head length); *Head volume* (head length x head breadth x head height); *Facial index* (facial breadth x 100 over facial length x 2); *Facial length over*

[14] Sheldon, W. H. Ability and facial measurements. *Person. J.*, 1927, vol. 6, no. 2.

head volume; Facial breadth lower over facial breadth upper; Eye width over head volume; Eye width over facial breadth upper; Eye width over facial breadth lower; Nose length over head volume; Nose length over facial length; Nose length over facial breadth upper; Nose length over facial breadth lower; Forehead projection over chin projection; Nose prominence (the projection of the nose over and above the average projection of the chin and forehead); *Neck thickness over head volume.*

All the measurements and these indices were correlated with the five social traits and with the two criteria of mental ability. The outcome was the same as before. There were no high correlations, but there was that same persistent low correlation between physical, social, and mental traits. There was a fairly clear tendency for all the simple breadth measurements to correlate positively with the four social traits, sociability, perseverance, leadership, and aggressiveness, and most of these measurements showed a low negative correlation both with mental test scores and with emotional excitability. But it was no particular measurement or group of measurements that showed this tendency. It seemed rather to be the phenomenon of simple largeness of feature that produced the relationship. The correlations between the indices and both social traits and mental ability were uniformly low. They revealed nothing beyond what was revealed by the correlations with simple measurements. Indeed, the use of such specific ratios appeared only to obscure a little of what direct correlation there was between simple physical bigness and social traits.

These results were certainly not heartening. We had gone a step beyond the work of predecessors and had demonstrated only too clearly that further progress on this particular trail alone could but complicate and obscure the picture. Specific measurements taken from even the most exact three-dimensional representation of the body structure provided no more of an indication of ability on mental tests than did Viola's crude morphological index, yet both methods yielded the same irritatingly persistent promise that deeper down lay something very interesting.

In 1930 Paterson[15] published a summary of the research that had been reported in this field, and in his concluding chapter (p. 269) he wrote:

Search in the realm of gross anatomy for a physical correlate of intellect has yielded uniformly negative results. It appears that such structural characteristics as height and weight are correlated only slightly with intelligence, narrowly defined. Even measurements of head size and shape are found to be relatively independently variable with respect to intellect, and skeletal development measured by precise X-ray photography yields either zero or low correlations with intelligence. The same may be said of dentition. Physiological development, measured in terms of pubescence, is found to be relatively unrelated to mental development, and so are complicated morphologic indices of bodily build.

Paterson had arrived justifiably at a pessimistic conclusion. That striking optimism of Naccarati and the flush of enthusiasm for correlational anthropometry had paled out in soberer light. It had become clear that the missing vital link between psychology and physical anthropology was not to be found in anthropometry and statistical precision alone, however valuable these two aids might later prove to be.

In the meantime another development had begun which seemed to offer greater prospect than had the correlation coefficient, the calipers, and the mental test. This was the method of clinical observation as employed by the psychiatrist Ernst Kretschmer.

KRETSCHMER'S STUDIES OF TYPES

Following Kraepelin, psychiatrists have found it expedient to describe most of the so-called nonorganic psychoses in terms of two general types, known as *manic-depressive* and *schizophrenic*. The former condition is often referred to as

[15] Paterson, D. G. *Physique and Intellect.* Century Psychology Series. New York: D. Appleton-Century, 1930.

circular insanity, because of the cyclical nature of the disorder. The patient is at one time excited, flushed, expansive,
manic, and at another time profoundly depressed. The extremes sometimes follow one another in rotation. Yet the
patient typically remains well oriented to time and to his
immediate spatial and social environment. In schizophrenia
(split mind) the patient becomes cut off from orientational
reality, and may seem to live in a world of his own creating.
The two extremes are apparently pathological intensifica-
tions of fundamentally divergent types of normal mental
outlook. The intensely social, "extraverted" person becomes
manic-depressive in mental illness, while the "introverted,"
shy, "queer" one tends toward schizophrenia.

Kretschmer made the observation that most of his circular
psychotic patients appeared to belong in the macrosplanchnic
group, whereas schizophrenics were generally microsplanchnic. He did not use this terminology, however, but revived
the Greek terms *pyknic* (compact) and *asthenic* (without
strength) to refer to macrosplanchnic and microsplanchnic
physiques respectively. He also reintroduced the French idea
of a third type, different in kind from the other two. This
he called the *athletic type.*[16]

Note now (Table 1) the recurrent persistence of this fundamental idea of polar types as it crops out in many different
language forms, from Hippocrates's day to our own. In this
table the classifications listed in column 1 correspond approximately with what we call endomorphy, those in column
2 correspond with mesomorphy, and those in columns 3 and
3b, with ectomorphy. Those classifications falling in column
3a appear to represent mixtures of mesomorphy and ectomorphy.

Table 1 presents by no means an exhaustive list. Scores

[16] In later editions of his book Kretschmer abandoned this third type
(athletic) and fell back upon a dichotomy consisting of the two types, pyknic
and leptosomic.

TABLE I

CLASSIFICATIONS OF CONSTITUTIONAL TYPES

Source	Nationality	1	2	3a	3	3b
Hippocrates (460–400 B.C.)	Greek	Habitus apoplecticus (short, thick)			Habitus phthisicus (long, thin)	
Halle (1797)	French	Abdominal	Muscular	Thoracic		Nervous, cephalic
de Troisvèvre (1821)	French	Abdominal	Muscular	Thoracic		Cranial
Rostan (1828)	French	Digestive		Respiratory		Cerebral
Walker (1852)	English	Nutritive beauty (Venus)	Locomotive beauty (Diana)			Mental beauty (Minerva)
Carus (1852)	German	Phlegmatic	Athletic	Asthenic		Cerebral
Wells (1869)	American	Vital	Motive		Mental	
di Giovanni (1877)	Italian	Third combination	Second combination (Plethoric)		First combination (Phthisic)	
Beneke (1878)	German	Rachitic	Carcinomatous		Scrofulous, phthisical	
" -Rokitansky (1878)	German	Hyperplastic	Normal		Hypoplastic	
Huter (1880)	German	Ernährungstypus	Krafttypus		Empfindungstypus	
Manouvrier (1902)	German	Brachyskeletal (Microskeletal)	Mesoskeletal		Macroskeletal	
Stratz (1904)	French	Xantodermic (Racial)	Leucodermic (Racial)		Melanodermic (Racial)	
Virenius (1904)	German	Connective	Muscular	Epithelial	Nervous	
Sigaud (1908)	Russian	Digestive	Muscular	Respiratory	Cerebral	
Bean (1912)	French	Hypo-onto-morph (Hypo-phylo-morph)	Meso-onto-morph (Meso-phylo-morph)		Hyper-onto-morph (Hyper-phylo-morph)	
Bryant and Goldthwait (1915)	American	Herbivorous	Mesoplastic (Normal)		Carnivorous	
Mills (1917)	American	Hypersthenic	Sthenic		Asthenic (Hyposthenic)	
Brugsch (1916)	German	Wide chested	Normal chested		Narrow chested (Asthmatic)	
Viola (1919)	Italian	Megalosplanchnic (Macrosplanchnic)	Normosplanchnic		Microsplanchnic	
Davenport (1923)	American	Fleshy biotype	Medium biotype		Slender biotype	
Stockard (1923)	American	Lateral	Intermediate (Normal)		Linear	
Aschner (1924)	German	Broad	Normal		Slender	
Bauer, J. (1924)	Austrian	Hypersthenic habitus (Arthritic habitus)	Sthenic habitus		Asthenic habitus	
Draper (1925)	American	Gallbladder			Ulcer	
Kretschmer (1925)	German	Pyknic	Athletic		Leptosome (Asthenic)	
MacAuliffe (1925)	French	Round			Flat	
Weidenreich (1926)	German	Eurysome			Leptosome	
Pende (1927)	Italian	Hypervegetative			Hypovegetative	

of these classifications are to be found in the literature. We have included here only the better known ones. The list begins with Hippocrates's famous twofold division, and it may be noteworthy that a number of contemporary writers have tended to return to this most elemental of morphological dichotomies (Draper, MacAuliffe, Weidenreich, Pende). Yet the majority of the historical attempts at classification have resulted in trichotomies. The French have in some instances used a fourfold system of types (Halle, Rostan, Sigaud). Possibly Rostan's original classification of man in terms of the *type digestif, type musculaire, type respiratoire,* and *type cérébral* is a more useful one than the more common trichotomy which in the present generation is most closely associated with Kretschmer. It is our own point of view that the *type respiratoire* (a slender, large-chested type) is best described as a mixture of mesomorphic and ectomorphic tendencies.

Like Viola and Naccarati, Kretschmer attempted to differentiate his types in terms of a system of anthropometric measurements. These he presents in three tables which, condensed, appear as follows (Table 2):

TABLE 2

PRINCIPAL AVERAGE MEASUREMENTS OF KRETSCHMER'S THREE PHYSICAL TYPES[17]

	Pyknic Type		Athletic Type		Asthenic Type	
	Men	Women	Men	Women	Men	Women
Height (cm.).......	167.8	156.5	170.0	163.1	168.4	153.8
Weight (kilos).......	68.0	56.3	62.9	61.7	50.5	44.4
Shoulder width......	36.9	34.3	39.1	37.4	35.5	32.8
Chest (mean of insp., expir.)...........	94.5	86.0	91.7	86.0	84.1	77.7
Stomach............	88.8	78.7	79.6	75.1	74.1	67.7
Hips..............	92.0	94.2	91.5	95.8	84.7	82.2
Forearm (circum)....	25.5	22.4	26.2	24.2	23.5	20.4
Hand (circum)......	20.7	18.6	21.7	20.0	19.7	18.0
Calf (circum).......	33.2	31.3	33.1*	31.7	30.0	27.7
Leg (length)........	87.4	80.5	90.9	85.0	89.4	79.2

[17] These figures are taken from the original German edition of Kretschmer's book (*Körperbau und Charakter*). The English translation contains a number of errors.

Paterson[18] was disturbed by Kretschmer's presentation. He points out that even with these measurements there is a good deal of jumble and confusion in the description of the material. He comments (p. 233):

. . . There are a number of rather puzzling features in this Table. . . . If one becomes puzzled at the outset by the principal measurements differentiating between types, he is certain to become outright bewildered when he attempts to follow the verbal descriptions of the types. They are interspersed with numerous references to specific cases, and are concerned, to a considerable extent, with distinctions not only between the three main classes but also between each of these and intermediate classifications. Asthenic and athletic features occur simultaneously in the same individual. There may also be asthenic-hypoplastic, or asthenic-pyknic interference in structure, pyknic mixture, dysplastic, uncataloguable forms, etc. In speaking of certain asthenic-pyknic traits found in one and the same individual Kretschmer states, "We could reel off here, and with other types, innumerable mixtures of such a kind: there is absolutely no single criterion which cannot be varied by and combined with marks of another type."

This somewhat impatient reaction of a well-trained scientific mind to what is, nevertheless, perhaps a brilliant advance in the field of constitutional study, illustrates the conflict between a creative and a logical kind of thinking. Paterson knew the danger that lies in typologies, but Kretschmer knew that there is something at the bottom of his observations. With Kretschmer, insight and an observant eye came first, tools of quantification were to be applied later. Paterson, critical and accurate in the use of scientific tools, could not tolerate their careless handling, a fault of which Kretschmer is undoubtedly guilty.

Throughout his book Kretschmer is engaged in a Laocoön-like struggle with the manipulation of types and their interminable intermixtures. He becomes deeply entangled in

[18] Paterson, D. G. *Physique and Intellect*. Century Psychology Series. New York: D. Appleton-Century, 1930.

the verbal descriptions of these mixtures, and with only three fixed points of reference to work from, is virtually defeated at the outset in his effort to establish scientifically valid cor-relations between physical and mental patterning. The diffi-culty lies simply in the fact that Kretschmer's conception of polar types implies a trimodality of distribution which is untrue to life. There are not three kinds of people—there is a continuous distribution of people, and of physiques.

Kretschmer's failure to grasp the idea of varying *com-ponents*, and his consequent effort to describe the variations of human morphology without the aid of structural *variables*, left his work open to criticism from so many quarters that the position of constitutional research may have been more weakened than strengthened by what is in some respects one of its brilliant contributions. Yet Kretschmer remains the first modern student to demonstrate anything approximating a quantitative relation between physical constitution and a specific clinical manifestation. His description of cycloid and schizoid temperament, and his verbal descriptions of physique are literature for any library.

The wonder is that Kretschmer could fail so completely to order his material against scalable components and yet demonstrate any statistical relationships at all. His attempt to handle human morphology with three types is comparable to trying to build a language with three adjectives. Accord-ing to his actual findings, he observed 260 psychopathic in-dividuals, 85 of whom had been classified psychiatrically as *circulars* and 175 as *schizophrenes*. These he found to be distributed morphologically as shown in Table 3.

The conclusions drawn by Kretschmer are as follows:

1. There is a clear biological affinity between the psychic disposition of the manic-depressives and the pyknic body type.

2. There is a clear biological affinity between the psychic disposition of the schizophrenes and the bodily disposition

TABLE 3
"PHYSICAL AND PSYCHIC DISPOSITIONS"
(After Kretschmer, p. 35)

	Circular	Schizophrene
Asthenic..........................	4	81
Athletic..........................	3	31
Asthenico-athletic mixed.............	2	11
Pyknic...........................	58	2
Pyknic mixture....................	14	3
Dysplastic.......................	—	34
Deformed and uncataloguable forms...	4	13
Total........................	85	175

characteristic of the asthenics, athletics, and certain dysplastics.

3. And vice versa, there is only a weak affinity between schizophrene and pyknic, on the one hand, and between circulars and asthenics, athletics, and dysplastics, on the other.

Kretschmer states that these cases were all of German Swabian stock, and that of the circulars 43 were men and 42 were women; of the schizophrenes 125 were men and 50 were women. He believes that "The female physique is less *significant* on the average, particularly with regard to the form of the face, and the development of the muscles and fat." He included in the material "a carefully arranged mixture of fresh and old cases, people of every age, and every occupation."

Quite a large number of other investigators have repeated Kretschmer's work, and although in the publication of their findings there has invariably been some confusion as to the technique of ascertaining the physical types, on the whole a fairly definite general agreement with Kretschmer's main finding has been reported. Several American psychiatrists have become followers of Kretschmer, and two or three attempts have been made in this country to transform his concept of types into statistical variables. Of these the best known and perhaps the most carefully executed is that of

Wertheimer and Hesketh.[19] At the Henry Phipps Psychiatric Clinic these investigators revived in shortened form what is actually the morphological index of Viola, with some of the trunk measurements omitted. They classified 65 male patients by Kretschmer's method, calculated the morphological indices for these patients, and demonstrated that all the Kretschmer asthenics were in the microsplanchnic range, and the pyknics in the macrosplanchnic range. They then correlated morphological index with psychotic temperament, and found much the same distribution that Kretschmer had reported. That is to say, the macrosplanchnics were on the whole manic-depressive, and the microsplanchnics were predominantly schizoid.

REVIEW OF THE STATUS OF THE PROBLEM

The foregoing summary sketches in general outline the problem of constitution as it existed when we contemplated a research project in this field a dozen years ago. The picture then seemed to exhibit a small but fairly clear constellation of facts and indications. These were as follows:

1. The concept of types had been useful in the study of personality, but, like the poles supporting a clothesline, it provides only end suspensions for distributive classifications. As the line becomes filled, the notion of types recedes and finally vanishes altogether, perhaps submerged under a smooth distribution. Yet at the outset a concept of types is a necessity. Such a concept is found in the early stages of development of almost every descriptive system. The path of progress is from the notion of dichotomies to the concept of variation along dimensional axes.

2. The elaborate refinement of anthropometry and of its attendant mathematics had proved not in itself a satisfactory substitute for a meaningful plan of study. The supremely

[19] Wertheimer, Frederick I., and Hesketh, F. E. The significance of the physical constitution in mental disease. *Med. Monogr.*, vol. 10, Baltimore: Williams & Wilkins, 1926.

0777147

accurate measurement of irrelevant data cannot in the long run fulfill the function of a systematic study of personality.

3. Although the concept of types had proved inadequate, and although the indiscriminate application of refined mathematics had been futile, there remained reasonable evidence that relations between physical and mental characteristics do exist. Working with normal material, Naccarati demonstrated this fact unmistakably, and Kretschmer showed it even more clearly with abnormal individuals. But these relations appeared to lie deeper and to be far more complex than either Naccarati's method or Kretschmer's method presupposed.

The difficulties involved in developing a systematic method for the study of personality were only too painfully apparent as we contemplated the general problem. A principal stumbling block lay in language. There was not one but many approaches to personality, and each had a jargon of its own. (We are perhaps destined for a long time to struggle with this particular difficulty.)

There were at least five academically respectable and more or less scientific attacks on the problem of constitutional description. These were (1) Anatomy and Physical Anthropology, (2) Physiology and Physiological Chemistry, (3) Clinical Medicine and Pathology, (4) Psychology and Psychiatry, and (5) Sociology and the other so-called Social Sciences. Already independent and specialized in their individual approaches to the problem, these groups appeared to be further diverging, not converging. What we wanted was an attack on personality capable of utilizing and focusing whatever was common to all these groups without sacrificing precision, and yet, if possible, without sacrificing the perspective of the whole individual. It appeared evident that the best and safest place to start was with the study of the living body.

CHAPTER III

DEVELOPMENT OF THE TECHNIQUE
OF SOMATOTYPING

FOLLOWING the studies based upon Viola's morphological index (see Chapter II) we undertook at the University of Chicago to classify 400 male undergraduate students on the basis of Kretschmer's threefold morphological typology. Upon statistical examination of the measurements recommended by Kretschmer, it appeared possible to classify only about 12 per cent of this group as clearly athletic, about 9 per cent as asthenic, and about 7 per cent as pyknic. The remaining 72 per cent appeared to be mixtures. Furthermore, a large number of these boys showed conspicuous inconsistencies within different regions of their bodies. After working over this material repeatedly, and after experimenting with a great many physical measurements, we felt that an adequate classification of physique would have to be founded upon (1) the study of a much larger number of cases of homogeneous age, (2) a method of attack which viewed the human physique as made up of an intermixture of components rather than as an example of a type, (3) a procedure for dividing the body into segments or regions for the purposes of comparative measurement and classification, and (4) a technique of comparison based upon permanent photographic records rather than upon isolated anthropometric measurements alone. In succeeding pages we shall follow the development of procedures designed to meet these four criteria.

THE PHOTOGRAPHIC TECHNIQUE

The first important step was the standardization of a photographic technique. Pictures were needed which would reveal the whole body, front, back and side views, on a single film—pictures sufficiently free from distortion to ensure reliable anthropometric measurements from the films. The equipment finally adopted, and still used, consists of a simple Corona type of portrait camera, 5″ by 7″, with a special sliding back which exposes one-third of the film at a time. These backs are constructed in such a manner that the part of the film which is being exposed always lies directly in line with the lens. Either film pack or cut film may be used. The vertical dimension of the individual being photographed corresponds with the short diameter of the film. Experiment showed that by using a long-focus lens (9½″) and by focusing horizontally upon the center of the body, it is possible to obtain full length pictures with all visible parts of the body sufficiently free from photographic distortion. That is to say, length and breadth measurements taken on such films agree consistently with the same measurements taken anthropometrically upon the living body.

The subject stands on a pedestal so placed that the backs of the subject's heels are in a vertical plane lying a measured distance from the center of the front of the lens. This is the distance at which the image of an individual 80 inches tall falls just within the short diameter of the 5″ by 7″ film. The pedestal is constructed to revolve between three stops placed at intervals of 90 degrees. Thus exact frontal, profile, and dorsal pictures can be taken without any movement on the subject's part. Artificial lights are used, and are adjusted to the physical surroundings available. A light-gray background is most satisfactory. We usually use the f-16 opening of the shutter, an exposure of 1/5 second, and lights adjusted accordingly.

With this equipment a series of standardized photographs

of 4,000 undergraduate male students was collected at several midwestern and eastern universities. The ages of these subjects ranged from 16 to 20, with the mean at 18 years, 3 months. In this series the racial element was disregarded, except that Negroes and Orientals were not included. It was simply a mixed series of Europeans, and was approximately 10 per cent Jewish.

This series served as the basis for a standardization of a descriptive classification of the patternings of the morphological components in the population studied. This basic classification rests upon the simplest possible procedure.

IDENTIFICATION OF THE COMPONENTS

With so large a sampling of physical variation at hand (4,000 cases), it was easy to select for special study several dozen extreme examples of each of three pronounced variants. To those who may wonder why *three* extremes were chosen, it should be pointed out that in a large random sample it is precisely three extreme types which stand out. Repeated combing of the population for what might reasonably be called a fourth basic type of extreme variation simply yielded nothing at all. We were not committed to find three first-order variants—and only three. It is, indeed, fair to state that we rather expected to find more than three. We were initially reluctant to accept the conclusion that only three fundamentally different extremes can be isolated.

The three variants which we found correspond, approximately, to Kretschmer's three types—pyknic, athletic, and asthenic. But it soon became apparent that these terms are neither very appropriate nor entirely univocal. *Pyknic* means compact. Our extremes of type 1 are not compact, but are round and soft. They are made of loose, flabby tissue. They float in water, and are markedly lacking in strength. Their bones are small, and their bodies are of relatively low density. Such people are physically weak.

Much of the confusion associated with Kretschmer's terminology arises from the fact that his term "pyknic" actually applies to a physique combining endomorphy and mesomorphy.

Athletic is a functional rather than a structural term. Our extremes of type 2 are not always athletic. They are massive, solid people with large bones, big joints, and heavy muscles. These variants are actually more compact than are the extremes of type 1. Sometimes they are slow of movement, awkward, and "muscle-bound."

Asthenic means weak, or without strength. Such a term would seem to apply just as aptly to type 1 as to type 3. Extremes of type 3 are often singularly spry. Despite their slender limbs and bodies, they are not infrequently good at minor athletics, and they are often great walkers. Kretschmer's later term "leptosomic" (delicate bodied) describes reasonably well this third type of variant.

We rejected Kretschmer's terminology for the reasons given above and because we sought a set of terms more homogeneous in form and more "meaningful" in implication. In order better to justify the final selection of the three terms *endomorphy, mesomorphy* and *ectomorphy* we turn now to a consideration of certain facts relating to the three extreme variants in terms of whose characteristics the three components were defined.

In the course of autopsy work at the University of Chicago, and at the University of Wisconsin, it was possible to examine, to measure, and to weigh the principal internal organs of several examples of each of the three type variants.[1] We found that individuals of type 1 are endowed with relatively enormous intestines, liver, and other digestive viscera. In these people the gut is both longer and heavier than in the other variants. It should be pointed out, however, that these data are not completely adequate, because our observations are based principally upon the study of middle-aged individuals, whereas our techniques for constitutional dif-

[1] These, however, were not all extreme variants.

ferentiation rest mainly upon the study of a large series of college students.

Nevertheless, in a series of ten male bodies predominantly of type 1 the mean total intestinal weight was 1,473 grams, and the mean intestinal length was 1,115 centimeters. The mean stature was 66.3 inches, the mean body weight 179 pounds, and the mean age 59 years. In a parallel series of thirteen male bodies predominantly of type 2 the mean intestinal weight was 1,085 grams, with a mean intestinal length of 963 centimeters. In this group the mean stature was 68.4 inches, the mean weight 163 pounds, and the mean age 54 years. And in a series of eleven male bodies predominantly of type 3, the mean intestinal weight was 786 grams, with a mean intestinal length of 871 centimeters. In this group the mean stature was 69.8 inches, the mean weight 141 pounds, and the mean age 60 years.

These data strongly support the findings of Bryant,[2] Goldthwait,[3] Bean,[4] and Swaim.[5] Bryant and Goldthwait, working independently, described two extreme types, corresponding to our variants of type 1 and type 3. These they called, respectively, the herbivorous and carnivorous extremes. Goldthwait, in the Shattuck Lecture in Boston (1915), presented photographs of his "herbivorous and carnivorous men." These photographs are excellent illustrations of our extremes of type 1 and type 3. Bryant found that in the extreme herbivorous type the length of the small intestine varied between 25 and 30 feet, whereas in the extreme carnivorous type the small intestine ranged from 10 to 15 feet in length. Swaim, working in the Harvard Medical School, found that in the carnivorous type the small intestine ranged

[2] Bryant, J. The carnivorous and herbivorous types of man. *Boston Med. and Surg. J.*, 170, 795, 1914; 172, 321, 1915; 173, 384, 1915.

[3] Goldthwait, J. E. An anatomic and mechanistic conception of disease (Shattuck Lecture). *Boston Med. and Surg. J.*, 172, 881, 1915.

[4] Bean, R. B. The two European types, *Amer. J. Anat.*, 31, 359, 1923.

[5] Swaim, L. T. Thirty-nine cases as regards intestinal length and nutrition, *Boston Med. and Surg. J.*, August, 1912.

from 10 to 20 feet in length, and from 20 to 25 feet in the herbivorous type. Swaim found the large intestine in the herbivorous type to range from 5 to 8½ feet, whereas Goldthwait gives 3 to 5 feet as the usual length of the large intestine in the carnivorous type.

Bean described three types of extreme variants. These he called the hypo-ontomorph (corresponding to our type 1), the meso-ontomorph (type 2), and the hyper-ontomorph (type 3). The hypo-ontomorph (literally the underdeveloped or unevolved) has a fat, round body, short extremities, and a relatively enormous preponderance of visceral mass. The meso-ontomorph has a strong, massive, powerful physique, with a relatively small forebrain (cerebrum) but a large cerebellum. The hyper-ontomorph has a light, linear physique, extremely small visceral mass, and a relatively large cerebrum with a small cerebellum. Bean gives the length of the small intestine as from 12 to 15 feet in the hyper-ontomorph, and from 20 to 25 feet in the hypo-ontomorph.

Such data suggest that in the extremes of type 1 the digestive viscera, especially the gut, hold a more or less predominant position in the organic economy. In these people the most manifest external characteristic is a conspicuous laying on of fat, which is an indication of predominance of the absorptive functions—the functions of the gut—over the energy-expending functions. Now, the functional elements of the digestive system are derived, embryologically, almost entirely from the endoderm, the innermost of the three original embryonic layers. We came quite naturally, therefore, to refer to the extremes of type 1 as those exhibiting a condition of *endomorphy*. Those whose physiques show a predominant endomorphy we call *endomorphs*, and such bodies are described as *endomorphic*.

It is of some interest to note that not all the internal organs are large in extreme endomorphy. In our autopsy work we found what seemed at first an inconsistency. Although the endomorphic stomach, intestines, liver—in short, all the digestive organs—were uniformly large, the heart and kidneys were usually of only moderate size, and the arteries varied from a moderate to a rather small size. Except in certain cases of pathological hypertrophy, it was only in extremes of type 2 that we found very large hearts and large arteries.

Now, bones, muscles, connective tissue, and the heart and blood vessels (for the most part) are derived from the mesoderm, the second embryonic layer. It is precisely these structures which predominate overwhelmingly in the variants of type 2. We therefore call these variants *mesomorphs*, and the morphological aspects exhibited by them we name *mesomorphy*.

In the extremes of type 3, surface predominates relatively over mass, and the surface structures—the skin and its specialized derivatives—predominate over the internal structures. The principal derivatives from the embryonic ectodermal layer are the skin itself, hair and nails, sense organs (exteroceptors), and the nervous system, including the brain. Relative to total bodily mass all these organs are conspicuous in the bodily economy of the extreme variants of type 3. The mean weight of the extreme type-3 variant (male), who is 68 inches tall and 18 years of age, is about 108 pounds. The extreme endomorph of this height and age weighs about 240 pounds. Yet the brain and the sense organs of each are of about the same size and weight. Relatively, therefore, the ectodermally derived tissues are strongly predominant in the type-3 variants. Hence, we have named them *ectomorphs*, or persons exhibiting *ectomorphy*.

These terms are polysyllabic and difficult—that we realize. We should welcome simpler appropriate designations, but we have found none as suitable as endomorphy, mesomorphy, and ectomorphy. Hence, somewhat as an experiment, we suggest these terms in the hope that time may stabilize their usage—or reveal better ones.

These, then, are the names applied to the three extreme variants in a "normal" population. We make the assumption that these individuals are extreme because they are dominated each by a different structural or morphological component. The nature of each of the components is revealed by the characteristics manifested by the respective extremes. (This, reduced to its simplest terms, is the operational definition of the components.) Just what are the characteristics the extremes have in common and how the components interact when mixed in various proportions will provide the subject matter for most of the remainder of this volume.

MORPHOLOGICAL CHARACTERISTICS OF THE THREE EXTREMES

In order more explicitly to record the characteristics of the three extreme variants, and thereby to define the three morphological components, we turn now to a check list of the more obvious differentiae.

The check list was prepared as a preliminary step in defining the criteria for ordering the 4,000 pictures in fifteen serial arrangements. The plan of procedure in making the rank orders was as follows: (1) To define criteria for determining by inspection the relative strength of each of the three basic components in each of five regions (see p. 54) of a given physique. (2) To apply these criteria and by inspectional (anthroposcopic) methods to arrange the whole series of pictures into three serial orders for each region of the body—one order for the endomorphic component, one order for the mesomorphic component, and one order for the ectomorphic component. This procedure determined approximately what combinations or patternings of the components actually occur in life. (3) To sharpen these classifications, scale them, and render them precise and objective by the application of detailed anthropometric criteria.

The first of these steps, preparation of a check list for the definition of criteria, was carried out principally by a detailed study of one hundred relatively extreme examples of each of the three variants. These examples were selected by inspection from the 4,000 cases. Included in these check lists are some additional comments on characteristics revealed by later studies but not immediately evident from the photographs.

CHECK LISTS OF INSPECTIONAL CRITERIA (MALE)

Type 1 Dominance: Endomorphy (the first component)

Roundness and softness of body. The anteroposterior diameters and lateral diameters tend toward equality in the head, the neck, throughout the trunk, and in the limbs.

Central concentration of mass. Predominance of abdominal and thoracic volume over the extremities. Predominance of abdomen over thorax. Predominance of proximal segments of limbs over the distal segments. Rounding and "hamming" of thighs and upper arms. High, square shoulders with soft contours. Short neck.

Head large and in full-blown endomorphy almost spherical. Face wide, lower facial breadth approximates upper facial breadth.

Smoothness of contours throughout. No muscle relief. Even the deltoid, trapezius, and gastrocnemius relief is gone in extreme endomorphy. No deltoid pyramiding.

Short, tapering limbs. Weak extremities, comparatively small hands and feet.

The neck forms an obtuse angle with the chin in the lateral view.

Upon palpation, bones are small. X-ray reveals bones of thin cortex. Inspectionally, bony projections are not seen.

The vertebral column appears relatively straight in the lateral view, varying sharply from the typical "S curves" of the other two types. This appearance is due somewhat to subcutaneous padding about the back, although it is likely that the pressure from the tightly filled abdominal and thoracic cavities may tend to straighten the vertebral column during the growth years.

The trunk is relatively long when the third, or ectomorphic, component is low. The chest is relatively wide at the base, the waistline is high and faintly indicated, and the greatest transverse breadth of the body below the waist is likely to fall well above the iliac crests rather than at the bitrochanteric level. The lower costal margins are relatively high, and the ribs form a wide angle with the vertebral column and with the sternum. There is always some development of the breast in the male (usually pseudo-breast resulting from fatty deposit). The whole trunk, with its tendency toward the spherical form, gives the impression of being under moderate pneumatic pressure. There is no dimpling at the lateral aspects of the buttocks, but instead a round, "pneumatic" fullness.

The outer line of the thighs, in the frontal and dorsal views, reveals what has been called the feminine contour or feminine ellipse. This outer curve is continued in the calves. When the first component is predominant but only moderately strong in the body, with a weak second component, the resemblance to the normal female contour may be quite marked.

The skin is soft, smooth, and velvety, resembling the skin of an apple. Contrary to a common prejudice, the endomorph is not particularly hirsute. (Hirsutism is almost evenly distributed among the morphological variations. See p. 78.) The endomorphic pubic hair shows the so-called feminine pattern. There is often hair at the breasts, over the scapulae, and sometimes over the deltoids. Massive chest hair is rare in endomorphy. A premature tendency toward baldness is often seen, even in youth. This is a round, even baldness, beginning at the top of the broadly domed head and spreading peripherally in an almost perfect circle, leaving a highly polished surface. Endomorphs with a low second component have characteristically fine hair texture. The hair lies flat against the head and is rarely recalcitrant or difficult to comb. Similarly, the ears lie flat and are about equally developed as to lobe and pinna. The nose does not protrude in the lateral view. The whole endomorphic head is constructed on a spherical plan. The hard palate is wide, low, and of parabolic shape, in sharp contrast to the narrow, high, ectomorphic palate.

The genitalia are hypoplastic. The penis is short and small and may be almost completely hidden within the pubic hair. Undescended testes are common. The foreskin is frequently too long. The corona is nearly always small.

Type 2 Dominance: Mesomorphy (the second component)

Squareness and hardness of body. Rugged, prominent, massive muscling. Large, prominent bones. Sharp, high muscle relief. The transverse diameters (shoulders, forearms, calves) approach and in some parts of the body exceed those of the endomorphs, but the anteroposterior diameters are far less than those found in endomorphy.

The trunk is large and heavily muscled, but the central concentration of mass is entirely absent. The limbs are heavily muscled throughout, massive, and of variable length. The most conspicuous characteristic of arms and legs is the relative prominence and massiveness of the distal segments. Forearm thickness approaches and may equal the thickness of the upper arm. The wrist is heavy and massive, as are the hand and fingers. There is no peripheral weakening, no 'hamming' of the upper arms.

Thoracic volume predominates over abdominal volume. The thorax is relatively wide at its apex as compared with its base, and there is a relatively slender waist as compared with the endomorphic waist. The shoulders are broad, the trunk usually long and upright, and the trapezius and deltoid muscles are invariably massive and prominent. Neither length of trunk nor length of limb, however, is a constant feature. There are extreme mesomorphs with short limbs and with short trunks. The pelvis is sturdy and powerful, with broad hips. (The narrow hips often seen with an "athletic" physique are presumably due to the presence of the ectomorphic component.)

Both arms and legs are evenly proportioned as to proximal and distal segments, although total length may vary greatly. The same is true of finger segments, although both long and short fingers are found in extreme mesomorphy.

The head varies greatly in size. The bones are invariably heavy and prominent, as are the muscles. The head shows heavy supraorbital ridges, prominent and massive cheekbones, heavy, square jaws. When examined by X-ray photography, the bones of the mesomorphic head and face are found to be thick and heavy. The same is true of the other bones throughout the body, but the fact is externally more conspicuous in the face because of the great complexity of bone in that region. Both moderate brachycephaly and moderate dolichocephaly are common with extreme mesomorphy, and likewise head height varies rather independently of this component. The facial mass is relatively great as compared with the cephalic mass. The head strongly suggests the cubical shape.

The neck is usually fairly long, and the transverse diameter predominates markedly over the anteroposterior diameter. This is because most of the neck muscles are laterally placed. The most conspicuous feature in this area of the body is usually the pyramiding of the powerful trapezius muscles on either side of the neck.

Because of the sloping contours formed by these trapezius muscles, in conjunction with a long neck, mesomorphic shoulders sometimes seem relatively low, although they are actually not low. The clavicles are heavy and prominent. Owing to deltoid development, and to massiveness of the muscles associated with the deltoids, the shoulders usually project laterally, well out from the trunk.

The line of the back as seen laterally is relatively straight in the thoracic region, that is to say, there is little thoracic rounding; but there is a relatively sharp inward bowing low in the lumbar region. In predominant mesomorphy this low, sharp "lower bow of the S" constitutes a striking characteristic. The appearance is due to a relatively straight back, with prominent muscularity of the buttocks. The lower part of the sacrum is pulled out dorsally, so that the sacrum lies in a relatively horizontal position.

In the frontal view the abdominal muscles are prominent and thick and always show a knotty, muscular rippling at Poupart's ligament. In the dorsal view a muscular dimpling is nearly always seen at the lateral margins of the buttocks.

The ribs are strong and heavy, forming an angle with the vertebral column intermediate between that of the endomorphs and that of the ectomorphs.

The waist is low, often very low. The thoracic segment of the trunk predominates over the abdominal segment.

The skin is thick and coarse with large conspicuous pores. It takes a deep tan readily and holds it for a long time. On exposed parts of the body the skin typically becomes permanently darkened, even in youth, and assumes a rich, leathery quality. The mesomorphic body is rich in connective tissue, and the skin is both thick and tightly bound to the subcutaneous tissue below, so that wrinkling, wherever it occurs, is of a heavy, coarse character. In the mesomorphic face, long, heavy folds appear in place of the more numerous and finer lines of the ectomorphic face. Because of its thickness and large pores, we have sometimes likened this skin to the skin of an orange.

The hair is generally coarse and may be either luxuriant or sparse. Hirsutism is highly variable. In the extreme mesomorphs, bodily hair is rarely luxuriant, but the pubic hair follows the so-called masculine pattern. Hair growth is slower in mesomorphy than in ectomorphy, perhaps because the hair is usually coarser. A notable characteristic of mesomorphic skin is a firm, elastic vigor—the skin quickly springs back into place when lightly pinched. Baldness is variable: when it appears, it usually appears first on the front of the head.

The face is both long and broad, with the nose strong

at the base. The lips are thick, well muscled, and firm. It is nearly impossible to confuse this massive, bony, hard, and muscular face with the soft, round, bland endomorphic face, or with the fragile, sensitive ectomorphic face.

The skull shape varies greatly. Usually it is of the so-called low-vaulted form, with low forehead. The dome is occasionally high, with a long, gently sloping forehead.

The genitalia are nearly always well developed and are compact. The scrotum is relatively thick and firm.

Type 3 Dominance: Ectomorphy (the third component)

Linearity, fragility, and delicacy of body. Small, delicate bones. Slight, 'thready' muscles. The anteroposterior diameters are extremely reduced. The transverse diameters are reduced, but not so sharply so.

The shoulder-droop is a constant feature: it is always present in extreme ectomorphy. The trunk is relatively short, and the limbs are relatively long, but the individual is not necessarily tall. The general suggestion of decentralization of structure is strong. The abdomen is flat, relatively short, and of shallow depth. In sharp contrast with mesomorphy, the lumbar curve is flat and high and the thoracic curve is relatively sharp and elevated. That is to say, relative to the mesomorphic physique, lumbar lordosis and thoracic kyphosis are pronounced.

The thorax is relatively long as compared with the abdomen. It is flat and receding from the nipple level to the clavicle, and it is usually narrow. The costovertebral angles are acute. The ribs are delicate and prominent. The shoulders are narrow and lacking in muscular relief. There is no bunching or bulging of the muscles at any point on the body. The rounded shoulders are carried well forward and produce a marked clavicular hollow. Thus, the arms often seem to hang in a plane anterior to the plane of the body. The shoulder girdle lacks muscular support and padding, and the scapulae tend to wing out posteriorly.

If the individual has been under a dietary regime to gain weight, as is often the case, the small abdomen will be scaphoid above and enteroptotic below, owing to poor abdominal musculature. In general, the ectomorphic abdomen protrudes only below the navel.

Both the arms and the legs tend to be relatively long in the distal segments—an exact opposite to endomorphy. Extremely weak thighs and upper arms are constant features of ectomorphy.

The fingers and toes are usually fragile and long, but not always conspicuously long. Knuckles and joints are small and are *not* prominent. When such prominence occurs, apart from pathology and inflammation, it is due to the presence of a degree of mesomorphy. This is an important point in making the differential diagnosis between the true ectomorph and an emaciated person of some other physical constitution.

The neck is long and extremely slender, with poor muscling and, when mesomorphy is at its minimum, with no trapezius support. The neck projects forward, forming an angle with the line of the back. The head is righted or leveled by the muscles of the back of the neck. These muscles are therefore, as a rule, a little better developed than the other neck muscles, and the extremely ectomorphic neck usually has an anteroposterior diameter nearly equal to its transverse diameter. Both these diameters are small.

The head as a whole is slight. The most constant feature of the head is the relatively small facial mass as compared with the cranial mass—a direct antithesis to mesomorphy. The features of the face are uniformly small, sharp, and fragile. If there is no endomorphic interference, the face presents a sharply triangular appearance, with the apex at the delicately pointed chin. The bridge of the nose is low and narrow and the nose itself is sharp, like a slender prow. The delicate zygomatic arches are clearly discernible but are not prominent unless there is mesomorphic interference. The lips are delicate and thin. The upper part of the ears, the pinnae, typically project laterally, and the pinnae are usually better developed than the lobes, which are often closely attached to the sides of the head. In the lateral view the chin is seen to be hypoplastic and somewhat receding. The lower jaw is often inadequate to carry the crowded teeth, and the hard palate is of a restricted U shape—long, narrow, and restricted anteriorly.

The head is frequently of more or less irregular shape, with bosses common. Sometimes the frontal area projects well forward and produces a high, straight, or even a bulbous forehead.[6] The top of the head is often flat, and occasionally somewhat scaphoid. Marked occipital projection is common and the result is often an exceptionally long head. Dolichocephaly predominates in ectomorphy, but is by no means inevitable. The relatively wide head is a common variant, and when this occurs, the sharp contrast with the narrow and hypoplastic facial structure is striking.

The supraorbital ridges, inion, and other bony projections are slight and inconspicuous unless there is a mesomorphic complication. The head, although small as a whole, often seems too large for the slender, poorly supported neck. The bones of the head and face when seen by X-ray photography are thin and fragile, like those of a young child.

The skin is thin and dry. The epidermis tends to slough off actively. The exposed skin surfaces, especially on the backs of the hands and on the neck, are likely to show fine wrinkling even in youth, in sharp contrast with endomorphic skin which frequently remains smooth and fresh looking in old age. We sometimes speak of ectomorphic skin as resembling the outer skin of an onion. The skin color is typically poor, that is to say, pale and ashy. This skin will not tan well, but burns easily, peels quickly, and returns rapidly to its pale color. Ectomorphs, with their relatively great bodily surface area, experience difficulty in maintaining an even

---

[6] Depending, of course, upon the secondary local influence of the other two components.

temperature. They do not easily tolerate the heat of summer, and Caucasian ectomorphs are frequently unable to live in the tropics. Similarly, they do not tolerate extreme cold and are more easily frozen than are the more massive people.

The skin lacks both elastic tissue and connective tissue. It is loosely bound to the underlying structures, and returns slowly to position when lightly pinched.

The hair is usually fine, often extremely fine, and it grows rapidly. When several thousand bodies are carefully examined, it is found that the secondary hair of ectomorphic people is of nearly the same abundance as in the case of endomorphy and mesomorphy, although it is perhaps a little less conspicuous because of its rather finer texture (see p. 78). Heavy hirsutism is sometimes seen in extreme ectomorphy. Baldness is rare when the ectomorphic component is strongly predominant. The head hair typically tends to grow forward, or in several directions, and the hair is hard to comb or to keep in place. The pubic hair varies greatly. It is sometimes luxuriant, tending to follow the *linea alba* upward to produce the so-called masculine triangle. Sometimes it is extremely scant, and it then usually exhibits the feminine triangle. There is much more variability of this characteristic in ectomorphy than in the other two extreme types.

The genitalia show marked linearity and, in comparison with the rest of the bodily development, are as a rule hypertrophic, unless there is endomorphic interference. The scrotum is typically long and permits the testicles to hang loosely. The left testicle is usually lower than the right. The penis is likewise characteristically long, with a well-developed corona.

These, then, are the characteristics which distinguish the three principal types of male physique as they occur in extreme variations. It should be emphasized again that these differentiae were selected for listing because they are the qualities exhibited by the extreme variants which any experimenter can readily pick from a large population. They were chosen because the variants exhibit them. They were not, initially, used to decide which individuals are variants. Thus, the procedure was strictly empirical and no *a priori* criteria were admitted. Extreme variants were isolated by inspection and then studied in detail. Hence it is clear what *initially* were the defining operations for each extreme type of physique: the extremes are those which an experimenter can reliably discriminate and pick from the population. This procedure is no novelty. The taxonomist separates the horse from the ass because they are obviously different. He then proceeds to study and record the characteristics of each beast. Later, when he has completed his description and compiled his check list, the student can, of course, use the check list to decide whether a given animal is horse or ass—or neither. The preceding check lists were devised on analogous principles.

APPLICATION OF THE CHECK LIST. ANTHROPOSCOPY

When we came to examine the entire photographic series of 4,000 individuals, scrutinizing each physique with reference to all the characteristics described in the check list, it became apparent that the absolutely pure variant probably does not exist. Though many physiques showed a strongly predominant trend toward one of the polar extremes, we could find no single individual who did not somewhere in his body also exhibit minor local characteristics belonging to one of the other two polar types. Every one of the 4,000 boys was dysplastic in the sense that he revealed at least some trace of all three of the polar morphologies. But this fact does not compel us to agree with those who teach that the task of physical classification is therefore necessarily a hopeless one.

It seems reasonable that if, in place of the idea of fixed types, three elemental structural components are postulated, then perhaps any human body, or for that matter any object, can be meaningfully described as a patterned mixture of these three more or less interdependent variables. The problem then becomes one of devising simple operations for scaling the three components. Further, if we then arbitrarily regard the body as a composite of several discrete topographic regions, and if the components of each region are measured separately, we have a descriptive method which makes possible a quantitative study of disharmony within the physical personality of an individual. Such a method would seem to enable us to study conflict at the morphological level.

Through the substitution of the concept of a continuous series of component intermixtures for that of types, the problem was changed from one of establishing a trichotomy to one of devising a sufficiently flexible and reliable scaling technique to reflect a trivariant distribution of physiques. And by the addition of the idea that the body is a composite structure consisting of a number of statistically separable units, the problem was further changed from that of a simple exercise in physical anthropology to that of standardizing a basic classificatory technique capable of handling the problem of dysplasias.

The body, then, was divided into five regions. The head, face, and neck constitute the first region. The second region is the thoracic trunk. The third region consists of the arms, shoulders, and hands. The fourth region is the abdominal trunk. The fifth region includes the legs and feet.

The next step was a purely anthroposcopic one. It was necessary to set up a preliminary framework for the more exact scaling of the three components. The photographs were arranged in fifteen ascending series, each series based upon the inspectionally estimated value of one component in one bodily region. The estimation of a component's value was based simply upon picture-to-picture comparisons in the light of the check list presented above. No anthropometry or other measuring devices were used in making these preliminary arrays. From previous experience with statistics, we knew that detailed quantification at the wrong time can confuse a study as completely as it can clarify it at the right time. In setting up the general framework, we needed to avoid calipers and decimal points.

Nevertheless, this preliminary anthroposcopic work was necessarily a laborious task. It was not done all at once, but was spread out over the course of several years as new groups of photographs accumulated. However, the general plan has been constant from the beginning, and in the final standardization of the technique, as later presented, the 4,000 photographs upon which the present norms are based were reexamined, rearranged, and finally remeasured.

Each of the fifteen series thus arrived at consisted of an array of 4,000 progressive variations of a component strength in one bodily region, as determined by inspection. We needed next to reduce these series to some simple scale which could be practicably applied and which could be correlated with anthropometric measurements. After some experimentation we elected to reduce each series to a simple scale of 7 points, although it was even then obvious that a much finer scale could be used accurately. The next question was that of where to place the intermediate points of the 7-point scale. The extremes (points 1 and 7) were clear enough, but should the mid-points (points 4) fall at the medians of the distribution or at the approximate mid-points on a scale of progression of the component? It was clear by inspection that under the latter criterion all the distributions, for the first and third components at least, would be somewhat skewed. That is to say, there were more individuals conspicuously low than conspicuously high in endomorphy and ectomorphy. Yet it was clear that what we were trying to scale was the strength of these components, and not the distributions of individuals. We wanted ectomorphy 4 to indicate a point halfway between ectomorphy 1 and ectomorphy 7, *in terms of ectomorphy,* not in terms of incidences.

But, for a given component, there is no perfectly satisfactory way to determine points on a scale of progression, for any quantitative measurement taken on a picture or on a living body is necessarily a measurement weighted by all three components. Furthermore, the logic of these researches requires that measurements be used only after they have been correlated with the component groupings—they cannot be used as primary indicators of the strength of a single component. Indeed, it is difficult to conceive of any statistical device by which anthropometry could be used for locating *ab initio* the intermediate points for scaling single components. Yet we had to have the approximate location of such points before we could determine intermixtures of the components represented in the sample of physiques with which we were concerned.

The method adopted temporarily to meet this difficulty was that of estimating by inspection first the approximate mid-point of each series, and then intermediate points until each progression was divided into six equal-appearing increments. These estimates were checked by several associates (principally graduate students in psychology) and a remarkably high agreement between independent estimates was found. And the anthroposcopic classifications were repeated until the experimenter was able to sort the entire series of pictures in almost perfect agreement with previous sortings. Meanwhile new sets of photographs were obtained, and these were sorted by the same system. We found that two sorters (see p. 101) were able independently to classify a new set of pictures and to arrive at nearly perfect agreement.

At this point, then, the state of the research appeared to be as follows: Clearly, by following simple empirical procedures we had devised a method of physical classification which appeared basically sound and highly practical. We had permanent records of most, if not all, of the recurrent patternings of physique in a large population, and we knew the approximate relative frequency of all these combinations. We had an indicated technique for estimating dysplasia—by comparing the components in different bodily regions—and had already begun to note certain correlations between physical constitution and both clinical and psychological characteristics. On the other hand, this method of physical classification was still essentially a subjective one. Obviously, the procedure needed to be rationalized and placed upon the more firm foundation of objective measurement.

THE PROBLEM OF THE ANTHROPOMETRIC OBJECTIFICATION OF THE ANTHROPOSCOPIC METHOD

The next step, then, was to discover what anthropometric measurements would serve to differentiate not only each of the three components but the degree of its manifestation. Consequently, it was at this point that resort was had to a technique of taking measurements from the photographic negatives.

We had accurate measurements of height and weight for all the individuals whose photographs had been taken, but no other measuremental data for the group as a whole. Height was taken against a wall scale. Weight was taken on several successive occasions, when feasible. In 1926[7] we had found that by carefully standardizing a photographic technique it is possible to take anthropometric measurements of diameters which agree not only with the same measurements taken on the living, but also with one another when successive photographs are taken of the same series of subjects. In the experimental phases of the standardization of the photographic method, it was found that diameter measurements of the head, neck, trunk, arms, and legs taken with needle-point dividers from sharp negatives are more reliable than are similar measurements taken on the living. Indeed, it appears that there is no precisely accurate anthropometric technique for measuring soft parts of the body, except a photographic one. Linear measurements on the *curved* sur-

[7] Sheldon, W. H. Ability and Facial Measurements, *Person. J.*, 1927, Vol. 6, No. 2.

face of body parts, on the other hand, cannot be taken accurately from photographs, for the depth dimension is lost.

Kretschmer and his followers had used simple circumference measurements almost entirely in their efforts to establish
a technique of anthropometric rationalization of Kretschmer's
threefold typology. Our own procedure, on the other hand,
was to run a few simple experiments with measurements of
diameter taken from the films. We found that by using an
ordinary light box, with a ground-glass window against which
to place the negative, together with a device for holding the
negative in position, it was possible to measure diameters
with adequate precision. Fine, replaceable needles should be
used, and the dividers should be equipped with a delicate
screw adjustment. The measurements can be read off directly
under a magnifying glass against a special steel rule graduated to tenths of a millimeter.[8]

With this equipment we found that two experimenters,
after a few hours' practice, could measure these diameters
from sharp negatives at the rate of about 120 measurements
per hour, and with excellent agreement, i.e., with a mean
disagreement of less than 1 per cent of the measurement.
This was true, of course, only in the case of diameters taken
at specific and clearly marked anatomical points. Where the
boundary points had to be located by secondary measurements preliminary to taking the diameter measurements,
more time was needed, and the risk of error was slightly
greater.

However, of the 17 diameter measurements on the basis
of which we have finally standardized the anthropometric
technique, only three have to be taken in this latter manner
(see p. 54). In practice, this anthropometric work is best done

[8] The ordinary ½ mm. rule can be used almost as accurately. The measurements are recorded in $\frac{1}{10}$ mm. units. When the ½ mm. rule is used, it
is necessary to interpolate the scale to fifths of a division. While accurate,
this method is a little hard on the eyes. The photographic images can, of
course, be projected and enlarged to any desired size provided the proportions
remain the same.

one step at a time for the whole available series of photographs. A high standard of efficiency and accuracy cannot be maintained when the work is done one picture at a time, or when all the measurements are taken on a picture before proceeding to the next individual, as is the rule in anthropometry on the living subject. This advantage of being able to do anthropometry one step at a time is considerable and probably accounts in large measure for an increase in accuracy over what we have been able to attain in anthropometry on living bodies.

Initially we experimented with a great many measurements of diameter in an attempt to determine what diameters best differentiate fine gradations of component variation. Almost all such measurements clearly differentiate ectomorphy from the other two components, for as ectomorphy rises nearly all diameter measurements fall sharply. Even the simple height-weight ratio, or, as we use it, height over the cube root of weight, is by itself a fairly accurate index of the third component for the body as a whole. Indeed, the accurate measurement of the third component in a physique generally offers little difficulty. Ectomorphy is so sharply defined and unconcealable a factor that an untrained person can ordinarily be taught in a few hours to gauge it anthroposcopically to within half a degree on a 7-point scale, or to within one degree on a 15-point scale. It is in the matter of accurate differentiation between the two massive components (endomorphy and mesomorphy) that the difficulty and the challenge present themselves.

In the beginning we took many more diameters than are necessary for accurate somatotyping on a 7-point scale. At one time we used five different facial diameters, four neck diameters, eleven trunk diameters, six arm and seven leg diameters—thirty-three in all. The principal reason for using so many of these measurements was a desire to reveal fine differences between dominances of the first and second components. The first component corresponds essentially to a central concentration of mass. The second component reflects a relatively even distribution of mass and strength and thickness of structure, even at the peripheries and extremities of the organism. Such differences are sufficiently pronounced that the trained eye experiences no difficulty in perceiving them, but it is not easy to demonstrate minor variations in terms of a small number of fixed linear measurements. Calipers cannot see. The human body is so plastic a structure that its variation of detail seems infinite.

We needed, therefore, to translate into anthropometric language certain trends of bodily proportion which could be seen clearly in the perspective obtained by viewing the body simultaneously from three orthogonal directions, but which could not always be seen, and might even seem to be contradicted, from the perspective of a single linear measurement. The problem was much like that of topographic mapping. One could scarcely expect to map a terrain by studying it from but a single vantage point. Consequently, differentiation between the first and second components could not, at the beginning, rest upon anthropometric measurements alone, but had always to be supported by anthroposcopic judgments. Combined with these judgments, however, the anthropometric measurements make possible an unequivocal differentiation of these two components. Just how this differentiation is effected will be made clearer when we consider the actual technique of somatotyping (Chapter IV).

From the beginning, all the measurements used were expressed as simple ratios to stature. This step escapes for the time being the problem of absolute size. For many purposes size is a factor of great importance, but in constructing the norms for somatotyping, size is placed in the denominator and is canceled out of the reckoning.

By experimenting with a large series we were able to determine approximately how many of these measurements were necessary to establish objective discrimination among the morphological entities we were attempting to define. Also we were able to select and retain those measurements which yielded the best discrimination. Had we elected to use a finer scale than the 7-point scale, it would have been necessary perhaps to standardize the anthropometric procedure on the basis of a greater number of measurements than those described below, but for the anthropometric standardization of a 7-point scale for each of the three components, the 17 measurements here presented, together with the ratio of height to the cube root of weight, are adequate.

THE MEASUREMENTS USED

Each of the following measurements is divided by the height of the subject[9] in order to convert it into a ratio. The positions at which these measurements are taken are shown in Fig. 2.

I. *First region*

FB$_1$ (Facial-Breadth-One). Photographic diameter taken at the highest level of the junction of the pinna of the ear with the skin line of the head (otobasion superior). Occasionally it is obscured slightly by hair, but it can then be located accurately by following the projection of the skin line upward to the correct level. Frontal picture.

FB$_2$ (Facial-Breadth-Two). Photographic diameter taken at the lowest level of the junction of the lobe of the ear with the skin line (otobasion inferior). Frontal picture.

NTap (Neck-Thickness-Anteroposterior). The shortest photographic anteroposterior diameter of the neck. Lateral picture.

NTt (Neck-Thickness-Transverse). The shortest transverse photographic diameter of the neck. Frontal picture.

[9] To arrive at an accurate measure of height, we use the height taken on a wall scale and translated into its equivalent linear distance on the film. Measurements of height made from the pictures are inaccurate, both because of postural variation and because of the tendency of the hair to obscure the top of the head.

II. *Second region*

TB₁   (Trunk-Breadth-One). The distance between the upper-most visible points in the photographic lines formed by the posterior axillary folds. Dorsal picture.

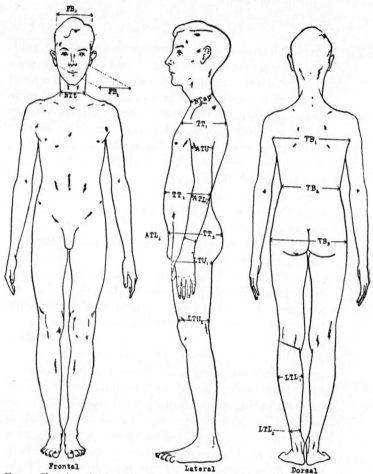

Frontal   Lateral   Dorsal

FIG. 2. Showing the locations on the body at which the 17 diameters are measured.

TT₁   (Trunk-Thickness-One). Horizontal anteroposterior photographic diameter of the trunk taken at a point midway between the level of the center of the nipple and the most anteriorly projecting point of the sternoclavicular junction. Lateral picture.

TB$_2$ (Trunk-Breadth-Two). Minimum transverse photographic diameter taken at the narrowest level of the waist. Dorsal picture.

III. *Third region*

ATU   (Arm-Thickness-Upper). Anteroposterior photographic arm diameter taken at the level of the mid-point between the photographic center of the cubital fossa, and a point on the skin overlying the greater tuberosity of the humerus and lying immediately beneath the anterior tip of the acromion process. This point should be marked with a dermographic pencil before the picture is taken, but can be located with fair accuracy if such a precaution is omitted. The measurement is taken in a plane perpendicular to the axis of the arm. Lateral picture.

ATL$_1$ (Arm-Thickness-Lower-One). Photographic forearm diameter taken at the level of greatest thickness below the elbow, in a plane perpendicular to the axis of the forearm. Lateral picture.

ATL$_2$ (Arm-Thickness-Lower-Two). Photographic diameter taken in a plane perpendicular to the axis of the forearm, at a level two inches proximal to a point on the skin surface immediately over the most anterior photographic projection of the styloid process of the radius. A grid consisting of two-inch squares is usually photographed into the pictures, chiefly for its value in locating exact horizontals. The two-inch measurement is laid off on the arm simply by adjusting the dividers to the exact width of one of these squares. (Also, on the pedestal on which the subject stands a distance of exactly two inches is marked off.) For this measurement to be valid, the back of the hand must lie in a plane approximately at right angles to the axis of the camera. Lateral picture.

IV. *Fourth region*

TT$_2$ (Trunk-Thickness-Two). Minimum horizontal anteroposterior photographic diameter taken at the level of the waistline. Lateral picture.

TB₃   (Trunk-Breadth-Three). Maximum horizontal transverse photographic diameter taken at the widest level of the hips. The points are usually found over the trochanters, but in high endomorphy they are frequently above the iliac crests, and in high mesomorphy they are often well below the trochanters, as is much more frequently the case with women. Dorsal picture.

TT₃   (Trunk-Thickness-Three). Horizontal anteroposterior diameter taken at the level of a point on the body surface directly over the symphysis pubis. This point is easily defined photographically as the vertex of an angle formed (in the lateral picture) by the skin line of the abdomen and the anterior line of the pubic hair. Lateral picture.

V. *Fifth region*

LTU₁   (Leg-Thickness-Upper-One). Horizontal anteroposterior photographic diameter of the leg taken at the level of the center of the photographic angle formed by the subgluteal fold. Lateral picture.

LTU₂   (Leg-Thickness-Upper-Two). Horizontal anteroposterior photographic diameter of the leg taken at the level of the photographic center of the slight fossa or hollow seen immediately above the patella. In the rare cases (of extreme endomorphy) in which this fossa cannot be seen photographically, the measurement is taken at the superior margin of the patella. Lateral picture.

LTL₁   (Leg-Thickness-Lower-One). Maximum photographic transverse calf diameter taken at the level of the greatest thickness of the calf, or gastrocnemius muscle, in a plane perpendicular to the axis of the lower leg. Dorsal picture. Left leg.

LTL₂   (Leg-Thickness-Lower-Two). The minimum photographic transverse ankle diameter. Taken at the narrowest point in the ankle, not necessarily in a plane at right angles to the axis of the leg. Dorsal picture. Left leg.

It should be emphasized again that these 17 diameter measurements have been selected, not by a preconceived logic, but by trial and error. They were originally included, along with a much larger series of measurements, because of their photographic availability and reliability. They were retained because they yielded relatively sharp and constant differentiation among physiques which also differed anthroposcopically. We have no assurance, on the other hand, that this is the best possible set of measurements—we are still experimenting in the hope of discovering better ones. Furthermore, it should be pointed out that the division of the body into these five regions is essentially arbitrary. At various stages in the research we have used a greater number of regions as our units. Depending upon the precision and detail one is interested in, the number of measurements and of regions could be multiplied indefinitely. With only five regions we occasionally encounter puzzling disharmonies within a region, particularly disharmonies between head and neck, but the method to be outlined below adequately takes care of most of such discrepancies.

THE FINAL CONSTRUCTION OF THE SCALES

The technique of somatotyping was built up by combining anthroposcopy with a detailed consideration of the anthropometric measurements just listed. Henceforth we shall designate a somatotype by three numerals, one for each component. These three numerals indicate the degree to which a subject exhibits each of the three components. The numeral 1 stands for the lowest observed amount of the component; the numeral 7 stands for the most extreme dominance by the component.

We first selected, by inspection of the photographs, unquestioned examples of the four somatotypes 711 (extreme endomorphy), 171 (extreme mesomorphy), 117 (extreme ectomorphy), and 444 (the physique falling at the mid-point of all three scales).[10] Next we recorded the photographic measurements of these types (every measurement expressed as a ratio to stature) and studied their interrelations. These measurements determine 18 different anthropometric series (including the ratio of height to cube root of weight). After these four basic somatotypes had been fully bracketed in terms of anthropometric measurements, photographs representing intermediate somatotypes were tentatively isolated by anthroposcopic examination and their measurements taken. These measurements were studied in relation to the several series of measurements obtained from the four basic somatotypes.

Now, at this point in the procedure, where we were correlating anthropometric measurements with relatively small anthroposcopic differences, it appeared desirable to introduce a change of method. Instead of deciding what anthropometric values serve to differentiate the intermediate somatotypes by taking the measurements solely from the examples selected by inspection, we checked these values by *interpolating* in the series of anthropometric measurements determined by the four basic somatotypes. This procedure is necessary, for one thing, because a perfect "bull's-eye" example of a given somatotype rarely if ever occurs in nature. These interpolations are of a rather complex nature, for they must be made within a system which is three-dimensional rather than two-dimensional.[11] All in all, therefore, a large amount of "cutting and trying" was necessary ultimately to establish the anthropometric measurements capable of defining in a three-dimensional "space" those points which we now call the somatotypes. Time, and the reader's patience, do not permit

[10] The possibility of finding a 444 in the general population raises certain interesting theoretical issues which will be dealt with in Chapter V.

[11] The actual process of determining and defining the somatotypes was greatly facilitated by the construction of a series of experimental models made from cubical blocks which were attached together in various constellations. As a somatotype was defined, a block representing it was placed in the appropriate position within a hollow cube (see Fig. 9).

us to review in detail all the experimentation and testing of hypotheses—both good and bad—which characterized the early stages of this part of the research. The problem was much like a jigsaw puzzle in three dimensions. But once the two parts of the research—the anthroposcopy and the anthropometry—are pieced together, the result is a complete and useful picture.

Anthropometric correlates for the independent somatotyping of each of the five regions of the body were determined by the procedure outlined briefly above. The final outcome is shown in the appendix (p. 265). There we see, in tabular form, the anthropometric measurements which characterize and differentiate the various somatotypes. These tables make it possible with complete "objectivity" to determine an individual's somatotype.

THE NUMBER OF SOMATOTYPES

Since it is possible, from anthropometric tables, to determine the measurements of a given somatotype, we can describe what a person having that physique would look like. But this fact does not mean that such a physique will necessarily be found in nature. Certain somatotypes appear not to have been created. Let us consider, for example, the somatotype 713. Even in the first sorting of the pictures we found several excellent examples of the striking 712, although we saw that this somatotype is rare. The presence of the 712 suggested the possibility that out at the periphery of the distribution we might find a 713. From the anthropometric data it was possible, by means of a kind of three-dimensional extrapolation, to predict almost exactly what the measurements of the 713 must be. Among the 4,000 photographs there were three or four which looked, from inspection, like candidates for the 713, but when the anthropometric measurements were taken it was plain that they were not of this somatotype. As yet we have never found a 713. Probably it does not exist.

The objective anthropometric definition of the rare somatotypes which fall near the peripheries of the distribution of
human physiques has been a slow and laborious task. The
tedious complexities to be encountered in making three-
dimensional interpolations and extrapolations in 18 series
of anthropometric measurements can readily be imagined.
Of the 76 somatotypes which we have isolated and described,
and of which we have available photographic and anthropometric records, the 50 or so which are relatively common
could have been described just about as accurately during
the first year of this work as now. It is the definition of the
rarities that has made this part of the task both toilsome and
slow. Even now it is by no means certain that our descriptive
system embraces quite all the variations of nonpathological
male physique that are to be found. Nevertheless, among
almost 10,000 photographs taken to date, none has appeared
which could not be classified into one of the 76 somatotypes
described in this volume. This final number, 76, represents
an increase of 6 over an original 70 somatotypes tentatively
isolated by means of anthroposcopy alone.

Table 4 illustrates the position of the 76 somatotypes
among the 343 *theoretical* possibilities, in a simple two-
dimensional scheme arranged as a progression of the first
component. (The number of somatotypes would be 343 if
it were equal to the number of all combinations and permutations of the numerals 1 to 7 taken three at a time.) Only
the somatotypes represented by the bold-face numerals occur
in nature. Note that the sum of the components ranges between 9 and 12 (see p. 120). There are many more somatotypes extremely low in a component than extremely high
in it. That is to say, there are many more 1's than 7's. An
individual can be at 1 in two of the components, but he
can be at 6 or 7 in only one component. Except for the rare
551 and the excessively rare 515, the level of 5 is reached
in only one component of a physique. With two other rare

TABLE 4

ILLUSTRATION OF THE POSITIONS OF THE 76 SOMATOTYPES
AMONG 343 THEORETICAL POSSIBILITIES

111	211	311	411	511	611	711
112	212	312	412	512	612	712
113	213	313	413	513	613	713
114	214	314	414	514	614	714
115	215	315	415	515	615	715
116	216	316	416	516	616	716
117	217	317	417	517	617	717
121	221	321	421	521	621	721
122	222	322	422	522	622	722
123	223	323	423	523	623	723
124	224	324	424	524	624	724
125	225	325	425	525	625	725
126	226	326	426	526	626	726
127	227	327	427	527	627	727
131	231	331	431	531	631	731
132	232	332	432	532	632	732
133	233	333	433	533	633	733
134	234	334	434	534	634	734
135	235	335	435	535	635	735
136	236	336	436	536	636	736
137	237	337	437	537	637	737
141	241	341	441	541	641	741
142	242	342	442	542	642	742
143	243	343	443	543	643	743
144	244	344	444	544	644	744
145	245	345	445	545	645	745
146	246	346	446	546	646	746
147	247	347	447	547	647	747
151	251	351	451	551	651	751
152	252	352	452	552	652	752
153	253	353	453	553	653	753
154	254	354	454	554	654	754
155	255	355	455	555	655	755
156	256	356	456	556	656	756
157	257	357	457	557	657	757
161	261	361	461	561	661	761
162	262	362	462	562	662	762
163	263	363	463	563	663	763
164	264	364	464	564	664	764
165	265	365	465	565	665	765
166	266	366	466	566	666	766
167	267	367	467	567	667	767
171	271	371	471	571	671	771
172	272	372	472	572	672	772
173	273	373	473	573	673	773
174	274	374	474	574	674	774
175	275	375	475	575	675	775
176	276	376	476	576	676	776
177	277	377	477	577	677	777

exceptions, the 461 and 641, if an individual is 6 in one component, he cannot be higher than 3 in any other component. Except for the 731 and 371 (both extremely rare), if an individual is 7 in one component, he will not be higher than 2 in any other component. It is important to note that five of these exceptions represent a massing of the first two components against the third, while the sixth, the 515, represents an alliance of the first and third against the second. From this one should predict that the statistical incompatibility, or negative correlation, between the first two components will be somewhat less than that either between the first and third or between the second and third. In men there is a much higher negative correlation between the second and third components than between either the first and second or the first and third (see p. 138).

The six somatotypes named above as exceptions are the six which had to be added to the original 70 predicted by anthroposcopy alone. All of them are rare, but as a group they represent a distinct tendency in the distribution of male physiques to depart from a symmetrical balancing of the three components, and they express a differential incompatibility among the components.

(For a table showing the distribution of the population among the somatotypes see Table 23a, p. 268.)

THE POSSIBILITY OF USING OTHER NUMBERS OF SOMATOTYPES

The procedure outlined above yields 76 somatotypes, simply because we measure the components in terms of a 7-point scale, and in the following pages we shall continue to treat the problem of morphology as though the varieties of human physique could be adequately differentiated by means of a classificatory scheme involving 76 categories. It must not be forgotten, however, that the creation of these 76 classes is essentially an arbitrary procedure. There is no magic to the number 76—it is merely the number we obtain when we elect to use a 7-point scale and ignore fractional values on this scale. As a matter of fact, when we use the fractional value ½ (as we often do) and designate a somatotype, for example, as 5 2½ 3½ (ordinarily written 523-534) we make an implicit assumption that the number of distinguishable somatotypes is nearer four or five hundred than 76, for we are then using 15-point scales for the three components. (The *precise* number of somatotypes to be obtained from 15-point scales has not yet been determined.)

The important aspect of somatotyping is not the number of somatotypes, but the fact that human physiques are measured in terms of three basic components. These components can be scaled against *continuous* scales, and it is only for purposes of convenience that we divide these scales by means of 7 points at equal-appearing intervals. Given sufficient refinement of method, these scales could be subdivided indefinitely. Conversely, the coarseness of the units used can be made greater at will.

To those who are accustomed to schemes which classify physiques in terms of three or four "types," 76 categories may appear unwieldy and unnecessary, and for certain kinds of research fewer somatotypes would undoubtedly be of some advantage. There are two methods by which the number could be reduced. Either fewer scale divisions could be used for gauging each component, or neighboring somatotypes obtained with the 7-point scales could be combined into single categories. The redivision of the scales would necessitate a complete revision of the anthropometric tables (Tables 23 to 40, Appendix I), which would be a considerable undertaking. Consequently, for most experiments requiring fewer categories, it would appear advisable to combine certain of the closely related somatotypes. Which ones are to be combined depends, of course, upon the investigator's purpose, but as an example of what can be done to reduce the number of somatotypes, we might make the following combinations.

Descriptive Classification	Somatotypes Included
1. Extreme endomorph	711
2. Strong endomorph	622, 522, 533
3. Moderate endomorph	433
4. Mesomorphic endomorph	721, 731, 641, 631, 621, 632, 543, 542, 541, 532
5. Mesomorph-endomorph	551, 442
6. Ectomorphic endomorph	712, 613, 612, 623, 523, 524, 534, 514
7. Ectomorph-endomorph	515, 424
8. Extreme mesomorph	171
9. Strong mesomorph	262, 252, 353
10. Moderate mesomorph	343
11. Endomorphic mesomorph	271, 371, 461, 361, 261, 362, 352, 453, 452, 451
12. Ectomorphic mesomorph	172, 163, 162, 263, 253, 154, 254, 354
13. Ectomorph-mesomorph	244
14. Extreme ectomorph	117
15. Strong ectomorph	226, 225, 335
16. Moderate ectomorph	334
17. Endomorphic ectomorph	217, 216, 316, 326, 325, 415, 425, 435
18. Mesomorphic ectomorph	127, 126, 136, 236, 235, 145, 245, 345
19. Balanced	444, 434, 344, 443

This particular procedure would thus produce 19 categories, or 19 somatotypes newly defined. Certain purposes might be better served by the use of a coarser "mesh" of this sort.

On the other hand, there are experiments and correlational studies for which it might be best to select certain widely separated somatotypes. A study might concern only the extreme somatotypes, the 711, 171, and 117, and be designed to reveal their psychological differences. Actually an experiment of this sort might lead to anomalous results, for our own observations indicate that traits correlated with a component often fail to reach their maximum expression in the morphological extremes. These extreme physical variants are, in a sense, abnormalities of nature and they must be treated as such. Hence a study of the sort we are discussing ought probably to concern the groups:

a.	621	612	622	623	632
b.	261	162	262	263	362
c.	126	216	226	236	326

But these are only suggestions. It is presumptive to prescribe how another investigator should proceed.

NOTE ON THE SOMATOTYPING OF WOMEN

We have not yet been able to secure an extensive series of standardized photographs of women. Consequently, such somatotyping of women as we have done rests on the anthroposcopic techniques alone and has little claim to scientific reliability. Using only the inspectional method of study, we have tentatively somatotyped several series of pictures of women students. Most of these were merely "shadow pictures" taken on bromide paper for purposes of postural study, and they are, of course, relatively worthless for anthropometric purposes. Nevertheless, we have contrived to classify a series of 2,500 such pictures, and, pending the availability of more adequate photographs, this preliminary somatotyping is regarded as a prediction and an approximate estimate of the probable distribution of somatotypes among women.

Such a predictive distribution is probably not sufficiently accurate or valid to be taken at face value, but it is of interest to note that the same 76 somatotypes that are found among men *seem* to occur among women, and no more, although the distribution of the population among the somatotypes is different. Endomorphy, and physiques combining a strong first and third component against the second, are much commoner in women than in men. Mesomorphy, and the strong combination of the first and second components against the third, are commoner in men.

In Appendix 2 is included a series of impressionistic drawings of young women representing 9 different somatotypes—three examples of a marked predominance in each component. These drawings were done for the most part from shadow pictures and they are not to be taken as anthropometrically correct. But the proportions are correct enough to lend the drawings a certain educational value for the beginning student of somatotyping.

SECONDARY VARIATIONS

The three components, endomorphy, mesomorphy and ectomorphy, in terms of which we designate the 76 basic somatotypes, are what we might call first-order morphological variables. They are primary variables in the sense that when the dominance of one of them is extreme the result is a physique easily recognized as a basic variant. In addition to these first-order variables we may conceive of second-, third-, and even nth-order morphological factors. The human physique is so complex that the number of specific aspects in terms of which. one could make a rank order of the population seems almost unlimited. Length of ears, width between the eyes, crowding of the teeth, sitting height, asymmetry of features, length of foot, etc., etc., are obvious secondary variations. The order we assign such variables must depend, of course, upon the purpose they are to serve. For the purpose of constructing a primary schema of morphological variation the endomorphic, mesomorphic, and ectomorphic components seem the most adequate first-order variables available.

Other aspects or components of variation are of great importance in the study of physical constitution and psychological personality. Which of these aspects are to be considered second-order and which third-order is a matter for empirical investigation. Our own studies thus far have revealed at least three secondary variables which merit the close attention of the student of constitutional psychology. These aspects include dysplasia, gynandromorphy (bisexuality), and what we call a textural aspect. In addition to these variables the following discussion will treat the problem of hirsutism (hairiness)—a secondary variable which is of considerable interest to the anthropologist but which has as yet failed to reveal its importance in the study of personality.[12]

DYSPLASIA

This variable is defined as any inconsistent or uneven mixing of the three primary components in different regions of the body. We refer to the dysplasia in a physique as the d-index. Its measurement is of the simplest nature, once the somatotyping of the five regions of the body has been completed, for the dysplastic index is merely a mathematical indication of the degree of disagreement between the separate or partial somatotypes of the five bodily regions. We compute the dysplasia by finding, for each component separately, the sum of the differences between each region of the body and each other region and adding these differences for all three components.

Suppose, for example, that we wish to calculate the dysplasia in a physique whose somatotype in each of the five regions of the body is as follows:

Region	Somatotype
I.	361
II.	252
III.	451
IV.	362
V.	352

[12] There are, of course, many variables which, through the ingenuity of the anthropologists, have been related to one another and to cultural and racial characteristics. Some of these are pigmentation, cephalic index, and numerous other measurements made upon the head. Many of these variables could be profitably studied in their relation to somatotypes, but the present study has not undertaken this task.

For the intercomparison of the five values of the first component we see that there are ten matchings to be made: I with
II, III, IV, and V; II with III, IV, and V; III with IV and V;
and IV with V. The sum of the disagreements (differences
found in these ten pairings) is 8. Similarly, there are ten
pairings to be made for the second component, and the sum

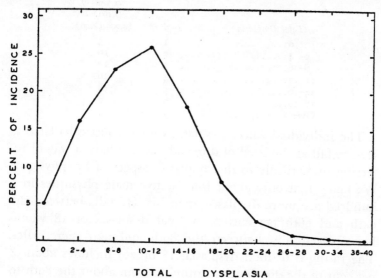

TOTAL   DYSPLASIA

FIG. 3. Showing the percentage of the male population characterized by
different amounts of dysplasia.

of their differences is 6. For the third component, the sum
of the differences is also 6. The total dysplasia for the three
components is, then, represented by the sum of 8 plus 6 plus
6, or 20.

Figure 3 illustrates the amount of total dysplasia found by
this method in the group of 4,000 college men. The range is
from 0 to 38, and the distribution is skewed to the right.
By dividing this range into seven steps which, except at the
extremes, are numerically equal, we derive a 7-point scale
of the d-index which is useful and convenient for the study

of individuals. The values of the dysplasia corresponding to these seven degrees of the d-index are expressed in Table 5.

TABLE 5

This table relates total dysplasia to the index, d, and shows the approximate distribution of the population against this index.

Total Dysplasia	d	Approximate Per Cent of Distribution (4,000 Cases)
0	1	5
2– 4	2	16
6– 8	3	23
10–12	4	26
14–16	5	18
18–20	6	8
Over 20	7	4

The individual whose dysplasia we have just calculated is seen to fall at the level of d 6, and we now have a way of referring numerically to the dysplastic aspect of his physique. We know that only about four or five male physiques in a hundred are more dysplastic than his. He falls between the 94th and 96th percentiles. A total dysplasia of 18 would have placed him between the 89th and 93rd percentiles. The rating d 6 (total dysplasia, 18 or 20) includes about 8 per cent of the distribution, running from about the 89th to about the 96th percentile.

In a sizable series of cases the third component uniformly shows more dysplasia than the second, and the second shows more than the first. Table 6 illustrates the distribution of dysplasia for the three components separately, and Fig. 4 presents the same data in graphic form. These data are typical of all the material studied thus far, but we do not know how to explain the greater dysplasia in the third component. It may possibly constitute an indirect support of Viola's well-known contention (see p. 15) that the third component represents a hyperevolute characteristic which would likely manifest itself as relatively local bodily specializations rather than as an even development of the body as a whole.

TABLE 6

This table gives the number of cases (in 1,000) which reveal various degrees of dysplasia in each component, and in the three components as a whole. (From an unpublished study by C. W. Dupertuis, of Presbyterian Hospital, New York City.)

Total Dysplasia	First Component	Second Component	Third Component	All Three Components
0.................	507	348	258	60
4.................	272	353	358	161
6.................	190	224	231	96
8.................	16	30	73	140
10.................	15	37	66	94
12.................		4	7	160
14.................		2	6	81
16.................		2	1	87
18.................				53
20.................				27
22.................				19
24.................				11
26.................				2
28.................				5
30.................				2
34.................				1
36.................				1
Means.............	2.51	3.47	4.31	10.22

The measurement of dysplasia promises to become a tool of value in the study of conflict both morphological and psychological, and perhaps therefore in the study of genius and of delinquency. This possibility is discussed in Chapter VII.

It is fairly clear that there is greater dysplasia in the female body than in the male, or at least that there are greater extremes of dysplasia. In the clinics we have seen, under anthroposcopic inspection, female physiques carrying a total dysplasia of 40 or even 46. It is not uncommon to find female bodies with highly endomorphic legs and highly ectomorphic upper segments (arms, upper trunk, head, and neck). But we cannot measure female dysplasia with scientific validity until we first can somatotype an extensive series of the "normal" population in order to establish norms. This we have not yet been able to do. In the study of dysplasia among psychotics, however, we have had better success. The preliminary study of a series of about 3,500 psychotics, mostly schizophrenic, reveals a distinctly higher dysplasia among these patients than among college students, and it also reveals several recurrent and apparently characteristic dysplasias (see p. 239).

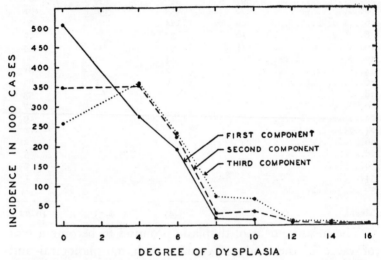

FIG. 4. Showing the number of cases in 1,000 having various degrees of dysplasia within each of the three components. These curves show that the greatest average dysplasia occurs in the third component. No point is recorded for a degree of 2 because this value is mathematically impossible under the present method of computation.

GYNANDROMORPHY

A conspicuous characteristic of a physique is the extent to which it presents traits ordinarily associated with the opposite sex. Every human body is both male and female in the sense that the rudimentary beginnings of both sets of sexual equipment are present. Ordinarily only one set of sexual characteristics is developed and functional, but in most bodies there are more or less prominent traces of what are called the secondary traits of the other sex. A highly masculine physique, or a highly feminine physique, is one relatively lacking in such traces. The Italian group of clinical anthropologists (di Giovanni) were the first, we believe, to use the term gynandromorphic (of female-male form) to refer to this phenomenon of morphological bisexuality. As an abbreviated terminology we use the term "g-aspect," or "g-index," in this connection. A man of high g-index has conspicuous feminity in his body. A woman of high g-index is conspicuously masculine.

When the g-index is high in the male, there is an intrusion of softness throughout the body. The hips are widened, the pelvis is broader and of feminine form, the feminine arrangement of pubic hair is conspicuous, there is a fullness and rounding of the buttocks and lower abdomen, often there is a pronounced fatty simulation of mammary development and sometimes there is functional glandular tissue in the breasts. There may be a rounding of all bodily contours. The bones are small, and the arms are relatively small or underdeveloped (they are both short and slender) as compared with the legs. The outer curves of the thighs reveal a full, even sweep which may extend from the knee to the waistline. These curves simulate the lower half of the typical figure-8 contour of the female body. The outer curve of the lower leg is well developed, in contrast to the flatter inner (gastrocnemius) curve. The upper arms and thighs tend toward fullness, the skin is soft and velvety with an even subcutaneous upholstering, and the features of the face tend to be small, with softened relief. Long eyelashes are the rule.

The scaling of gynandromorphy as we now do it, is simple. The photographs within each somatotype are arranged in ascending order of gynandromorphy. This is done by paired matchings. Next we rate the photographs on a 7-point scale of gynandromorphy. Successive numerals are assigned as nearly as possible to equal-appearing intervals. Given a sufficient sampling of a particular somatotype, it is possible to establish a standardized scale for the g-index. Then, after a new photograph is somatotyped, the g-index is determined simply by matching the photograph against the standard scale for the same somatotype. In Fig. 5A we see two examples of the somatotype 442—note the difference in gynandromorphy. To attempt to interpret the g-index without regard to somatotype would, of course, be misleading. The first step in a morphological description must in some way include a definition of the basic form, or architecture, for otherwise we might soon find ourselves matching the secondary characteristics of horses against those of hippopotami.

On the other hand, it is obvious, even to superficial inspection, that the various somatotypes differ among themselves in the extent to which they exhibit gynandromorphy. The typical 425 is much more bisexual than the typical 245. Hence it is of interest to make cross-comparisons among the somatotypes. This can best be done by setting up a master scale of the g-index from a rank-ordering of a large "normal" population. Armed with this scale we can readily determine what degree of gynandromorphy is typical of a given somatotype. Then, from the scale determined for the members of that somatotype we can decide whether a given individual has more or less g than is "normally" expected. It is this latter aspect—the amount of g relative to other members of his group—which appears to be of the more importance in the study of an individual's personality and conflicts.

In assigning the g-index to a male photograph, the following specific criteria are taken into consideration:

1. The extent to which the features suggest femininity. Feminine facial characteristics include principally smallness of feature, softer and rounder relief (not necessarily the endomorphic roundness of the whole), small, oval eyebrows, long eyelashes, delicate alae of the nostrils, a small mouth with full lips.

2. Rounded delicacy of the shoulders and relative weakness of the arms. Feminine arms are both shorter and more delicate, as compared with the legs, than are masculine arms.

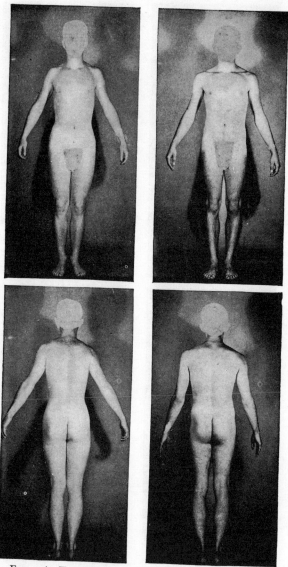

FIG. 5 A. Two individuals of the same somatotype, 442, showing different degrees of gynandromorphy. These physiques are of the same somatotype in all regions of the body except the second (thoracic trunk). The individual on the left is higher and the one on the right is lower in gynandromorphy, than is the average 442.

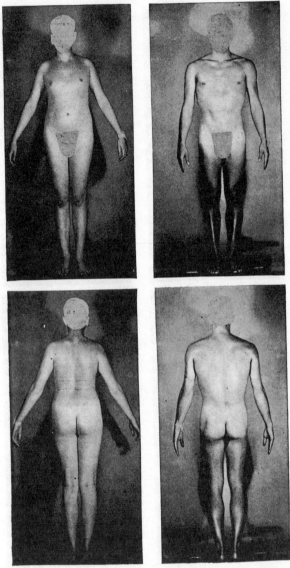

Fig. 5 B. Two individuals of different somatotype showing different degrees of gynandromorphy. The individual on the left is of a somatotype, 523–524, normally high in gynandromorphy. The individual on the right is of a somatotype, 262–172, normally low in gynandromorphy.

3. Disproportionately wide hips.

4. The hour-glass, or figure-8, appearance of the body as a whole (especially in the dorsal photograph). This involves a high waist, softly molded shoulders, a full sweep of outer curve from waist to knee, and full, "pneumatic"-appearing buttocks. Also, the groins (frontal photograph) and the inner surfaces of the thighs are relatively full.

5. Sparsity of secondary hair, and feminine distribution of the pubic hair.

6. Feminine softness of the subcutaneous finish of the entire body. Like the feminine softening of the features of the face, this is a characteristic which can be readily differentiated from gross endomorphic form, although a very high g-index does not often occur in a physique with a very low endomorphic component.

7. The presence of breast formation.

8. Prominence of the outer curve of the lower leg as compared to the inner curve (bulge of the gastrocnemius muscle).

THE TEXTURAL ASPECT

Men cannot forever ignore the problem of systematically gauging the quality of human stock. A projected social science which completely waives the question of the texture of human material has no more chance of survival than an engineering science that ignores the texture of its building materials. There is perhaps as much difference between a fine human face and a coarse one as there is between endomorphy and ectomorphy, but this secondary *textural* variable is more elusive and more difficult to objectify than are the three primary components. The importance of the problem of quality, however, is attested by the fact that the language we speak is rich in modifiers expressing quality and texture in human beings. Examples: fine, clean-cut, refined, aristocratic, well-bred, thoroughbred, noble, etc., etc.

Systematic recognition of qualitative differences in human stock is likely, in a democracy, to be discouraged, but quality is readily enough accepted as a differentia for horses, and informally sometimes for the neighbor's children. Men become fairly expert at gauging the "thoroughbred" aspect of a horse, but they sometimes remain squeamish at the thought of judging the degree to which they themselves are thoroughbreds. Perhaps a certain wisdom resides in such squeamishness, for there has never been a clear statement of the criteria by which human texture can be gauged. Yet the textural variable is there, and to deny it is an act of willful blindness. One thing is clear, however: it is patently impossible to deal meaningfully with this aspect until the study of basic morphology rests upon a stable and well-tested foundation. We must segregate individuals according to the first-order variables before we establish norms for secondary aspects. Otherwise, it would be like comparing the textural details of an apple with those of an orange.

The somatotyping techniques are admittedly not yet sufficiently developed to justify an extensive discussion of the quality-variable, or t-index, as we sometimes call it. We shall not at present attempt to define the t-index beyond the simple statement that within each somatotype there is a fairly clear gradation from very coarse to very fine physical texture, and that it is easy to arrange a series of standardized pictures in an ascending order of textural fineness, provided the pictures all fall within the same somatotype. We do not, as yet, undertake to compare the textural fineness of a 117 with that of a 171, for these two are different animals. Such cross-comparisons may later prove feasible, but norms and standards need first to be established within the separate somatotypes.

We scale the textural aspect just as we do the g-aspect. We arrange the cases *within* a single somatotype into a rank-ordered series, and then we apply a 7-point scale. The coarsest appearing texture is assigned the numeral 1 and the finest appearing texture is given the numeral 7. Once a standard series has been scaled in this manner, other instances of the same somatotype can be graded by comparing them with the standard series. In this fashion quality or texture can be measured with a precision which is at least comparable to the accuracy with which wine tasting and silk grading can be performed. In all three of these estimations the objective criteria of the judgment are difficult to define, but useful scales can nevertheless be constructed.

In order to discover with what reliability the textural aspect can be scaled, an experimenter (Sheldon) rated 1,000 somatotyped photographs which had already been arranged in 75 somatotype groups. The photographs were rated on a 7-point scale. These ratings were recorded and the series in each somatotype reshuffled. A month later the 1,000 ratings were repeated. The product-moment correlation between the two series of ratings, for the whole 1,000 cases, was + .93. With the somatotype established, it seems possible accurately to gauge the t-index, at least so far as statistical reliability is a criterion of accuracy.

It is of interest at this point to note that within a given somatotype there is a high correlation between the t-index and the fineness of the hair of the head. Although the matter remains to be explored, it may eventually prove possible to use the diameter of the hair as one objective correlate of the texture of the body. Another hypothesis to be explored is the possibility that apparent coarseness of texture might correlate with the gross size of the individual cells of various parts of the body.

At present we should not want to undertake to interpret a rating of the t-index except within its own somatotype. Furthermore, we have as yet discovered no statistically demonstrable relationship between the t-index and other personality variables. Nevertheless, it is a reasonable hypothesis that as we continue to explore motivational and other personality variables such relationships may emerge. In the meantime we regard the t-index as a kind of insurance against a future scientific "futilitarianism."

HIRSUTISM

Followers of Kretschmer and others have assumed that luxuriance of body hair is a trait directly related to mor-

TABLE 7

HIRSUTISM IN 1,000 COLLEGE STUDENTS

(From an unpublished study by C. W. Dupertuis, of Presbyterian Hospital, New York City)

Somatotype	Number of Cases	Mean Hirsutism	Somatotype	Number of Cases	Mean Hirsutism
117	5	2.40	371	1	2.00
126	7	2.29			
127	5	2.80	415	3	1.00
136	2	3.00	424	13	2.54
145	8	3.00	425	6	2.17
154	4	3.00	433	24	3.00
162	5	3.40	434	44	2.75
163	6	2.83	435	3	3.00
171	6	3.50	442	28	2.86
172	3	3.33	443	54	2.80
			444	38	2.92
216	6	3.00	451	5	3.40
217	3	2.67	452	21	3.19
225	20	2.55	453	12	2.92
226	18	2.44			
235	53	2.68	514	3	1.67
236	6	2.33	522	4	2.75
244	53	2.83	523	6	2.67
245	9	2.78	524	7	2.43
252	11	3.27	532	14	3.21
253	34	2.97	533	22	2.86
254	15	3.00	534	11	3.09
261	7	3.00	541	5	3.60
262	22	2.95	542	14	3.79
263	6	3.00	543	8	3.00
271	2	4.00			
			612	1	5.00
316	5	1.60	613	2	2.00
325	18	2.89	621	2	3.50
326	2	1.50	622	6	1.67
334	55	2.67	623	6	3.00
335	30	2.47	631	5	2.40
343	38	2.82	632	6	2.67
344	46	2.57	641	1	3.00
345	11	2.82			
352	20	3.20	711	2	2.00
353	49	3.00	712	4	4.00
354	11	3.00	721	3	3.00
361	5	4.00	731	1	1.00
362	10	3.30			

phological structure. Kretschmer associated hirsutism with his pyknic type, and absence of body hair with his asthenic type. On the other hand, we have found no correlation at all between endomorphy and hirsutism, and only a low negative correlation between ectomorphy and hirsutism. In our series there is a low positive correlation between mesomorphy and hirsutism.

The study of body hair was carried out by inspection of the photographs. Two independent investigators rated total hairiness of trunk, arms, and legs on a 5-point scale. On this scale, 1 means almost total absence of body hair, with extremely sparse pubic hair; 5 means extreme and generalized hirsutism. The three intermediate numerals refer, so far as possible, to equal-appearing increments in hirsutism.

Table 7 gives the mean ratings on hirsutism, by somatotypes, for a series of 1,000 college students. Examination of the table will reveal that there is a slight tendency for the heavy, massive somatotypes—the endomorphic mesomorphs —to develop more hairiness than is seen among the slender ectomorphic somatotypes. But when the components are considered separately, it is the mesomorphs and not the endomorphs who have this slight preponderance of hair.

Table 8 presents two sets of product-moment correlations between hirsutism and the three morphological components. The first series is from a study (unpublished) of 1,000 cases by C. W. Dupertuis. The second series is from a study of 1,700 cases by Sheldon.

TABLE 8

PRODUCT-MOMENT CORRELATIONS BETWEEN
HIRSUTISM AND THE MORPHOLOGICAL
COMPONENTS

(Results obtained by two experimenters)

	Endomorphy	*Mesomorphy*	*Ectomorphy*
Dupertuis (1939)....	.04	.22	−.23
Sheldon (1930)......	−.03	.27	−.24

CHAPTER IV

HOW TO PROCEED IN SOMATOTYPING

IN THIS chapter we shall outline step by step the procedure to be followed in the determination of an individual's somatotype. The technique,[1] as presented here, is designed for practical use. Its purpose is to provide for the classification of individuals at the level of physical constitution in such a manner that parallel studies of personality at other levels of investigation can be carried out efficiently and meaningfully. The particular measurements which we have adopted for standardization are not necessarily the only ones suitable to the purpose, but they are a group of measurements which (1) can be taken accurately and rapidly from photographs and (2) provide a foolproof objectification of the technique.

From the point of view of the anatomist or physical anthropologist, a classification of somatotypes is but the beginning of a morphological study. The physical anthropologist wants to know the correlation between general somatotype and the numerous specialized skeletal measurements from which he makes his racial classifications. From the point of view of the clinician and psychologist, when the somatotyping is completed the stage is set, and the study itself is ready to begin. The groundwork is then laid for an investigation of, let us say, somatotype and immunities and susceptibilities to disease, or between somatotype and

[1] Actually, two techniques for somatotyping are outlined in this chapter. The second is a purely "objective" anthropometric technique, but its efficient use depends upon the availability of electrical or mechanical aids for sorting anthropometric data. A machine for this purpose has been constructed (see Fig. 8).

psychological attributes. The following sections tell how to proceed in the first steps of a project in constitutional research.

Somatotyping begins with photography. Using the procedure outlined above (p. 30), we obtain, on the same film, three views of the human body. As the second task, we measure the photographs. The measurements taken are those listed in the previous chapter (p. 54), and they are taken from the film (negative)—not from the print. Each of these measurements is divided by the individual's height and multiplied by 100 in order to express it as a percentage of stature. Then with a set of photographs at hand, and with the anthropometric measurements recorded, we complete the somatotyping by the following specific steps. Two investigators should work together and check one another at each step.

Step 1. The photographs are examined, and by inspectional study (anthroposcopy) an estimate is made of the approximate strength of each component for the body as a whole. This judgment is ordinarily made from the inspection of a print rather than the negative. How well and accurately this can be done depends, of course, upon the training and experience of the investigators. A well-trained "somatotyper" should be able to gauge the component strengths with such accuracy that the further steps in the procedure will modify his estimate little. (For an example of the reliability with which this anthroposcopic estimate can be made see p. 101.)

From this point on we shall demonstrate the procedure by somatotyping the physique shown in Fig. 6A. This boy is 19 years old. We shall refer to him as P.

First impression: distinct predominance of the third component, with the first stronger than the second. Anthroposcopic estimate: 325.

The recording of this estimate completes step 1. We conclude that P is probably in the neighborhood of the point defined by the somatotype 325. How do we know this? At this stage we have based our estimate upon the detailed inspectional criteria set forth in Chapter VI, together with those unverbalized criteria that one accumulates through practice and experience with somatotyping. The final somatotype at which we shall arrive after we consider P's anthropometric measurements may be slightly different from the anthroposcopic estimate, but not so different as to change the order of predominance among the components. It is both quite easy and quite necessary for the investigator to acquire the ability to tell by inspection of the photographs which of the components is dominant in a physique and which is weakest, or to detect the near equality of the components when two or more are closely balanced. *Note:* In making the anthroposcopic estimate either for the body as a whole or for the individual regions (see below) it is better to record the components as equal unless the dominance is distinct and certain.

Step 2. We check the somatotype estimated in step 1 against the somatotype indicated by the ratio of P's height divided by the cube root of his weight. This ratio is 13.8. Using this ratio as an index, we enter Table 23 (Appendix 1) to find what somatotypes exhibit this or a similar ratio. The procedure in entering Table 23 is as follows. We lay a rule (a transparent one is best) along the row of figures opposite the ratio-index 13.8, and note which somatotypes occur in this row. We find the 235 and the 325. Now, the somatotype 235 is one in which the second component is higher than the first. But this contradicts the order of dominance observed in step 1. Therefore, we do not consider the 235 as a possibility, but only the 325. Next we consider in Table 23 the two rows adjacent to the row headed by the ratio-index 13.8, i.e., the rows opposite 13.7 and 13.9. Here we find the somatotypes 245, 335, 415, 145, 225, and

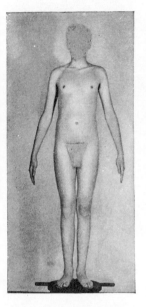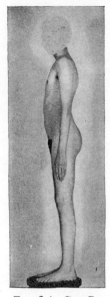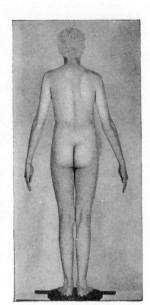

FIG. 6 A. Case P

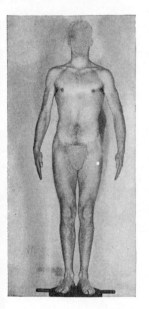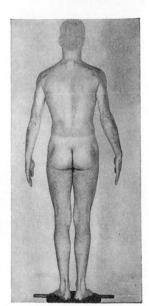

FIG. 6 B. Case Q

326. Of these we consider as candidates only the 415 and the 326, because all the others either disagree with the observed dominance among the components or deviate from the anthroposcopic estimate by more than one degree in some component. Next we consider the somatotypes two rows removed from 13.8, i.e., the rows opposite 13.6 and 14.0. Here we find the somatotypes 345, 425, 236 and 316. Of these, for the same reasons as stated above, we consider only the 316 and the 425. This procedure is then repeated for the somatotypes found three and four rows removed from 13.8. The only good candidates here are the 435 and the 216, respectively.

At this point we make a table like the following:

TABLE 9

Ratio	Rank				
	0	1	2	3	4
13.8	325	326 415	316 425	435	216

This table records the somatotypes occurring in the rows at various removes from the ratio-index 13.8. The number of rows removed determines the *rank* of the somatotype. We have, then, in Table 9, the various somatotypes to one of which P might reasonably belong, according to the criterion height over the cube root of weight, and we have these somatotypes recorded roughly in the order of their probability. This table agrees with the anthroposcopic estimate. So far, so good.

At this point let us state the rules relating to the construction of Table 9 and of the tables shortly to be considered.

The eligible somatotypes for a given ratio-index are those which (1) do not deviate by more than one degree in each component from the anthroposcopic estimate, (2) do not reverse or

contradict the relative dominance among the components as determined by the anthroposcopic estimate, and (3) are ordinarily
not, in the table, more than four rows removed from the ratio-
index.

There are exceptions to this last rule. Such exceptions,
although rare, arise when some marked dysplasia exists *within*
one of the five bodily regions. Of such dysplasias, the most
common is the one which arises from structural disharmony
between head and neck. An example of this dysplasia will
be presented below (see p. 93).

Step 3. We are now prepared for a detailed consideration
of P's physique. We proceed to examine him region by
region and to make an anthroposcopic estimate of his somatotype in each of the five bodily regions. These estimates
we record as follows:

Region	Estimate
I. Head and neck	425
II. Thoracic trunk	325
III. Arms and hands	326
IV. Abdominal trunk	425
V. Legs and feet	425

Step 3, therefore, is similar to step 1. It is an essential
step, because it guides us in the use of the anthropometric
tables and guarantees that the procedure to follow will not
become confused. It prevents the investigator from having
to decide from a single linear measurement whether a physique belongs among the pronounced endomorphs, mesomorphs, or ectomorphs. The situation is simply this: A
particular linear measurement may not differentiate, for example, between an endomorph and a mesomorph, just as
one measurement might not differentiate between a cow and
a horse. But inspection will make it clear which kind of
animal is being considered. If our subject is clearly an endomorph, the mesomorphic somatotypes need not be considered, and our anthropometric measurements will then

tell us *which* endomorph he is. How this result is achieved will be demonstrated in the next step.

Step 4. This part of the procedure is similar to that of step 2 except that the ratio-indices (ratio of diameter to stature expressed as a percentage) by which we enter the tables (Appendix 1) are those obtained from the diameter measurements made in the five regions of the body. For each region we construct a table similar to Table 9. These tables follow.

TABLE 10

REGION I

(Head and neck)

Measurement	Ratio	Rank				
		0	1	2	3	4
FB₁	8.2	425 424 334	415 325 435 434 335 515	—	326	316
FB₂	7.3	325	415 316 326 334 335	425 435 424 434 515	—	—
NT_{ap}	5.7	—	326 316	325 415 424 334	434 335 515	425 435
NTT	5.9	415	325 326 316 515	425 424 335	435 334	434

Table 10 is obtained by entering Tables 24, 25, 26, and 27 (Appendix 1) by means of the appropriate ratio-index. Keeping in mind that the anthroposcopic estimate for this region is 425, we record under rank o the somatotypes which satisfy these two criteria: (1) they do not deviate, in any component, by more than one degree from the anthroposcopic estimate and (2) they do not reverse or contradict the observed dominance among the components. Under rank 1 we record, by the same two criteria, the somatotypes in the rows at one remove from the ratio-index. In a similar manner we fill in ranks 2, 3, and 4. The rank, then, shows at what remove from the measured ratio-index the somatotype falls.

Next we find which somatotype in Table 10 has the lowest mean rank. (Add the ranks for all four measurements and divide by four.) In this case we find that the somatotypes 325 and 415 have the same mean rank of 1.0. This tie is re-

TABLE 11

REGION II

(Thoracic trunk)

Measurement	Ratio	Rank				
		0	1	2	3	4
TT$_1$	11.0	325 335 334 424	425 435 434 326 316 225	226 216 415	—	—
TB$_1$	17.4	415 326 226	216 316 325 425 225	424 335 435	334	434
TB$_2$	15.4	—	435	425 335 434 424	325 415 334	326 316 225

Indicated somatotype: 335, 424, 325, 425, 435 (mean rank = 1.3)

solved by reconsidering the anthroposcopic estimate (see p. 98) for region I, which was 425. When we reexamine P's head and neck with a view to determining which of these two somatotypes the region as a whole approximates more closely, we choose the 415 rather than the 325. Therefore, we record 415 as the somatotype of region I.

For the other regions of the body the procedure is precisely similar. Hence, we shall merely present the tables from which the regional somatotypes are determined. In building each of these tables the experimenter kept in mind the appropriate anthroposcopic estimate in order to guide the selection of somatotypes from the tables in Appendix 1.

Here in region II we find five somatotypes tied for the lowest rank. These are "neighboring" somatotypes—as they will almost always be. We have yet to find a case of two or

TABLE 12

REGION III

(Arms and hands)

Measurement	Ratio	Rank				
		0	1	2	3	4
ATU	5.2	326 325	316 226 225 335 415	425	435 216	217
ATL$_1$	4.1	—	316 217 216	326 226 415 225	325 425	335 435
ATL$_2$	3.4	326 226 325 225 415	216 316 335 425 435	—	217	—

Indicated somatotype: 326 (mean rank = 0.67)

more somatotypes tied for the lowest rank where the difference in any component is greater than 1. To resolve a tie involving three or more somatotypes we merely average the numerals for each component and record this average to the nearest integer. Hence, in region II we record 425 as the final somatotype. This outcome differs but slightly from the anthroposcopic estimate.

TABLE 13

REGION IV

(Abdominal trunk)

Measurement	Ratio	Rank				
		0	1	2	3	4
TT_2	10.9	425 435 415 434	424 325 335 334 515	326 316	—	—
TT_3	12.9	425 435 434	415 335 325 424 334 515	326 316	—	—
TB_3	18.9	435 434 515	425 415 424	326 316 325 335 334	—	—

Indicated somatotype: 434, 435 (mean rank = 0)
Final somatotype: 435 (because 435 agrees better with the anthroposcopic estimate of 425).

That completes step 4. We have determined P's somatotype region by region. The original anthroposcopic estimates have been confirmed in general and corrected in detail. At this point the question is often asked as to what happens when the original estimates are bad ones. The answer is that

TABLE 14

REGION V

(Legs and feet)

Measurement	Ratio	Rank				
		0	1	2	3	4
LTU₁	10.0	425 415 424 334	325 326 316 335 435 434	515	—	—
LTU₂	7.2	435 434	335 425 424 515	326 415 325 334	316	—
LTL₁	5.8	325 415	425 335 326	424 435 515 334 316	434	—
LTL₂	3.4	425 335 334 515 424	325 435 434 415	326 316	—	—

Indicated somatotype: 425 (mean rank = 0.5)

if the error is slight and does not reverse a dominance it makes no difference, but if the error is large the investigator is certain to discover it before proceeding far. If there is a serious error in the anthroposcopic estimate, the necessary consistency within the tables will be lacking.

Let us, for example, assume an estimate which is so much in error that no reasonably trained "somatotyper" would have made it. We might estimate that in region V (legs and feet) P is 362 instead of 425. Instead of Table 14 we should then obtain Table 15.

TABLE 15

Measurement	Ratio	Rank					
		0	1	2	3	4	5
LTU_1	10.0	—	252 353	261 262 352	361 451 362 452 453	461 271	371
LTU_2	7.2	—	252	352 353	261 262 452 453	361 451 362	461
LTL_1	5.8	—	—	—	—	252	352 353 452 453
LTL_2	3.4	—	—	252 353	261 262 352 453	361 362 451 452	271

Here the indicated somatotype is 252, with a mean rank of 2.00. But the table itself indicates that a gross error has been made, both because no somatotypes fall at zero rank and because, for the measurement LTL_1, we have to go to the 4th rank to find *any* somatotypes answering the criteria stated on p. 83. These facts, together with the fact that no extreme dysplasias are visible in the body, should lead one to question the anthroposcopic impression, and to try another estimate.

It should be pointed out here that there is another way in which we could arrive at the correct somatotype, regardless of the anthroposcopic estimate. We could ignore the estimate and make tables recording, for all 17 ratio-indices, all 76 of the somatotypes, together with the ranks of each (see p. 103).

The lowest mean rank in each region would then give the regional somatotype. Thus, the technique of somatotyping *can* be made completely "objective," but without the aid of a tabulating and sorting machine the labor would be prohibitive. In the absence of such aid, it is best to gain proficiency at making the anthroposcopic estimates—for the better the estimates the greater the saving of time and labor.

If the investigator suspects his estimate he should, of course, try other estimates and find which yields the lowest mean rank for the indicated somatotype. But from the point of view of the practical application of this technique it can be said that an experimenter should not undertake to somatotype a series of cases until he can, with few exceptions, estimate the somatotype to within one degree in each of the components. This is not so high a standard as might at first be supposed.

Step 5. We return now to the case of P. The final step consists in averaging the values of the components for all five regions.

Region	Somatotype	Averages by components	
I.	415	1st	3.8
II.	425	2nd	2.0
III.	326	3rd	5.2
IV.	435		
V.	425		

In specifying the final somatotype for the body as a whole we drop the decimal .2, carry .4 and .6 (when they occur) as 1/2 and treat .8 as 1.0. Therefore, P's somatotype is 425. This agrees reasonably well with the anthroposcopic estimate. P looks a little less endomorphic than he is, because of his long arms and legs. Furthermore, when we reexamine Table 9 we find that P's correct somatotype is two ranks removed from that indicated by the ratio-index of height over cube

root of weight. In other words, this boy is somewhat underweight for his build. One use of Table 9 is to tell us this
fact. Nevertheless, P belongs to a family of somatotypes
which grow heavy at later ages. He will probably gain about
35 pounds before he is 40, and this increase will be concentrated about the lower trunk rather than distributed
throughout the body (see p. 162).

We can now compute the total dysplasia for this physique.
We record for each component the sum of the differences
between the five bodily regions (see p. 69).

Component   Dysplasia

1st	4
2nd	8
3rd	4

Total 16

P's index of dysplasia, d, then, is 5 (see p. 70). He is somewhat
more dysplastic than the average individual.

As a second example we shall somatotype an extremely
dysplastic physique (Fig. 6B). This case we shall call Q. He
is 19 years of age.

Step 1. First impression: second component strongly dominant; third component distinctly stronger than the first; first
component extremely low. Anthroposcopic estimate: 163.

Step 2. Height over cube root of weight: 13.1.

Table 16

Ratio	Rank				
	0	1	2	3	4
13.1	163	263 253 252	162	262 254	172 154

Step 3. Anthroposcopic estimate by regions:

I.	Head and neck	163
II.	Thoracic trunk	172
III.	Arms and hands	162
IV.	Abdominal trunk	163
V.	Legs and feet	154

Step 4.

TABLE 17

REGION I

(Head and neck)

Measurement	Ratio	Rank					
		0	1	2	3	4	5
FB$_1$	7.9	—	—	154	—	163 253	263 162
FB$_2$	7.3	154	254	163	263 253	162 252	262
NT$_{ap}$	6.3	163 252	253 162	172 262 263 254	154	—	—
NTT	7.0	262	162 172	252	263	163	253 254

Indicated somatotype: 163 (mean rank = 2.5)

Here we have an unusual dysplasia *within* a single bodily region. This individual is extremely tall. His neck is thick and muscular but his head is small and narrow for a man of his size. Consequently, Table 17 takes on an appearance which leads us to ask whether our anthroposcopic estimate is correct. Other possible estimates were examined but the value of the lowest mean rank for any somatotype could not be reduced below 2.5. This is the mean rank of the somatotype which agrees with the original estimate (163). Note that, because of the lack of consistency in this table, we included the 5th rank in order to ensure consideration of all possibilities.

This case serves to demonstrate the significance of the mean rank. When the lowest mean rank is high, as it is in Q's region I, we conclude that there is a marked dysplasia within this region. In other words, the lowest mean ranks for the various regions can be taken as measures of dysplasias within these regions. Although we have not, as yet, used these measures of *intra-regional dysplasia* for correlational purposes, they may be of considerable value in studies of conflict, at both the morphological and the psychological levels.

TABLE 18

REGION II

(Thoracic trunk)

Measurement	Ratio	Rank				
		0	1	2	3	4
TT$_1$	12.0	172 262	162 252 253 263	163	—	—
TB$_1$	21.3	172	262	162 263	163 252	154 253 254
TB$_2$	15.2	172	262 263	162 252 253	163 254	154

Indicated somatotype: 172 (mean rank = 0)

In marked contrast to region I, this table shows no dysplasia within region II. All three measurements give the somatotype 172 a rank of zero.

Table 19 shows another dysplastic region. The forearm is disproportionately thick.

TABLE 19

REGION III

(Arms and hands)

Measurement	Ratio	Rank				
		0	1	2	3	4
ATU	6.3	—	163 252 162 263	262 253 254	172	—
ATL₁	5.7	—	—	—	172	262 263
ATL₂	4.2	172	162 262	252 163 263	253	154 254

Indicated somatotype: 172 (mean rank = 2.0)

TABLE 20

REGION IV

(Abdominal trunk)

Measurement	Ratio	Rank			
		0	1	2	3
TT₂	10.2	163 253 254	154 162 252 263	172 262	—
TT₃	13.0	172 262 263	162 252 253 254	163	154
TB₃	19.4	—	262 172 162 252 263	163 253 254	154

Indicated somatotype: 263 (mean rank = .67)

TABLE 21
REGION V
(Legs and feet)

Measurement	Ratio	Rank			
		0	1	2	3
LTU₁	9.8	163 253 254	154 263 244	—	—
LTU₂	7.6	263	—	163 253 254	154 244
LTL₁	6.1	244	154	253 254	163 263
LTL₂	3.2	—	154 244	163 254	253 263

Indicated somatotype: 244 (mean rank = 1.25)

Step 5. Final averaging of the components for all five regions.

Region	Somatotype	Averages by components	
I.	163	1st	1.4
II.	172	2nd	6.0
III.	172	3rd	2.8
IV.	263		
V.	244		

Final somatotype: 1½ 6 3. This we write as 163—263, instead of using the fraction. This final result agrees well with the original anthropometric estimate and also with the indication obtained from the ratio-index of height over cube root of weight. The slight discrepancy of ½ degree in the first component points to the fact that Q is slightly underweight—perhaps by two or three pounds.

Dysplasia:

1st component		6
2nd	"	14
3rd	"	10
	Total	30

Q's index of dysplasia, d, is 7. Only about 1 per cent of the population is more dysplastic than he. Hence, we see in Q not only a lack of harmony within certain of the five regions of the body, but an inconsistency from region to region as well. Q demonstrates how an individual of a given somatotype may deviate sharply in some of the three or four diameters taken from a bodily region. But when this is the case it will be found that the measurements deviate in the other direction in other closely related diameters.

By depending upon seventeen diameters, instead of upon two or three, and by tolerating an adequate elasticity in the individual measurement, we find that throughout the body as a whole specific deviations cancel themselves out, and in every instance the anthropometric somatotype which finally emerges agrees with common sense. That is to say, it agrees in the main with what the trained eye finds in the anthroposcopic examination of the individual. If this were not so, the whole technique would be worthless, and the fact that it is so rests not upon chance but upon the history of the development of the method. From the beginning, every step has been taken in such a way that the two approaches, anthroposcopy and anthropometry, have proceeded together and have kept in plain sight of one another.

Since we use the anthropometry in this way, and depend upon a trend of many measurements rather than upon single measurements, it has often been suggested that a less precise technique of taking the measurements might be made to serve the purpose. Perhaps this is so, in the main, but nothing would be gained by lowering the anthropometric standards in such a manner, for even if the measurements were taken less carefully and with less precise instruments they could hardly be taken with significantly greater rapidity. Furthermore, it is our opinion that we have already reduced the number of measurements to a minimum for the purpose they serve.

We recommend that the beginning student of somatotyping follow the procedure as outlined. Nevertheless, practice and experience will teach him many minor short cuts and "dodges" by which he can shorten the labor.

SPECIAL NOTES AND CAUTIONS

1. It should be emphasized again that in making an anthroposcopic estimate the investigator should never indicate the dominance of one component over another unless he is certain of it. When in doubt call the components equal.

2. When two or more somatotypes are tied for the lowest mean rank the tie is resolved by one of the following procedures: (1) If two are tied, the tie is resolved in favor of the one which is closer to the anthroposcopic estimate. (2) If two are tied and are equally distant from the original estimate, the photograph is reexamined and the tie resolved in favor of the somatotype which appears the more correct anthroposcopically. (3) If three or more are tied, the tie is resolved by averaging the three components separately.

3. In making the anthroposcopic estimates it is well to have two or more investigators submit judgments independently. Furthermore, in making the estimates it is of great value to have available a key file of all 76 somatotypes in order that the method of paired comparisons may be used.

4. It should be remembered that small anthroposcopic errors will not invalidate the technique unless the dominance between at least two of the components is reversed.

5. For the ages 17, 18, and 19 the table for height over cube root of weight (Table 23) is highly reliable. (In a series of 1,000 college students 67 per cent fell within rank 1; 92

per cent fell within rank 2. All the cases fell within rank 3.) Therefore, beware of anthroposcopic estimates which do not check with this ratio-index. Either the estimate is wrong or there is a serious nutritional disturbance which ought to be evident to inspection.

At other age levels Table 23 is not necessarily reliable. New tables for these other age levels must be constructed as cases become available in sufficient numbers.

6. The individual tables giving the rank of the various somatotypes within each region (examples: Tables 10 to 21) should be carefully inspected for inconsistencies. If unusual discrepancies are found, it indicates either (1) that the estimated somatotype is wrong or (2) that there is a marked dysplasia *within* the region.

7. As a last step, the final somatotype, anthropometrically determined, should be compared with the somatotype anthroposcopically estimated and with the one indicated by the zero rank of the table for height over cube root of weight. If these three agree, all is well. If they disagree, one should ask why. If this question cannot easily be answered in terms of dysplasias or of a nutritional disturbance, an error at some point is indicated.

8. Finally, in using and interpreting the three numerals designating an individual's somatotype, the investigator should keep in mind their relative reliabilities. We do not measure all three components with equal precision (cf. p. 265). For 18-year-old men ectomorphy correlates so well with the anthropometric diameters (negative correlation) that this component can be measured to approximately a tenth of a unit of the 7-point scale. Mesomorphy correlates positively, but less highly, with the diameter measurements, and endomorphy correlates positively, but still less well, with these measurements. Furthermore, the measurement of endomorphy in 18-year-olds must be regarded as a prediction, made on a "bud," as to the future appearance of a full-blown "flower." At age 40 or 50 the measurement of endomorphy

would be easier and far more reliable, for then we would see the first component in full flower. Nevertheless, the prediction implicit in the measurement of endomorphy at 18 is sufficiently reliable to justify the use of a 7-point scale.

The three components contribute quite differently to the future change in a physique. In this sense ectomorphy is the most stable of the components. The extreme ectomorph changes scarcely at all from 18 to 100 years of age. Mesomorphy leads only to a general fullness throughout the body. Endomorphy contributes most to localized increases of bodily mass, and a person moderately high in the first component is subject to wide fluctuations in weight.

TRAINING OF THE INVESTIGATOR

Somatotyping is a relatively objective procedure. Yet a modicum of specific training and a preparatory background of basic academic instruction are necessary for doing it accurately. We consider the ordinary medical course in anatomy and a year's training in physical anthropology to be minimum prerequisites to the serious study of the technique. Beyond this basic background, it is necessary only to follow faithfully a standardized procedure. The final validity of the technique as outlined above rests upon the assumption that the investigator is competent to tell by inspection which component is dominant, if there is a clear dominance, and to recognize a relatively even balancing of the components when there is no dominance. It should be possible to teach, in six months, the principles of anthroposcopy to a qualified person who is willing to work. One should not, however, expect to accomplish proficiency in six days.

Figure 7 is of interest here, for it may constitute a source of encouragement to anyone interested in mastering the technique of somatotyping for practical application. These correlation regressions represent the degree of agreement between two anthroposcopic determinations of somatotypes (step 1 of the technique). The somatotypes were assigned independently, by Tucker and Sheldon, to a group of standardized pictures of 200 college men. These men were the first 200 of the entering class photographed at a midwestern

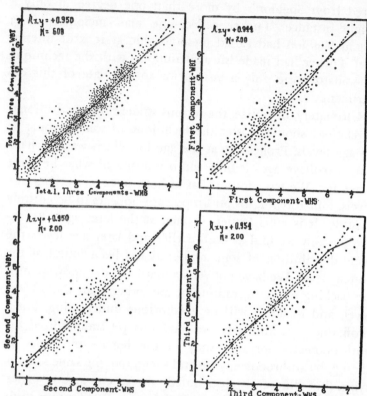

FIG. 7. Scatter diagrams showing the correlation between the anthroposcopic estimates of somatotype made independently by two investigators (W. H. S. and W. B. T.). The solid line shows W. B. T.'s average estimates for various values of W. H. S.'s estimates. The dotted line shows W. H. S.'s average estimates for various values of W. B. T.'s estimates.

college in September, 1937. Each experimenter followed only the method of anthroposcopy in assigning numerals to the three components. No anthropometry was done at that time and no resort was had to a key file of somatotypes for comparisons. The agreement between the two series of 600 estimates, 200 estimates for each of the three components, is represented by the product-moment coefficient, +.95. In the series of 600 specific estimates, Tucker's somatotype differed from Sheldon's by more than one degree in only a single instance. Tucker called one man mesomorphic 3 whom Sheldon had called mesomorphic 5. It is of interest that Tucker had made his acquaintance with the technique of somatotyping only a year prior to the date of this experiment.

Ultimately, of course, the serious student of constitutional psychology should master the technique of somatotyping at all age levels. Proficiency at the age for which we now have norms (college age) is only the beginning of what he must strive for. We have found that at both later and earlier age levels, somatotyping by anthroposcopy appears to be entirely feasible. It is much easier, in fact, at the later ages. By anthroposcopy we find at both earlier and later age levels the same distribution of somatotypes as has been found at the 18-year level. We have not yet standardized the anthropometric backing of the technique at any other than the 18-year level, and to do so will be a laborious undertaking, but a profitable one. Similarly, we have not yet standardized the anthropometry for the study of the female physique, although by anthroposcopy we find there, too, the same somatotypes (but differently distributed) that occur among males. On the whole, a scientific method for the classificatory study of physique at all age levels seems clearly in the offing, but it is still not fully developed.

Even the comparatively slight contribution that somatotyping has already made to this study can scarcely be mastered and comprehended without effort. But if we can master it at all, and can establish a scientific procedure at this level of investigation, the way will be open for a new attack on the problems of medical immunology, on studies of temperament, and on racial and anthropological investigations.

SOMATOTYPING WITHOUT ANTHROPOSCOPY

The technique of somatotyping outlined in the preceding pages involves an anthroposcopic estimate and an anthropometric check. The advantage of the anthroposcopic estimate is that it facilitates the use of the anthropometric tables (Tables 23 to 40). What is perhaps even more important, it minimizes the possibility of making a serious error as the result of a clerical mistake. If the somatotype obtained from the tables does not agree with what an inspection of the physique reveals, we ordinarily proceed to check each step of the anthropometry. Only when both anthroposcopy and anthropometry brings us to the same result are we satisfied with the outcome.

The question is often asked, however, as to whether by objective anthropometry alone the somatotype can be determined. Given only the height and weight of a subject plus the 17 ratio-indices determined by measurements on his photograph, could the experimenter arrive at the same somatotype obtained by the procedure just described? The answer is Yes. With one slight qualification, the anthropometric methods presented in this volume are adequate to meet the requirement of complete objectivity—a requirement which appeals to many. The minor qualification refers to the problem of resolving a situation where the ratio-indices for a given region of the body determine equally well two different somatotypes. This is the two-way tie referred to on p. 86.

The procedure for somatotyping without the aid of anthroposcopy is as follows: Tables are constructed similar to Tables 9 to 21 except that *all* the somatotypes occurring at each rank are recorded instead of only those satisfying the criteria listed on p. 83. As many ranks are used as are needed to ensure that the somatotype having the lowest mean rank has been bracketed. If necessary, all 76 somatotypes may be listed for each ratio-index. Then the mean rank for each somatotype listed is determined and that somatotype having the lowest mean rank is designated as correct for the bodily region concerned. However, when two regional somatotypes are tied for the lowest mean rank the tie must be resolved by the experimenter's deciding from an inspection of the photograph which best fits that particular region of the body. Except for this minor concession to "subjective" judgment, the completely "objective" technique of anthropometry has proved adequate for deriving somatotypes.

Most of the vast amount of clerical labor involved in the completely "objective" technique of somatotyping can be obviated by the machine shown in Fig. 8. This is merely a device for determining from anthropometric measurements the mean rank of a given somatotype—just as in the procedure outlined above. But instead of entering the tables of Appendix I and tabulating the somatotypes as in Tables 9 to 21, the operator throws a switch corresponding to the given somatotype and observes a pattern of lights on the board before him.

On the vertical board are 18 rows of lights—one row for each anthropometric index. Corresponding to each value of each index is a light below which is printed the value of the index. A slider with 9 holes in it can be moved along each row of lights. A switch for each somatotype turns on in each row the light corresponding to the value of the index appropriate to that somatotype. In other words, the tables of Appendix I are wired into the machine (more than 1300 separate wires).

The procedure in using this machine is as follows: The 18 anthropometric indices are determined in the usual manner. The center of each slider on the vertical board is moved to a position coincident with the measured index. Then, the switches for the various somatotypes are closed until the one is found which turns on the series of lights falling nearest the centers of the sliders. The holes in the slider are numbered in such a way as to facilitate the determination

Fig. 8. A machine for determining the somatotype from anthropometric measurements. Procedure: The anthropometric measurements are made on a photograph. A slider is set to the measured value of each of the 18 anthropometric indices (horizontal scales). By turning a switch (one switch for each somatotype) the operator turns on a light (seen as a bright spot on each slider) corresponding to some one value of each anthropometric index. The operator's problem is simply to determine which switch will turn on lights nearest the centers of the sliders. The somatotype corresponding to that switch is the somatotype of the individual.

of the mean rank of the somatotype. The procedure is applied to each of the five bodily regions separately.

If an anthroposcopic estimate of the somatotype is made first, the operation of the machine can be speeded up because the anthroposcopy tells approximately which switches to close. Nevertheless, the machine can be used independently of an anthroposcopic estimate.

LABOR AND COST

By the method outlined earlier (see p. 30) we can conveniently photograph about 100 people in an eight-hour day. The measurements (see p. 54) can be taken, with a good setup at the rate of about 120 measurements per hour. When one investigator works with a recorder, or when two investigators work together and alternate at taking the measurement, about 55 photographs can be measured per day. The anthroposcopic step in somatotyping, that is to say, the inspectional comparison and serial classification of the photographs according to the relative strengths of the components (see p. 81), can be carried out conveniently at the rate of 75 pictures per day. The final step, that of applying the detailed anthropometric criteria and arriving at the exact somatotype, can be done comfortably at the rate of about 20 pictures per day.

Thus, with two investigators working together under reasonably favorable conditions, the photographing of 1,000 cases can be done in 10 days. The measuring of the photographs ought to be finished in 18 days. Anthroposcopy should be done within 14 days, and the final somatotyping should be carried out in about 50 more days. One thousand individuals can be correctly and accurately somatotyped by two men working together for 90 working days, or in less than four months. The two final steps, anthroposcopy and the application of anthropometric criteria, can be carried out by one experimenter, but it is not the wisest procedure for one person to do this work alone. It ought to be done independently by two investigators and the work of one should be checked against that of the other. (Machines to aid in sorting and classifying would, of course, greatly facilitate the procedure.) It is estimated that with the somatotyping machine (Fig. 8) the time required to somatotype 1000 cases could be reduced by 30 days.

The cost, aside from the time of the investigators, is moderate. High-grade 5″ by 7″ film (cut) can be bought in quantity through an institution at a cost of about 8 cents per film, or at about 14 cents per film in film pack. Developing is a negligible expense, and prints, although desirable for the anthroposcopy, can be dispensed with if necessary. Add a cent per picture for the cost of lights. In our work we have used the film pack because of the less likelihood of getting the film out of the correct plane in the film carrier at the time of photographing, and also because of greater convenience. The original cost of the camera, lens, special back, screen, and light standards, should not be much over $150. A good revolving pedestal for the subject can be made for $25, and should be constructed with ball bearings. For the anthropometry, a large airy (open) light box is needed—one with a slope convenient for working. A steel rule divided to ½ mm. is adequate. A pair of fine dividers (screw-controlled) with replaceable needles and a large reading glass mounted on a stand complete the equipment. The measurements are read under the glass.

We developed the entire method using this simple equipment. We have experimentally projected films on a ground-glass surface on which had been ruled a graduated grid, and have found that it is possible in this way to take the measurements on a larger scale without distortion. Such a procedure increases slightly the accuracy of the measurements. The disadvantage of this method is that it requires a projector.

Many times the question has been raised as to whether we could not greatly reduce expenses, for an extensive study, by taking the photographs with a miniature camera, on 35 mm. film, and projecting the images, either from negative or from positive, in a special reading desk like those now commonly used for "microfilm." There is no doubt that this can be done with practicability. Either a device will be necessary, however, which projects simultaneously three separate pictures in the reading desk or it will be necessary to use a miniature camera geared to expose one-third of the film at a time in exact center position. Otherwise the photographic technique would lose one of its principal advantages —that of viewing the whole body from three directions simultaneously. There is a possibility that with miniature equipment and with the consequent necessary enlargement of the image, a greater danger of error from distortion would creep in, but it should be possible to standardize the procedure sufficiently to eliminate such a danger. We have hitherto foregone the advantages of such equipment because of its prohibitive initial cost, and because the expense of photography actually constitutes a rather small part of the total cost of somatotyping.

CHAPTER V

SOME THEORETICAL CONSIDERATIONS

M ANY interesting problems touching upon the theory of measurement, statistics, and psychological judgment can be raised in connection with the theory of somatotyping. Not all these problems can be answered, but some of them merit more attention than they have received in preceding chapters. Many of these problems are what the practitioner of somatotyping might pigeonhole as "academic" issues, and perhaps justly, because they are mostly questions which do not bear upon the *practical* utility of somatotyping as a method and tool of constitutional study. Nevertheless, the nature of the variables, the erection of the scales, the functional interrelations and the geometrical interpretation of the components, the psychological judgment of equal-appearing morphological differences, and the frequency distribution of the somatotypes offer important topics for inquiry. Some of these we shall explore in the present chapter.

THE CHOICE OF VARIABLES

The theory of somatotyping is founded upon the assumption that it is possible to discriminate differences among human beings. That certain differences are obvious needs no argument—at least most of us do not confuse the identity of our friends. Actually, the formulation of a technique for somatotyping is difficult, not because people fail to differ morphologically, but because they differ in almost innumerable ways. There are unnumbered aspects or variables against which we could classify members of the human race, and with which of these we choose to operate determines the functional utility of our classificatory schemes.

Unfortunately, there are no rules for choosing adequate variables. All we can say is that the progress of a science depends in large measure upon the selection of the right ones for the purpose in hand. Much of nature reveals itself under such a complexity of aspects that sometimes only by laborious trial and error, coupled with precious insights, do men hit upon descriptive categories which reduce an apparent chaos to an ordered system of natural laws.

Consider what must have been the history of man's speculation about the blowing of the wind. How many hypotheses have been proposed and rejected, how many apparent correlations between the wind and everything from angered deities to sun spots have broken down, and how many kinds of "data" have been studied by meteorologists, both primitive and modern, is beyond guess. Even today, meteorological tables present a mass of data so chaotic that it seems foolish to look for simple laws among them, but the ingenuity and persistence of the weather man has not gone entirely un-rewarded. By constructing synoptic charts showing contours of equal atmospheric pressures over the earth, he can follow the movements of large masses of air and can tell the natives of a given region how hard the wind will blow on the mor-row. But the meteorologist has made only a crude beginning, and he is still experimenting with new variables and schemes for the classification of his data.

The story of man's speculation about man has been no less packed with weird notions than the history of his guesses about the wind. His urge to find order in the baffling com-plexities of human nature has led him through the ages to fumble with variables, aspects, schemas and classifications, many of which have been the fad of one generation and the scandal of the next. Almost every conceivable variable has been seized upon—from the shape of the brow to the position of the stars. On the relation of morphology to character

Aristotle gave us six chapters in which he argued, among other things, that the structure of the nose revealed the disposition of the man. And Aristotle's is but one of dozens of more or less discredited treatises. As their primary variables phrenologists took bumps on the head, graphologists took handwriting, physiognomists took facial features, and palmists took creases on the hand. Not that these variables are worthless for all purposes, but by and large they failed to provide the key to system and order in the study of human beings.

Scientific order and simplicity is, of course, a relative matter, and perhaps the data of anatomy, physiology, neurology, and psychology are so complex that a classification of the facts in such a way that simple laws can be induced may never prove as feasible as it is in a science like chemistry. On the other hand, there is no likelihood that men will ever give up struggling with new and beguiling classificatory schemes.

Ideally, the choice of variables for a descriptive classification of human bodies should try to satisfy what are essentially two pragmatic tests. The variables selected should be capable of unambiguous definition and should show "meaningful" correlations with other aspects of human beings. The first of these requirements provides for the practicability of the method; the second imposes a demand for what we might call fruitfulness. These two criteria are met, at least in part, by the choice of the three components: endomorphy, mesomorphy, and ectomorphy. These we regard, for the purposes of somatotyping, as first-order variables, and to them are added second-order aspects such as gynandromorphy, texture, and so on. As already pointed out (see p. 67), the designation of certain variables as first-order and others as second-order must be dictated by the investigators' purpose. The unambiguous, operational definition of the three first-order variables can be made fairly adequately at the present time, and the fruitfulness of the schema in providing "meaningful" correlations between physical constitution and such things as temperament, susceptibility to disease, and physiological functions appears to be at least sufficient to justify this book. The test of fruitfulness calls for much additional research. And if a more fertile system is discovered, the present one will have to make way.

Reduced to its simplest operations the definition of the three basic components is strictly ostensive. They are the aspects common to each of the three classes illustrated by the physiques pictured above in Figs. 1A, 1B, and 1C. These physiques were selected from the population because they appear to be extreme variants—just as objects that are red, green, and white could be segregated on the basis of the fact that they look different from other objects. To this simple denotative procedure for defining the components we next add the descriptive characterizations found in the check lists (pp. 37 to 45) and eventually the anthropometric measurements of these somatotypes found in Tables 23 to 40 (Appendix 1). These characterizations are far from exhaustive and undoubtedly many additional defining criteria could be added. It is to be hoped that eventually many more descriptive and functional relations might be discovered which will add significance and "meaningfulness" to these three morphological aspects.

Hence, at the outset, the method of somatotyping may be regarded as an arbitrary system for classifying human physiques—an arbitrary system which is practicable and reliable. From this point of view it is irrelevant whether the three components are in any sense basic biological "entities" which combine in the formation of a human body. The system remains a practicable system of classification regardless of the "meaningfulness" (biologically) of the components. Nevertheless it is of great interest to explore the biological relations among the three components, endomorphy, mesomorphy and ectomorphy. Their tentative identification with some aspect of the germinal embryonic layers is a step in this direction (see p. 32).

After we have isolated and characterized by ostensive definition three basic aspects of morphological variation, two questions present themselves. (1) Can these aspects be treated as variables which assume different values? In other words, can the population be rank-ordered according to the degree to which individuals exhibit more or less of a given aspect? (There are many human attributes against which such a ranking could not profitably be made. An example would be the aspect two-leggedness.) Then, as a corollary to this question there is the problem as to whether the three components can be regarded as *continuous* variables. (2) The second problem relates to the interrelations among the components. Can one of these three aspects exist independently of the others? In other words, could one or more components be completely absent? If not, in what proportions can they exist?

These questions bring us to the problem of the measurement of the components.

SCALES FOR THE MEASUREMENT OF MORPHOLOGICAL COMPONENTS

Examination of a large population reveals at once that the three aspects we have defined occur in varying degrees in different people. In fact, it is demonstrably possible to rank-order a given sample of the population against each of the aspects. And, although only *discrete* gradations of an aspect can occur in a finite population, the gradations are sufficiently fine to warrant the assumption that the aspects can be regarded as *continuous* variables. Hence, we postulate continuity in the gradation of each component—endomorphy, mesomorphy, and ectomorphy—and proceed to treat them as continuous variables.

Since these variables are complex, nonmetricized aspects of human beings, we must depend for their recognition and gradation directly upon the discriminatory capacities of a human observer, rather than upon some set of operations like those by which we measure length and weight. Thus, the situation is much like the one we face when we attempt the construction of scales for the measurement of psychological attributes of sensation, such as the loudness of tones or the saturation of colors.[1] This means, in a sense, that the morphological components are initially psychologically differentiable aspects—just as are all differentiae at the outset of a taxonomical inquiry. Part of the problem of somatotyping is to discover "objective" anthropometric correlates for these "subjective" discriminable aspects. But first we need a method for scaling the "subjective" aspects.

The procedure followed has already been outlined in Chapter III. The population (4,000 cases) was combed for physiques showing an extreme manifestation of each component. Then against each component separately a rank order of all the cases was made. At this point *numerals* were introduced. (We say *numeral* and not *number*, because number implies a kind of quantification not relevant here.) The numeral 7 was assigned to the maximum manifestation of each variable and the numeral 1 to the minimum. The choice of these numerals is arbitrary—any others, or even letters of the alphabet, could be made to serve at this stage of the research. But these numerals are probably as convenient as any when a 7-point scale is to be used.

Here we must raise a question as to the significance of the numeral 1. Why did we not, for example, assign the numeral 0? The answer is that zero would have implied a total absence of the component, whereas all we can say is that endomorphy 1 is the least amount of endomorphy we have thus far observed. We do not know what endomorphy 0 could mean. Even the most elongated physique has *some*

[1] See Stevens, S. S. On the problem of scales for the measurement of psychological magnitudes. *J. Unified Science*, vol. 9, 1940 (in press). For an amplified statement of the point of view adopted in this discussion, see Stevens, S. S. Psychology and the science of science. *Psychol. Bull.*, 36, 1939, 221-263.

roundness and softness to it. And so with the other components. In other words, every physique has some of all three aspects, and we arbitrarily assign the numeral 1 to the least amount we find, because we do not know what zero would mean for any of these variables.

Now, is endomorphy 7 the same amount of endomorphy as mesomorphy 7 is of mesomorphy or as ectomorphy 7 is of ectomorphy? The answer to this question is that we do not know. All we know is that these are the maximum values so far discovered. What complete, 100 per cent endomorphy would look like we can only guess. (It probably would not be found walking around.)

Given two points on a scale for each component, we can proceed to devise operations for defining other points. The next step, then, was to discover what appeared to be the mid-point in the progression of each variable from 1 to 7 and to assign to it the numeral 4. This is what the psychologist knows as an experiment in the bisection of a psychological distance. By this method he is able to construct useful and reliable scales.[2] Under this method successive bisections, or else the determination of equal-appearing intervals, can be used to define intermediate points on a scale.

Actually, the definition of the equal-appearing morphological intervals required to fill in the scales between 1 and 4 and between 4 and 7 was aided by the anthropometric series determined by measurements made on the physiques 711, 171, 117, and 444. This was the process of interpolation referred to on p. 59. Nevertheless, the scales for the morphological components are basically "psychological"—the anthropometric measurements merely provide them with "physical" objectification.

At this point we might raise the question as to what kind of scales these are. First, however, what different kinds of scales are there? Three basic types can be recognized. There

---

[2] Cf. Stevens, S. S., and Volkmann, J. The relation of pitch to frequency: a revised scale. *Amer. J. Psychol.*, 53, 1940 (in press).

are at least three different sets of rules by which we assign numerals to aspects of things, and it is because of differences among the rules that we have different kinds of scales and different kinds of measurement.

1. *Ordinal scales* are those we obtain when we assign numerals to a rank-ordered series of objects or aspects. We can assign to such a series any set of numerals whose order is determined, such as 1, 2, 3, 4 or 2, 4, 6, 8 or even 3, 7, 14, 15, 18. We could equally well use the letters of the alphabet, for only the *order* of our series needs to be reflected in the numerals or letters used.

2. *Intensive scales* result when we know the order of a series and also possess an operation to tell us when to assign *adjacent* numerals. A common operation for this purpose is the determination of a just noticeable difference. Then, if the numeral 6 is assigned to one value of an aspect, the numeral 7 could be assigned to that value of the aspect which appeared just noticeably greater. Another operation—one of more interest here—is the determination of an equal-appearing interval. Then, if the numerals 4 and 5 are assigned to two aspects differing by a certain perceived amount, the numeral 6 could be assigned to the value differing by the same amount from that labeled 5 as this one differs from that labeled 4.

3. *Extensive scales* are the sort we use in measuring length and weight. In these scales we know the order, the rule for assigning adjacent numerals, *and* we can say, in addition, that the value called 8 is twice as far from zero as the value assigned the numeral 4. Here we have a *unit* and a definable *zero point*.

From the brief definition of these three types of scales it is clear that the scales used in somatotyping are of the second kind—they are *intensive scales*. We cannot define the zero points on the scales used in measuring the morphological components and we have no fundamental *units*. But we do have an *ordered* variable and an operation (equal-appearing intervals) for assigning the successive adjacent numerals between 1 and 7. Of course, the anthropometric measurements themselves are made in terms of extensive scales (length and weight), but these measurements do not initially define the components nor the scales for their measurement—they merely serve to objectify these scales after they are erected. The search for the anthropometric correlates of the observed aspects of morphological variation is like hunting for a means of representing or describing the stimulus to an attribute of a sensation. But the anthropometric measurements only *partially* describe the stimulus to what one sees in the various somatotypes.

Since we measure the components only against intensive scales, we must beware of making certain kinds of statements. As already pointed out, we cannot say whether 7 on each scale represents the same "amount" of each component. Neither can we say whether the *difference* between 1 and 7 on the scale of endomorphy is the same as the difference between 1 and 7 on the other two scales. In other words, when we represent the three extreme variants as the corners of a triangle (see Fig. 10) we do not know whether the triangle is truly equilateral or not. (Not knowing the answer, in practice we draw it as equilateral.)

Nevertheless, although we have no true units, in the physical sense, for the measurement of endomorphy, mesomorphy, and ectomorphy, the usefulness of the component scales is not impaired. The difference between endomorphy 1 and endomorphy 2 is a definite, recognizable difference, as are the differences between all adjacent numerical values on the three scales. In terms of these equal-appearing differences we can unequivocally describe and classify human physiques.

A GEOMETRICAL REPRESENTATION OF THE SOMATOTYPES

When something is measured simultaneously in terms of three variables, it is often convenient to represent these variables by means of orthogonal coordinates. Thus, along each of three axes at right angles to one another we can plot the numerals 1 to 7 for each of the somatotype scales. Then, a

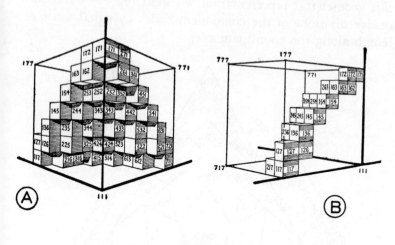

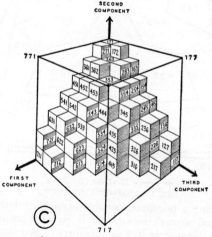

FIG. 9. Three perspective views of a cluster of blocks representing the geometrical distribution of 70 of the somatotypes. The heavy lines represent the orthogonal axes along which are scaled the three components. (Erratum: in Fig. 9A read 334 in place of 344.)

given somatotype is represented as a point in space at an appropriate position relative to the three coordinate axes. This scheme provides us with a formal model for representing certain relations among the somatotypes and with a means of carrying out certain mathematical analyses. In utilizing this geometrical representation we shall represent the successive divisions of the component scales by equal units of length along the coordinate axes.

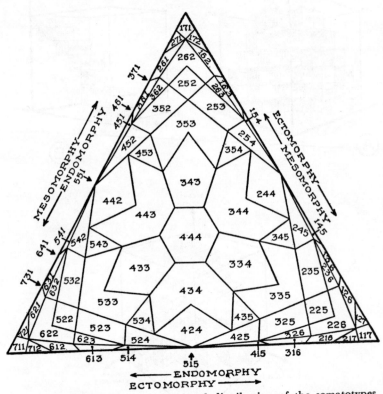

FIG. 10. Showing a two-dimensional distribution of the somatotypes. The area allotted to each somatotype is roughly proportional to the incidence of the somatotype in a population of 4,000 cases.

The distribution of the somatotypes in the three-dimensional "space" defined by three orthogonal axes can be visualized with the aid of Fig. 9. In order to facilitate the impression of perspective in these drawings, each somatotype is represented by a small cube instead of by a point. The intersection (origin) of the coordinates in these figures is at the point 111. The other lines completing the larger cube are added merely to define the boundaries of the region containing all the permutations and combinations of the numerals 1 to 7 taken three at a time. Actually six rare somatotypes (731, 371, 641, 461, 551, and 515) are omitted from Fig. 9, because their presence would distort the symmetry of the figures. These six somatotypes account for less than 0.5 per cent of the population of 4,000 cases.

In drawing C of Fig. 9 we view the distribution of somatotypes from a point along a line almost perpendicular to the surface approximated by the somatotypes. Seen from this angle the distribution is roughly triangular. Hence, in order to represent all the somatotypes on a two-dimensional surface we can construct a figure like that shown in Fig. 10. In this figure the area allotted to each somatotype is approximately proportional to the number of cases falling within the somatotype (cf. Table 23a, p. 268), but for the purposes of this illustration the areas are arbitrarily equalized for each member of the following 19 groups or "natural families" of somatotypes:

(1)	(2)	(3)	(4)	(5)	(6)	(7)	(8)	(9)	(10)
721	621	632	631	532	541	542	543	711	622
712	612	623	613	523	514	524	534	171	262
271	261	362	361	352	451	452	453	117	226
172	162	263	163	253	154	254	354		
217	216	326	316	325	415	425	435		
127	126	236	136	235	145	245	345		

(11)	(12)	(13)	(14)	(15)	(16)	(17)	(18)	(19)
522	533	442	443	433	731	641	551	**444**
252	353	424	434	343	371	461	515	
225	335	244	344	334				

Note that the common somatotypes are relatively central in Fig. 10, whereas the rare ones are peripheral. Note also that there are only three "natural families" of somatotypes which are incomplete. The 731 and 371 belong to a family of somatotypes which if complete would include also the 713, 317, 173, and 137, but if any of these latter exist, we have so far found no trace of them. If the family 641—461 were complete, the 614, 416, 164, and 146 would be present, but we have found none of these either. The family 551—515 would be completed by the presence of the 155, but it has not been seen. These six somatotypes, the 731, 371, 641, 461, 551, and 515, all of them representing incomplete families, are the six which we had to add when we came to apply anthropometric criteria to the classification (see p. 61). All of them are rare in the colleges, although it is probable that the 551, 461, and 641 and the 371 and 731 are much less rare in the general population.

THE INDEPENDENCE OF THE COMPONENTS

We have previously referred to the components, endomorphy, mesomorphy, and ectomorphy, as "more or less interdependent variables." This loose terminology refers to the fact that when a physique is high in one component it must be low in the others. Careful scrutiny of Fig. 9 reveals, however, that these variables are not interdependent in the sense that knowledge of two of them always discloses the value of the third. We find, for example, the somatotypes 451, 452, and 453. Thus, the value of the third component is not a function of the first two. On the other hand, the possible combinations of numerals are restricted to certain limits, *but within these limits the components behave as independent variables.*

Technically, we should say that the variables are independent but that their sum is limited by the boundaries given by the numbers 9 and 12. In a geometrical representation the boundaries within which the somatotypes lie are determined by two approximately spherical surfaces and by the three planes given by the equations: $x = 1$, $y = 1$ and $z = 1$. The restriction of the variables by these limits results in their being *correlated* variables.

A question frequently posed in connection with the theory of somatotypes concerns the *sum* of the numerals designating the values of the three components. As the system is now constituted this sum ranges from 9 to 12, but the question is: Why is the sum not constant? This question implies the supposition that a given individual should be regarded as being a certain percentage endomorphic, a certain percentage mesomorphic, a certain percentage ectomorphic, and that he should add up to 100 per cent. This is not, at first sight, an unreasonable assumption, but the conclusive evidence against it is the functional *independence* of the components apparent in Fig. 9. Geometrically this independence shows itself as a *thickness* of the region in which the somatotypes lie (most clearly seen in Fig. 9B).

If we restrict the designation of the somatotypes to whole numbers, the range of variation in one component, for fixed values of the other two, is never more than three units, and for some combinations near the peripheries of the distribution it is restricted to one unit. But the fact that independent variation in a component, even within restricted limits, is possible constitutes an important theoretical point. It answers definitively the question as to whether an individual's physique should "add up to 100 per cent." *The components cannot be regarded simply as expressions of the percentage-composition of a physique.* Actually there are 37 cases in which one component takes on three different values in the face of fixed values of the other two components.

If the functional independence of the components (within boundaries), which we find empirically, is valid and not an artifact,[3] we have added reason for regarding the three aspects of human physique, exhibited by the three extreme variants

[3] Possible artifacts: (1) The use only of whole numbers. This fact would account for a slight thickness of the region wherein the somatotypes lie—but only a slight thickness. This factor is far from sufficient to account for the thickness actually observed. (2) Errors in the evaluation of components. Errors of judgment are, of course, always possible, but the kind of *systematic* error which would produce the independent variability observed in the components we believe to be highly improbable. The final evaluation of each component is approached from several different angles, both anthroposcopic and anthropometric, and many checks and counterchecks are provided.

pictured in Fig. 1, p. 5, as genuine *components* of morphological structure.

THE SURFACE APPROXIMATED BY THE SOMATOTYPES

The distribution of the somatotypes in the space defined by three orthogonal coordinates approximates roughly to a curved surface. The nature of this surface can best be seen in drawing B of Fig. 9, where we view the distribution from one side. As we have already indicated, the region occupied by the somatotypes differs from a mathematical "surface" in that it has thickness. Nevertheless, the question can be asked as to what surface the somatotypes most nearly approximate. The "best fitting" surface, under the criterion of "least squares," could be obtained by conventional methods, but for our present purposes another approach is perhaps preferable.

It will be recalled that the scales for the three basic components were constructed by assigning the numerals 1, 4, and 7 to points along a series of photographs rank-ordered in terms of each component separately (see p. 48). The numerals 1 and 7 were assigned to the ends of each of the three rank-ordered series and the numeral 4 was assigned to the points which appeared equidistant from the ends of each series. Then, in order to enlist the aid of anthropometry for the task of locating the intermediate numerals on the component scales, several representatives of each of four somatotypes were selected and measured. These four were the 711, 171, 117, and the 444. It is not, however, a *necessary* consequence of the procedure that it should be possible, in the general population, to find a 444—a physique which falls at the mid-point on all three scales. Nevertheless, such was the empirical outcome.

Now, these four points, 711, 171, 117, and 444, which serve, in a sense, as points of anchorage for the system, determine a spherical surface in the three-dimensional space pictured in Fig. 9. The equation for this surface in terms of coordinates intersecting at 0,0,0, instead of at 1,1,1 can be written as

$$(x + 0.5)^2 + (y + 0.5)^2 + (z + 0.5)^2 = 60.75$$

where x, y, and z are the values (between 1 and 7) along each of the axes. Or in terms of the coordinates actually used in Fig. 9, where the intersection is at the point 1,1,1, this equation means that the center of the sphere would be at a point 1.5 units back along the coordinates in the negative direction from their intersection, i.e., at the point −0.5, −0.5, −0.5. The surface defined by this equation is not the one which best fits the points representing the 76 somatotypes, but it is a good approximation and near enough for present purposes.

Let us return now to the question relating to the sum of the components. Those who assume that the sum should be constant are implying that the previous equation should be written:

$$x + y + z = 9$$

Although we have shown, in the previous section (p. 120), that the most damaging evidence *against* this assumption is the functional *independence* of the components, a tentative acceptance of the assumption has some interesting implications regarding the component scales themselves. These implications we shall now investigate.

A POSSIBLE CORRECTION OF THE COMPONENT SCALES

The equation

$$x + y + z = 9$$

is the equation of the plane which cuts the three coordinate axes shown in Fig. 9 at the points 7,1,1, 1,7,1, and 1,1,7. The somatotype 444 would not lie on this plane, nor would most of the other somatotypes obtained by following the procedure outlined in the previous chapter. But admittedly, these somatotypes are obtained by the use of scales which are not necessarily linear. Hence, the problem arises as to whether, by altering the scales for the three components, we could force the somatotypes to approximate more closely to a plane rather than a curved surface, and make each physique more nearly add up to 100 per cent.

Let us assume that the first equation (for the spherical surface) "fits" the somatotypes. The problem then becomes one of finding the transformation-equation for altering each of the scales on the coordinate axes in such a way as to move each point on the sphere to a position both on the plane and on the line connecting the point on the sphere with the intersection of the coordinates. The functional form of this equation can be readily obtained, but its explicit form still eludes us. Fortunately, however, the problem can be solved for five specific points, and with the aid of these five points the curve in Fig. 11 can be drawn. (An identical curve could be drawn for each component.) This curve relates the scale (ψ value) actually used for measuring each component to the scale (ϕ value) which, if used, would move the somatotypes from the sphere to the plane. (We are neglecting, of course, the problem of thickness.)

Here the question presents itself: Is this correction reasonable? Is it credible to assume that the scales for somatotyping, which we have erected by means of inspection and psychological judgment, are skewed in the manner suggested by Fig. 11? Two factors (both as yet unsubstantiated), can be suggested as plausible reasons for the skewing.

First, we know from experiments on the construction of psychological scales for the measurement of pitch and of loudness[4] that the subjective judgment follows a kind of law of diminishing returns as the value of the physical stimulus (frequency and sound pressure, respectively) increases. This is analogous to what the psychophysicist calls Weber's

[4] See Stevens, S. S., and Davis, H. *Hearing: Its Psychology and Physiology*, New York: Wiley, 1938.

principle. The argument would be that in judging equal-appearing increments in endomorphy, for example, the observer's judgments obey this principle in such a way that a given increment in endomorphy, when endomorphy is high, appears smaller than the same "absolute" increment added

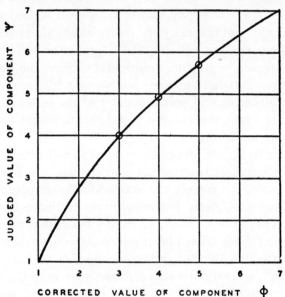

FIG. 11. A curve showing the relation of the component scale (ordinate) actually used in somatotyping to a scale (abscissa) which would eliminate the curvature of the three-dimensional surface near which the somatotypes lie. This curve might, under certain conditions, be used for correcting the somatotype scales (see text).

to a low endomorphy. In other words, if we had some "physical" means for measuring the "true" value of the endomorphy which is the "stimulus" to our judgment, we should expect the judgments of equal-appearing intervals in endomorphy to follow a curve like that in Fig. 11. Consequently, it is consistent with known facts about some kinds of psychophysical judgments to assume that the failure of the components to add up to 9 is due, at least in part, to a law of diminishing returns in the judgments upon which the scales for the components are based.

Secondly, the scales might be skewed by an understandable tendency of the observer to note the presence of morphological components more easily than he sees their absence. In other words, he might first note details which suggest considerable endomorphy, and then proceed to find signs of mesomorphy and ectomorphy, and to assign them relatively high values *without* revising his judgment of endomorphy. This tendency, if present, would tend to skew the scales for the components in a manner consistent with the curve in Fig. 11. Since the end points 1 and 7 of the scales are fixed, this tendency in the observer's judgments would raise the middle section of the curve.

These two factors, diminishing returns and a tendency to note presence more readily than absence, suggest that it might be reasonable to correct the scales for the components in such a way as to make the somatotypes lie more nearly on a plane. On the other hand, we cannot evaluate these factors, and hence cannot know how much to correct for them. If we had a "true" measure of each component (a measure of the "stimulus") we could discover the laws governing the psychological judgments of endomorphy, mesomorphy, and ectomorphy. Conversely, if we knew precisely the laws of judgment in a case of this sort we could deduce from the psychological judgments the "physical" scale for the measurement of the components.

In the foregoing discussion we have made the simplifying assumption that the somatotypes could be represented by points on a surface. Actually, however, the region occupied by these points has thickness, and no simple correction of the scales for skewness due to errors of judgment or to any other cause would restore all the points to a plane surface. As we have previously shown, this thickness of the region occupied by the somatotypes demonstrates that, within certain boundaries, the components are independent variables.

DISTRIBUTION OF THE POPULATION AGAINST THE SOMATOTYPES

We turn now to a consideration of the number of physiques, in a population of 4,000 cases, that fall within each of the 76 somatotypes. This distribution is recorded in Table 23A, p. 268. Fig. 10 (p. 118) shows that if the somatotypes were plotted on a two-dimensional surface and if the number of

TABLE 22

INCIDENCES OF COMPONENTS

	Incidence per 1,000	
	4,000 Men (By complete somatotyping technique)	2,500 Women (By anthroposcopy only)
First Component		
1.........................	50	27
2.........................	251	181
3.........................	319	265
4.........................	251	282
5.........................	95	183
6.........................	26	47
7.........................	8	15
Mean......................	3.20	3.61
Standard Deviation..........	1.2	1.3
Second Component		
1.........................	20	49
2.........................	131	239
3.........................	263	348
4.........................	324	210
5.........................	185	101
6.........................	63	49
7.........................	14	4
Mean......................	3.77	3.24
Standard Deviation..........	1.2	1.2
Third Component		
1.........................	43	59
2.........................	177	156
3.........................	271	234
4.........................	291	278
5.........................	161	196
6.........................	46	63
7.........................	11	14
Mean......................	3.53	3.64
Standard Deviation..........	1.3	1.3

cases in each somatotype were plotted vertically above the surface, the resulting distribution would be *roughly* bell-shaped. This distribution approximates—but not too closely—a "normal" surface, truncated by the three sides of the triangle forming the base.

The problem naturally arises as to the possibility of making the distribution more normal by correcting the component scales—a practice commonly resorted to in the construction of scales for psychological testing. We have already

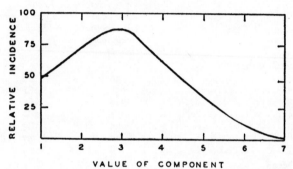

FIG. 12. Curve showing the theoretical distribution of a "normal" population against one of the component scales.

pursued an analysis suggesting a correction of the component scales. Would the same correction more nearly "normalize" the distribution of the population against the somatotypes? We shall attack this problem somewhat indirectly.

If we make the simplifying assumption that all possible somatotypes lie on the plane defined by the points 711, 171, and 117 we can plot a normal surface above this plane. This normal surface would extend beyond the triangular boundaries of the plane, but we could cut the surface at these boundaries. From this kind of plot we can calculate the form of the distribution against each of the components taken singly, i.e., we can determine the proportions of the cases falling at endomorphy 1, endomorphy 2, etc. This distribution of a truncated normal surface, taken against a single component is shown in Fig. 12. As we should anticipate, the distribution is skewed, because many more cases can be at 1 in a given component than can be at 6 or 7. It can be shown that no distribution, normal or otherwise, over a surface of this sort could yield a normal distribution against each of the three components simultaneously.

The simplifying assumption adopted for this formal analysis does violence, of course, to the empirical arrangement of the somatotypes—most of them do not lie on the plane. Nevertheless, it is of interest to compare the curve in Fig. 12 with the actual distribution of the population against the components, as recorded in Table 22 and plotted in Fig. 13. Data for women are included, but it should be pointed out that these data are tentative and may later be subject to thorough revision. The curves in Fig. 13 show a tendency, less marked, however, toward the same skewness exhibited in Fig. 12.

The skewness in these curves is, among other things, a function of the "linearity" of the scales used in measuring the components. Consequently, it is interesting to ask whether in these scales the kind of "error" suggested as due to "diminishing returns" and a "tendency to note the presence rather than the absence of a component" would cause more or less skewing in the curves of Fig. 13. The answer is that these "errors," together perhaps with a tendency for the investigator to avoid assigning to physiques the numerals at the *ends* of the scales, would reduce the skewness. Correction for these factors would skew the curves in the direction to make them resemble more the theoretical curve of Fig. 12. This fact does not, of course, prove that these "errors" are present in the scales *unless* we assume that nature has in reality distributed her population normally over the truncated somatotype surface. This assumption, although commonly made in the biological sciences, is somewhat gratuitous, and an adjustment of the units on the somatotype scales in such a way as to produce a normal distribution over the surface would

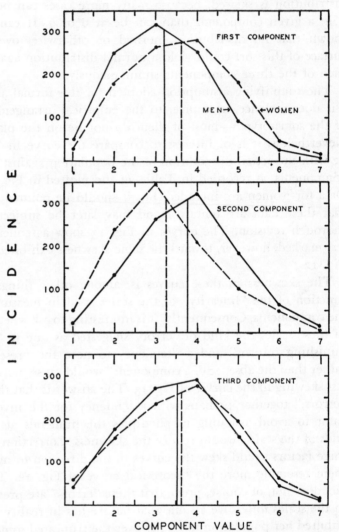

FIG. 13. The actual distributions (per 1,000) of the population against the three component scales. The solid lines represent men, the dashed lines women. The vertical lines are at the means of each distribution.

probably be premature. Besides, in this argument we have neglected the factor of thickness in the somatotype surface— a factor which would need to be considered before such a correction is made.

SUMMARY OF THE ARGUMENTS FOR AND AGAINST A CORRECTION OF THE COMPONENT SCALES

It is interesting to note that all four of the assumptions considered above point in the direction of a skewness in the component scales like that depicted in Fig. 11. These assumptions can be restated as follows:

1. That the distribution of the somatotypes should approximate a plane rather than a spherical surface, i.e., a given physique should "add up to 100 per cent."
2. That a law of diminishing returns (Weber's principle) operates in the judgment of equal-appearing intervals in a component.
3. That an observer tends, throughout the middle range of the scales, to overrate rather than underrate a component.
4. That the distribution of the population should be a truncated normal surface when this distribution is plotted over the somatotype surface.

It is consistent with these assumptions that the units at the upper ends of the somatotype scales are systematically too small.

Arguing, however, against a too hasty correction of the scales to bring them more nearly in line with these assumptions is the fact that the precise amount of the correction cannot, at present, be satisfactorily determined. Furthermore, it must not be forgotten that the three components are sufficiently independent to make it appear impossible ever to force all the somatotypes on to a surface lacking thickness.

It is conceivable, nevertheless, that a situation might arise in which a correction of the scales would be advisable. (A case in point would be one in which the *linearity* of the correlation-regression between a component and some measure or test, known to be itself *linear*, was of some importance.) In that case, the best approximation to the amount of the correction is probably that depicted by the curve in Fig. 11.

For the present we think it justifiable to leave the three scales for the components, endomorphy, mesomorphy, and ectomorphy, precisely as they are. These scales provide an adequate method for classifying human physiques according to three morphological variables. Furthermore, the technique of somatotyping advised in the previous chapter calls for an anthroposcopic estimate, i.e., a psychological judgment of the subject's physique. The systematic "errors" already present in the scales would presumably be present also in these judgments. Hence, if the scales agree with the judgments, somatotyping by inspection should be easier than if the investigator had to carry in mind a correction factor or had to apply such a factor to his estimate after he had made it.

CHAPTER VI

DESCRIPTION OF THE SOMATOTYPES

IN THIS chapter are set forth the principal characteristics of the 76 somatotypes. Many of the morphological characteristics that one should look for in anthroposcopy are described. Not every feature that will guide the experienced observer is listed, however, for a single book could scarcely contain an account of all the rich detail apparent to a thoroughly practiced eye. In addition to purely morphological description, the following pages contain some observations on non-photographable characteristics typical of the various somatotypes. For the most part these statements represent information gleaned throughout a decade of observation, but perhaps some of these generalizations will need revision when more systematic research is completed. The reader interested in the practice of somatotyping will find it instructive to study the points relating to morphology. Readers with other interests may find the remarks on those characteristics of the somatotypes that are not visible in a photograph to be of some suggestive value. Certain of these observations are amplified in Chapter VII.

It should be of some help for the reader to compare the descriptions of the somatotypes with the illustrative photographs, although the reader ought to be warned again that perhaps no living physique is a perfect example of a somatotype. The somatotype derives from an average of tendencies. The descriptions of the somatotypes were made with a large number of photographs spread out on a table. Each photograph was a correct example (anthropometrically) of the somatotype. Yet these photographs differed in many details.

The descriptions printed here are correct for the somatotype as a whole, but in some instances it has been impossible to select a single photograph which does not in certain details contradict the general description.

In studying the following sketches, we must bear in mind that no two physiques are exactly alike. The designation 117 refers to a mathematical point in a space defined by three coordinates, each of which is continuous. To label a physique 117 means simply that the physique falls nearer to that point than to any other. Since, in the whole three-dimensional range of human physical variation, a physique is arbitrarily classified in terms of its proximity to one of 76 such points, and since there are millions of discernible variations among physiques, we shall expect to find within the same somatotype examples which differ quite markedly in detail.

It cannot be too strongly emphasized that in describing somatotypes we are not describing people. The living human physique is a highly complex morphological unit which may, as a whole, approximate some mathematical point, but no physique is perfectly consistent throughout every region, and a perfect example of any somatotype is perhaps non-existent. On the relatively coarse 7-point scaling system which we use for statistical purposes, together with the even coarser 5-point division of the body into regions, a few physiques (about three or four in a hundred) turn out to be "bull's-eye" somatotypes, but this does not mean that two such physiques having the same somatotype are in any sense absolutely alike. They are only relatively alike, for their degree of morphological resemblance is a function of the fineness of the scale by which they are measured. In the following pages we find ourselves referring to the 76 somatotypes *as though* such categories were exhaustive, in the sense that every human body must necessarily fit one of these categories, but such is only an approximation to the truth. It is necessary to speak in terms of points of reference, and in the description of physique 76 points of reference are of relatively greater value for precision than are the traditional two points of reference or Kretschmer's three points of reference. But even a mesh of 76 holes is far too coarse to strain out the detailed individual variations of human beings. It is desirable to define these 76 reference points, not because there are only that many kinds of physique, but because such a skeletal framework makes possible a study of the intermixing of morphological components.

Since variations of the third component are by far the easiest both to measure and to recognize, we shall present the somatotypes in an order determined by the strength of the third component—beginning with those highest in ectomorphy.

THE SEVENS IN ECTOMORPHY

127

117

217

THE 117

This is the most extreme of the microsplanchnic physiques. The trunk is excessively flat, and is relatively narrow and relatively short. In the first region (head), we find a small, hypoplastic face, fragile features, and the moderately long, extremely slender neck. Both face and cranium are of variable shape in the 117. The cranium is occasionally of fairly large size, but the face is always small. The nose is usually both slender and short. The jaw is weak and receding. The upper trunk usually shows a sharp, high kyphotic curving of the vertebral column, with flat upper chest and marked lack of anteroposterior depth. The chest is fairly long, with acute costovertebral angles. The waist is rather low and is both extremely narrow and extremely flat. The iliac crests stand out prominently. The arms are like slender reeds throughout the whole of their length, with relatively little difference in the three arm measurements, and the legs are like jointed pipestems.

The general muscular tone of the 117 is fairly good. The posture is usually rather straight and upright, in contrast with the extremely slumped and overrelaxed 217. In this respect the 117 falls just about midway between the sprightly and often athletic 127, and the excessively weak, atonic 217. In the 117, with the first component so extremely low and with the skeleton so extremely light and fragile, there is a minimum of weight to carry and consequently the muscular equipment, though slight, may attain a high degree of relative efficiency. The muscles are long and slender, almost stringlike, and the 117 is generally spry and energetic. He is likely to be a great walker, striding with a long, springy up-and-down motion as though he had elastic coils in his legs.

THE 127

The 127 retains the extreme linearity of the 117, but carries a distinctly stronger skeleton and more powerful musculature. The face of the 127 is less hypoplastic than that of the 117, and may have a long, prominent, narrow nose, with a sharp, prowlike bridge. The 127 often has a fairly well-developed jaw, which typically comes to a sharp point and gives the face a distinctive triangular appearance. Dolichocephaly is a pronounced characteristic of this somatotype, though not of the 117. The 217 is more often brachycephalic than dolichocephalic. The neck usually shows a clear dominance of the transverse over the anteroposterior diameter, and the trapezius muscles are sometimes fairly well developed. The shoulders are broader than the shoulders of the 117, and the pectoralis and other chest muscles are better developed. The deltoid muscles stand out a little, as do the triceps. The upper arm has partially lost the reedlike appearance of the arm of the 117, and in its proximal segment there is the beginning of muscular relief and molding, but there is none of the soft, even inflation which marks the beginnings of endomorphy. The abdominal muscles have begun to be visible. The posture is straighter and the lumbar curve of the back is lower than in the 117. The waist is low, usually narrow, and the upper trunk, with its fairly broad shoulders, may show a pronounced "athletic" taper. The long arms and legs are likely to seem extremely fragile in their distal segments, partially because of the somewhat increased muscular reinforcement which is seen chiefly in the proximal segments. The distal segments of the limbs seem too long.

The 127 is usually tall, often extremely tall, and he stands straight and erect. Like the 117 he is fond of walking, but unlike the former, he is sometimes sufficiently strong and has sufficient endurance to participate in competitive athletics. The 127's are occasionally seen as basketball centers, baseball pitchers, or tennis players. This is apparently one of the healthiest physiques. All the ectomorphs who are lower in the first component than in the second seem to be peculiarly resistant to most of the contagious diseases, and they are long lived. These people tend to be hyperthyroid.

THE 217

The general appearance of the 217 presents a sharp antithesis to that of the 127. This is a slumped and overrelaxed physique, markedly lacking in the spryness and muscular tone of the 127 or even of the 117. It is such a physique as might cause apoplexy in a teacher of postural education. The facial skeleton is extremely frail and slight, like that of the 117, but there is a soft, subcutaneous deposit of fat which gives the face, and the whole body, a distinctly feminine molding. The head is rounder, and a little larger, than the head of the 127. The features are small, with the jaw and the nose almost always hypoplastic. The nose lacks the sharp beaklike quality of the nose of the 127, but is inclined to be short and pointed, or may be turned up slightly, with gently flaring alae. The lips are softer and more full than other highly ectomorphic lips. The neck is extremely slender in both diameters, with marked lack of muscular molding or relief. The Adam's apple, often prominent in the neck of the 127, is not visible in the 217. The trapezius muscle is low and undeveloped, with no pyramiding. The upper chest always appears badly collapsed and slumped anteriorly, while the more or less forward projecting abdomen below gives the impression that the contents of the body cavities have slipped downward. The waist is uniformly high, a characteristic which lengthens the lumbar curve of the back (as seen in the lateral picture). In general, weakness of the second component raises and lengthens the lower bow of the "S curve" of the spine. Strength of the second component lowers and sharpens this lower bow. The waistline rises with the first component and falls with the second. When the first component dominates over the second, the high waist and the weak spinal musculature combine to produce a characteristic sway-backed appearance, and the arms hang flaccidly.

In the 217 the iliac crests are typically covered by a thin endomorphic blanket, and there is an even fullness of the lower abdomen which is entirely absent in the two previous somatotypes. The trunk as a whole is a little shorter than in the 117, and distinctly shorter than in the 127, but these measures of length are more variable than the measures of breadth and thickness. The whole appearance of the 217, especially in the dorsal photograph, often suggests the feminine form. The outer curves from the waist to the knees approach an ellipse. The gynandromorphic aspect is so strong in all male somatotypes carrying predominance of the first component over the second, and in all female physiques carrying predominance of the second over the first, that we are inclined to regard gynandromorphy as a phenomenon correlated with the patterning of the components in a physique. Yet marked gynandromorphy is sometimes seen in a somatotype which ordinarily lacks it. It is perhaps under such circumstances that this phenomenon assumes a peculiar psychological importance.

The arms and legs of the 217 show the same distal fragility and great distal length that are seen in the other ectomorphic 7's, but there is just the beginning of endomorphic inflation over the proximal segments of the upper arms, the thighs are rounded and are beginning to fill out in their upper third, and the buttocks are fully inflated. That is to say, the lateral indentations of the buttocks, which are always seen in the dorsal photograph when the first component is distinctly the weakest component, are missing.

This is one of the weakest of physiques, although with the first component at 2, the 217 is outside the range of the so-called Froehlich syndrome (*dystrophia adiposo genitalis*), and it is rare to see a 217 with a suggestion of hypogenitalism. In the 316, however, this is a common phenomenon. Many of the Froehlich cases are 316's.

The 217 nearly always has poor muscular coordination, and is inept at every form of athletic exercise. When he sits down, he likes to slump in a heap, and to sit on about the middle of his spinal column. He gives the strong impression of languor. But there is some evidence that he carries more than his share of mental gifts. If unfortunate enough to fall into the clutches of an undiscriminating enthusiast for physical education, he may suffer most unhappily.

The 127 and the 217 look a little alike at long range, especially when clothed, but under careful examination they look quite different, and there is evidence that they are more different physiologically and psychologically than morphologically. It might be pointed out in this connection that, as we study personalities more closely from the point of view of the components, it becomes increasingly more evident that the determinants of both physiological and psychological personality probably lie more in the balancing of the components than in the absolute strength of any one component. Thus, it appears that if insight into constitutional psychology is to be had it will come from a study of the balancing of the components within a physique, as manifested in conflicts and dysplasias among the components, and not from any superficial correlation of endomorphy or mesomorphy or ectomorphy with mental and physiological patterns. The 217 and the 127 are possibly as different, psychologically and physiologically, as the 117 and 171.

One brief note on behavior may be permissible at this point. The 217's appear to have a distinct advantage in their remarkable degree of relaxation. They have the power of easy recuperation, and so do not overtax their energy sources. Persons of low second component but of still lower first are prone to live under tension and to carry on in irregular spurts of energy. Such spurts tend to overtax the energy sources of the individual and occasionally leave him high and dry and exhausted, like a flounder which the tide has left on the flats.

All strongly ectomorphic patterns are probably inclined to tuberculosis (Hippocrates called ectomorphy the *phthisic habitus*), but this belief remains to be proved. Our studies appear to indicate that as a group the ectomorphs are relatively immune to all the other common fatal diseases of early and middle life.

The 117 and the 127 remain at nearly the same weight throughout life. Typically they gain only a few pounds, perhaps but 2 or 3 pounds, in the thirties or forties. The 217 usually gains from 5 to 10 pounds in the twenties, and perhaps as much more between 30 and 45.

THE SIXES IN ECTOMORPHY

126		136	236
	226		
216		316	326

THE 126

This is a less fragile, somewhat more compact and stronger edition of the same morphological family that produces the 127. The extremities appear fragile and brittle, but the physique as a whole suggests action, speed, and clean quick movement. This is a tense and unrelaxed, if not indeed an unrelaxable, physical constitution, but the tenseness is "normal" and uniform, like the flaccidity of the 216. These appear to be fixed constitutional characteristics, not factors which "ought to be corrected."

The facial architecture is slight but firm, with sharp lines. All the features are small, cleanly chiseled. The still slender neck shows distinct muscle relief, with the strap muscles well outlined. The thoracic cage is flat but well lifted, and its anteroposterior dimension immediately below the level of the sternal incisure is nearly equal to that at the level of the tenth rib. The abdomen is small, flat and firm. The muscle outlines can be seen along Poupart's ligament. The trunk as a whole is relatively longer in relation to the arms and legs than was the case with the ectomorphic 7's. The trunk-limbs proportions approach those of the aesthetic ideal of artists who portray the slender physique. Neither arms nor legs show any trace of endomorphic padding or inflation in the proximal segments. They are completely clean of fat, or of feminine softness. The posture is straight, alert, eager. This is an athletic somatotype, adept at all games except those requiring weight and sheer strength.

THE 216

The 216 presents substantially the same contrasts with the 126 that were seen between the 217 and the 127. This is a soft, flaccid physique, with a relaxed, sleepy look. The face is rounder than that of the 126, but the bones are smaller and the jaw is usually hypoplastic. All the features are relaxed, the lips are more full, the tense muscle lines are absent, and softness pervades the whole structure of the face. The slender neck lacks muscle relief. Even the strap muscles of the neck can be barely made out. The head is usually carried far forward, the neck forming a sharp angle with the spine. The chest is narrow, flat, and shapeless above, and rather deeper below, where it merges with the flaccidly protruding abdomen. In the 216, even at 18, the abdomen often protrudes immediately above the symphysis pubis like the crown of a derby hat. The musculature is weak and lacking in tone.

In general, the musculature of the body wall may be likened to a system of elastic bands which by their different tensions and strengths mold and shape the anatomical contours. In those physiques in which the first component predominates over the second, especially where the third component is strong, it is as though the elastic used were thin and of poor quality. The body wall seems to stretch too easily, and to lack the contractile power needed to return the body to position and shape. It is this characteristic that is usually meant by the term "poor muscle tone." When the first component dominates, the molding power of the musculature is lost, and the body, like a raindrop, tends to assume the spherical form. If under such circumstances the third component is also high, then the spherical tendency is not lost but is scattered. It is not seen in the body as a whole, but it is seen locally at several points, such as the abdomen, the buttocks, around the breasts, the cheeks, and at the upper arms and upper thighs. The third component seems then to have the effect, not of destroying the spherical tendency, but merely of breaking up or elongating the single sphere into several smaller spheres.

In physiques in which the second component predominates over the first, it is as though the elastic bands were made singularly strong and heavy, and as though they were wrapped too tightly, thus molding the body harshly and forcing it toward angular, squared, rectangular proportions. If under such circumstances the third component is high, the harsh and angular tendency is not lost, but is diffused throughout the whole body where it appears as many sharp corners and jagged edges.

The arms of the 216 tend to appear even weaker and more fragile than they are, for they are almost totally without muscular relief. They are extremely weak in the distal segments, and are outlined (in the lateral photograph) against a slightly greater bodily mass than is the case with the 126. Also, the legs of the 216 are likely to appear weak and spindling in the distal segments.

The posture is slumped, languid, and suggestive of physical collapse. All muscular coordination is poor. Yet these people, like the 217's, are inclined to be resilient and adaptive, and to some tastes they are better company than is the tense, determined, and driving personality of the 126.

The 216 nearly always has a high voice. The 126, on the other hand, frequently has a deep, bass voice.

THE 226

The 226 is a much commoner somatotype than any of the five which we have just considered. In the ectomorphic wing (the ectomorphic 5's, 6's, and 7's) only two others are commoner. About 4 per cent of men are 235's, about 3 per cent are 335's, and about 2½ per cent are 226's.

The 226 looks slender, but normal. We are accustomed to seeing him every day and do not regard him as unusual. He is generally tall, often extremely tall, has a relatively small face, but a larger one than the extremes we have been considering, a slender neck, and a moderately long trunk with long arms and legs. He walks rather awkwardly, with long, deliberate strides and a springy, up-and-down motion, a little like that of the 117.

Theoretically the 226 combines the qualities of the 126 with those of the 216, but actually he is physically quite different from either. He lacks entirely the tense, hard lines of the former, and he also lacks the collapsed softness of the latter. Falling between two extreme tendencies, and representing as it does something of a balancing of them, this physique has many opportunities for the development of internal contradictions and of externally manifest dysplasias. The 226 is actually one of the most dysplastic of physiques, and it is rare to find one in perfect symmetry throughout the five regions of the body. Some of the dysplastic variations achieve bizarre proportions.

Note in the illustration that the 226 of low dysplasia is an aesthetically well-balanced physique. The long slender limbs match the similarly slender body, the posture is fairly erect without tenseness, and the thoracic and abdominal segments of the trunk are well balanced, with a moderately high waist and a well-proportioned head and neck. The height of the head and face, as seen frontally, is slightly greater than one-eighth of the total height. This is a good aesthetic balance for ectomorphy—not for mesomorphy or endomorphy. Textbooks usually give 1 to 7 as the "correct" proportion for the male. The 262 has about that proportion. In the 711 the proportion is about 1 to 6.

THE 136

In the 136 the angularity and sharp relief of the 126 are accentuated. The flesh is drawn tightly over the now much stronger skeleton, and the individual has a lean and hungry look, combined perhaps with the suggestion of a certain fierceness. Cassius may possibly have been a 136. Calvin may have been another.

Other characteristics are a long nose, stronger jaw, heavier supraorbital structure, slight pyramiding of the neck, wide shoulders, sharply tapering athletic chest, narrow waist, narrow hips, sharp muscle relief over the trunk and in the limbs, larger joints, and heavier bone in the wrists and ankles. This is still a slender and fragile physique, but in both the second and third components it is a full degree removed from the 127.

The 136 is a rare somatotype. Nevertheless, in the history

of the human race the 136's may have played a disproportionately prominent part, for they are often people of great stern-
ness of purpose and of unswerving determination.

THE 316

The 316, an even greater rarity than the 136, is actually a
softer and weaker physique than the 216 or 217. There is the
same minimum of muscular strength and support, but a distinctly greater endomorphic load to carry. The face is soft,
rather round and small, with hypoplastic features, and usually
with an excessively underdeveloped chin and a small mouth
and nose. The neck often seems even more slender and
pipestemlike than the neck of a 216 because of the greater
mass both above and below. The shoulders are narrow, soft
and frail, and are usually slumped forward. The upper chest
is more flattened than the chest of the 216, and the abdomen
is more protuberant and appears more flaccid. The back is
weak, the waist high, and the hips wide. The lower legs and
arms look like slender stilts which are strikingly white and
appear devoid of muscle. There are usually small breasts,
and the distribution of hair is distinctly feminine.

In the late teens the 316 often has underdeveloped genitalia, a condition then referred to medically as one exhibiting
the Froehlich syndrome. This condition is associated with
one form of hypopituitarism, although it is probable that
all the somatotypes in which the first component predominates over the second carry this same glandular characteristic
to a greater or less degree.

Which is more fundamental, the glandular patterning
or the constitutional factors determining the physical pattern, is perhaps a purely academic question. Instead of en-
gaging in such a controversy we need to apply energy first
to the standardizing of adequate descriptions of what is to
be seen and measured. The ectomorphs who are lower in
the second than in the first component probably are classi-

fiable physiologically in a hypopituitary group (posterior lobe). Similarly, the ectomorphs who are higher in the second than in the first component are apparently uniformly hyperthyroid. But is a 136 a 136 because he is hyperthyroid, or is he hyperthyroid because he is a 136, or are the two facts not causally related? We do not yet know the answers to such questions as these (see p. 230).

Many of the Froehlich cases are 415's or 514's. Quite a number of them are 613's. Possibly all the excessively rare 515's are of the Froehlich order. All Froehlichs are low in the second component.

THE 236

The 236 is a slender, upright physique, usually tall, and when not dysplastic, he has a symmetry and beauty of proportion that is aesthetically of the highest order. It is a lean, clean-cut body throughout. The muscular relief is sharp, but the muscles are long and slender and there is no muscular bunching. The diffuse endomorphic 2 softens all tendency toward jaggedness. The facial structure is further developed than is the case with the somatotypes of lower second component, and the general tendency is toward a triangular frontal appearance of the face, with a fairly strong jaw in profile. The shoulders are wide, and the still rather flat chest is usually well supported above. The abdomen is flat but not tightly pinched in. Arms and legs are long but well proportioned. The fingers and toes are often long, and hands and feet are narrow.

Such is the picture of the nondysplastic 236, but he is rare. This somatotype, like the 226, falls between two sharply diverging tendencies, and dysplasias are the rule. A common dysplasia is one which carries a markedly weak, collapsed chest, and a concentration of the first component about the lower trunk. For some reason, this kind of dysplastic 236 is disproportionately common among schizophrenic patients in mental hospitals, and also seems to be remarkably susceptible to tuberculosis.

In an informal study of over one hundred different historical pictures of the Christ, we found that about 30 per cent of the artists have pictured the Christian central figure as approximately a 236, and about 35 per cent of them have made him approximately a 235.

THE 326

The 326 contrasts with the 236 as the 316 contrasts with the 136, but less sharply so. The striking collapsed appearance due to the 1 in the second component is not present in the 326, and this somatotype is not often Froehlich.

The face appears larger and the features are heavier than in the 236. There is a suggestion of roundness in the face. The fine lines of the facial muscles are entirely absent. The eyes are larger, with relaxed or drooping lids, the nose broader, the lips fuller, and the whole face is relaxed. There is no detail of muscle relief in the body, and its absence is especially noticeable in the neck. The chest is relatively weak and flattened above, but there is nothing suggesting the complete collapse which marks the 316. The abdomen is a little more full and rounded than is the thorax, but the flaccid atonic protuberance of the 316 is not seen. The shoulders are fairly broad, and the waistline is definitely high—a feature which always distinguishes the 326 from the 236. The latter carries a rather low waistline. The line from waist to knee in the 326 strongly suggests the feminine ellipse, the buttocks are full, and there is a feminine fullness over the groins, in the upper thighs, and about the pubic region. Weakness is seen in the inner aspect of the lower thighs, the arms and legs are long in proportion to the rather short trunk, and the forearms and lower legs appear particularly weak. This is a somatotype which approaches the Froehlich pattern, but does not often reach it.

THE FIVES IN ECTOMORPHY

145	[155]		235		245	345
		225		335		
415	515		325		425	435

THE 145

The 145 is the next step in the 126—136 series, but this somatotype has reached and has slightly surpassed average male ruggedness, and therefore it presents characteristics which set it sharply apart from the 136. In the 145 we no longer see an overwhelming ectomorphy, but we see instead a fairly rugged and muscular youth who is also markedly lean and brittle in appearance. The drawn, alert, lean lines of the face are present, as in the 136, but the bones are heavier, the nose may have a high and medium-broad bridge instead of the sharp prowlike bridge of the 136, the cheekbones are likely to be prominent. The jaw is strong and may be somewhat squared, like the square jaws of the mesomorphs; the lips are thick and tight and are never seen gaping open, and the supraorbital ridges are likely to be fairly prominent. The eyelids are tense, and the eyes seem sharp and watchful. The muscle relief of the slender neck is sharp and clear, and the trapezius muscles have generally begun to pyramid. The chest is markedly flat above, but the shoulder girdle and upper thorax are erect and well supported. The outline of the scapula can be easily made out on the lean back, but there is no winging or flaring (a characteristic due to over-relaxation of the shoulder girdle). The shoulders are fairly broad, but the waist is less narrow than the waist of the 136, and the sharp athletic taper of the chest is therefore not seen quite so prominently. The abdomen is flat and seems tightly under control. There is sharp lateral muscular dimpling of the buttocks. The trunk is of variable length, but on the average it shows about the aesthetically popular proportion to length of limb. The arms and legs have lost much of the weakness in the distal segments which is so characteristic of extreme ectomorphy, and the preponderant length of the distal segments has also disappeared.

The 145 is usually a somatotype of moderate height, but he is sometimes tall. Like the near relatives in his morphological family, he enjoys singularly good health and seems to carry immunity to most of the contagious diseases. Also his physique is relatively free from dysplasias. He is rather rare, occurring about five or six times in a thousand, but among the five or six cases two or three will always be found to be excellent, relatively nondysplastic examples. Most of the extremely long-lived people appear to be ectomorphic 5. Many of them may be 145's.

THE 415

This is one of the most easily recognized of the somatotypes. Its hallmark is an extreme muscular weakness, a high, narrow waist which has endomorphic fullness both above and below, and an overwhelmingly feminine appearance of the whole bodily outline. With the second component at a minimum, and the first as high as 4, the weak muscular and skeletal equipment has about all that it can carry, but the 415 carries it fairly well, and does not typically show the signs of collapse that are beginning to appear in the 514 and that become more conspicuous in the 613 and 712.

The 415's range freely from the very tall to the very short. At 18 there is ordinarily no conspicuous accumulation of fat, and unless the individual overeats, there need be none throughout life, although the later development of the "bay window" is a phenomenon associated with weak abdominal musculature and, consequently, with a low second component rather than with a high first component. The face of the 415 is oval, although the facial skeleton is frail; the chin is weak, and the bony structures are hypoplastic. The upper chest is collapsed and the abdominal trunk is markedly predominant over the thoracic trunk. The hips are often wide.

The distal segments of the arms and legs are weak and seem disproportionately long, although not so extremely long as in the 316.

About 10 per cent of the 415's show the genital underdevelopment associated with the Froehlich syndrome. There is no question that this condition responds somewhat to the administration of pituitary and gonadal extracts, at least temporarily, although whether or not such treatment effects any permanent change in the sexual life and reproductive potentialities of the individual is a controversial question which has been under voluminous discussion. Certainly no such treatment brings about any change in the somatotype. Whether or not glandular treatment might effect a change in the somatotype if administered early, say from birth on, is another interesting and controversial question which we cannot yet answer (see p. 230).

We have studied the physiques of young children for some years with this question in mind, and the impression appears warranted that the somatotype is definitely fixed before birth. Certainly children can be somatotyped with approximate accuracy shortly after birth. But the question of the permanency of the somatotype must remain open until a research attack is brought to bear upon the matter—one which will involve standardized photographing of a large series of children at regular intervals from birth through childhood and adolescence to full maturity, and thereafter, if possible, until the processes of senescence set in (see p. 217).

THE 515

As yet we have never seen a physique which even strongly suggested the 155, and the 515 is so rare that its existence in the male may perhaps be regarded as controversial. Only one male in a total series of nearly 10,000 has been clearly classified as a 515. But there is no question as to the existence of this somatotype in the female, and the single male case is so clear cut that the inclusion of the somatotype in this series is probably justified.

Our 515 has a short, highly collapsed trunk, with an extremely high, narrow waist, definite breasts, plump "pneumatic" thighs, buttocks, and upper arms, and extremely long, ectomorphic arms and legs. The height over cube root of weight is 13.5. The Froehlich characteristic is marked. There is no pubic hair at 18, no photographically visible testicles, and a hypoplastic penis.

In a series of 200 unstandardized photographs (not taken by us) of Froehlich cases which we have had the privilege of examining, there were at least two who looked as though they might well be 515's.

THE 225

The 225, like the 226, is a fairly common somatotype which seems to represent a balance or intermediate stage between two competing tendencies, and this physique is usually found with marked dysplasia. Characteristically, the 225 is a little fellow, both slender and short, and in middle life he almost always has a "potbelly," about the size of a small watermelon. Supported by a second component of only 2, this tends to become the soft, jiggly sort of belly. The 225 does not often possess the graceful aesthetic appearance of the 226, but is typically just a small, inconspicuous physique. The face is slight, with unobtrusive, rather sharp features. The neck is slender, the chest is generally weak in the upper third, the waist is fairly narrow, with the waistline neither conspicuously high nor low, but the proportion between the abdomen and chest is good. There is none of the harshness of muscular and bony detail that is seen in the 145 and, on the other hand, at college age there is no protruding of the lower abdomen. The arms and legs are slender but they do not seem conspicuously long. There is no endomorphic inflation in the thighs or in the upper arms.

The 225 is physically inconspicuous unless he is tall, which is unusual. He is easy to overlook. But he is apt to be mentally gifted (see p. 178).

THE 235

The 235 is the commonest of the "ectomorphic constellation," and this physique has, among other things, apparently provided the most acceptable visualization of the Christian Messiah (see p. 155).

There is a sharp difference between the 235 and the 225. In the former, the entire body carries definite undercurrents of secondary dominance by the second component. That is to say, the second component dominates over the first. The facial structure is stronger and fuller than that of the 225. The 235 frequently carries what appears at first glance to be a strong jaw and fairly strong, determined features, although on close examination it can be seen that the bony framework is actually rather light. The neck is no longer strikingly slender, but is fairly well supported by muscular development, and the trapezii are usually well pyramided. The chest and shoulder girdle suggest slender strength, rather than collapse, or brittle weakness. The shoulders are typically wide and the rather low waist is narrow—a combination providing a good athletic taper. The abdomen is well under muscular control, is flattened anteriorly, and the abdominal segment of the trunk appears to play a distinctly minor role as compared with the thoracic segment. The thighs have lost the glaring weakness of the lower half which is so characteristic of extreme ectomorphy, and the still slender forearms and lower legs appear well matched to the respective proximal segments of the limbs.

THE 325

Both the 325 and the 235 abound in dysplasias, and therefore a "perfect" or "typical" example of either is especially hard to find. But in general these two somatotypes are in sharp contrast and it is easy to distinguish between them.

The differences are of the same nature, essentially, as those between the 216 and 126. The 235 suggests the Messiah. The 325 suggests relaxation. These two concepts are psychologically at opposite poles.

The 325 has soft, relaxed features, and the whole personality expresses overrelaxation. The lips lack firmness and often do not close tightly, the sharp muscular relief is absent, the shoulders are relatively narrow and often drooping, the chest is more or less slumped, the waist is high, the abdomen is relatively full and predominant over the thorax in the morphology of the trunk, the thighs and upper arms are relatively full as compared to the distal segments of these respective limbs, and the wrists are likely to seem extremely slender. In the 325 the ankles are sometimes swathed in an endomorphic blanket, giving them a thick and shapeless appearance, but this is far less common in the male than in the female. In the somatotypes of high endomorphy, this phenomenon is common in both sexes.

THE 335

The 335 is the second commonest of the markedly ectomorphic somatotypes in the male series. This is a highly dysplastic physique, and a difficult one to describe or illustrate, for there are many details in which it varies widely. There is no "typical" 335, and there is no specific hallmark which can positively identify it. In dealing with this, and other physiques which fall near the middle range of somatotypes, the only safe and unqualified descriptive statement that can be made is simply that when the scale values of the components for each of the five regions of the body are computed we can average them and obtain, for the body as a whole, a numerical value of each component.

Nevertheless, the 335 can be described as a heavier and softer 235, with wider hips and usually with a distinct gynandromorphic element throughout the body, or he can be described as a harder and stronger 325, with wider shoulders and better muscling, a lower waist and more evenly proportioned trunk, and a lower gynandromorphic element. The 335 is still a pronounced ectomorph but the sharpness of feature and the lean sensitivity of the body are blanketed with a softening first component, like a rock quarry with a carpet of snow.

THE 245

The 245 is a somewhat softened and heavier 145, or alternatively he is a stronger and harder 235. Mesomorphic 4 places a physique on the strong side of the mean of masculine muscularity and strength, and once the physique has moved across this line, the trend of the personality appears to change markedly. The tense sensitivity of the 235 is not usually seen in the 245. The latter is a fairly solid and clearly masculine personality. The facial structure is a little on the strong side, often with a prominent, square jaw, and with massive, prominent cheekbones. The neck is no longer conspicuously slender, but is muscular. The shoulders are wide, the chest well developed and well supported, and the waist is wider and more muscular than the waist of the 145. But the sharply athletic taper of the chest is usually less marked in the 245. The thoracic trunk of the 245 predominates clearly over the abdominal trunk, and the waist remains distinctly low. Both arms and legs are fairly long, slender, and well muscled. The 245 is ideally patterned for middle- and long-distance running, or for nearly any kind of minor athletics. Many of the best tennis players have been 245's.

THE 425

The 425 is a stronger and less collapsed 415, or alternatively a heavier and more visceral 325. The extremely weak neck, fragile facial structure, collapsed chest, and narrow shoulders of the 415 have all been somewhat strengthened, but this is still a weak physique. There is general relaxation and the suggestion of flaccidity throughout. The waist is

The following plates (Figs. 14 to 71) illustrate various of the somatotypes as they appear at college age. The order of appearance of the figures is based upon the strength of the third component. This is the order followed in Chapter VI where the somatotypes are described. The illustration of a given somatotype will not always check point for point with the description in Chapter VI because a thoroughly typical example—an individual combining *all* the features of his class—is rare and difficult to find.

The legend of each figure gives the general somatotype and is followed, in parentheses, by the five regional somatotypes. Thus "The somatotype 117–127 (117, 127, 117, 117, 127)" means that Fig. 14 is of the general somatotype 117–127 or 1–1½–7; and that region I (head and neck) is 117, region II (thoracic trunk) is 127, region III (arms) is 117, region IV (abdominal trunk) is 117, and region V (legs) is 127.

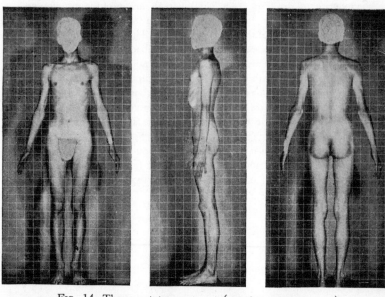

Fig. 14. The somatotype 117–127 (117, 127, 117, 117, 127)

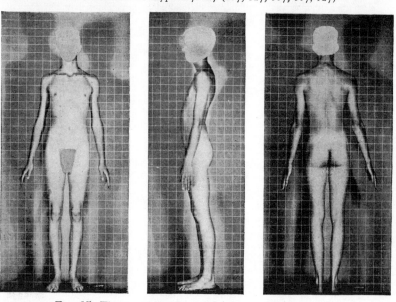

Fig. 15. The somatotype 217–216 (217, 217, 226, 217, 216)

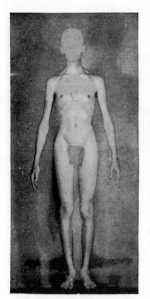

Fig. 16. The somatotype 127–217 (217, 127, 126, 127, 217)

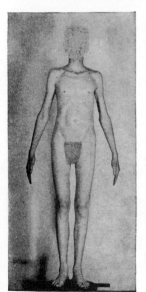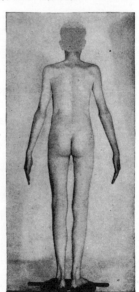

Fig. 17. The somatotype 217–127 (117, 217, 127, 226, 217)

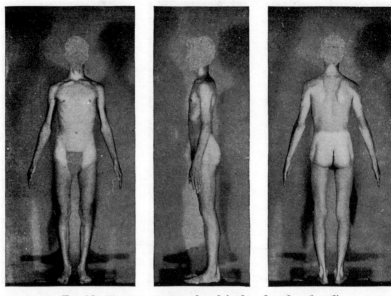

FIG. 18. The somatotype 126–136 (126, 136, 126, 136, 126)

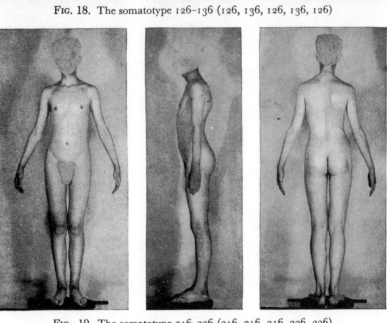

FIG. 19. The somatotype 216–326 (216, 216, 216, 326, 326)

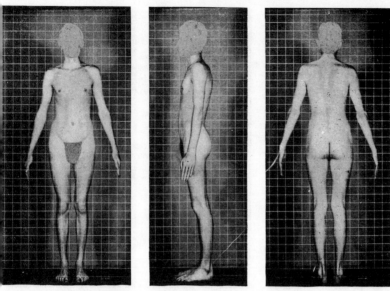

FIG. 20. The somatotype 226–226 (226, 226, 226, 226, 226)

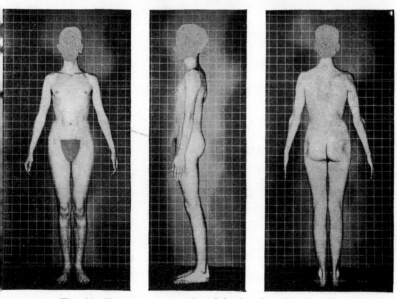

FIG. 21. The somatotype 316–316 (316, 316, 316, 216, 326)

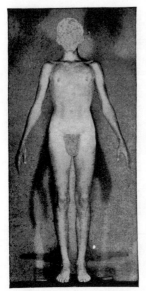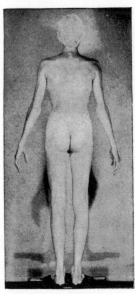

FIG. 22. The somatotype 236–236 (236, 235, 236, 226, 236)

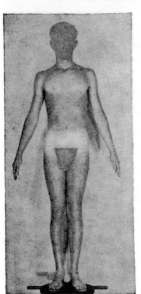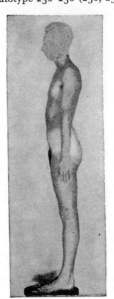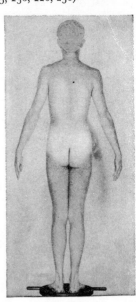

FIG. 23. The somatotype 326–326 (326, 326, 326, 326, 326)

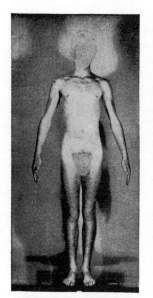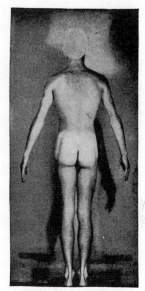

FIG. 24. The somatotype 145–145 (145, 145, 145, 145, 235)

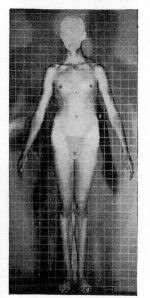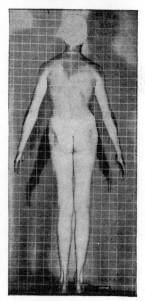

FIG. 25. The somatotype 415–425 (415, 425, 425, 415, 316)

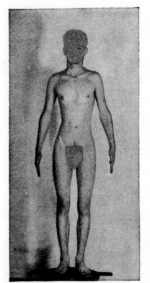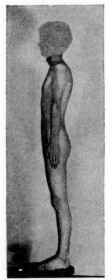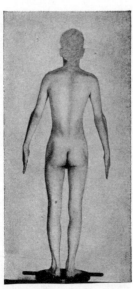

Fig. 26. The somatotype 225–226 (225, 225, 225, 127, 225). Such a striking ecto-morphic dysplasia of the abdominal trunk is extremely rare.

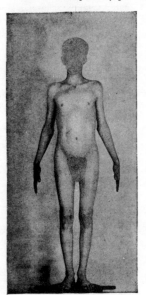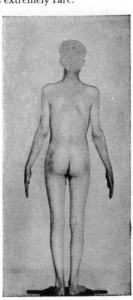

Fig. 27. The somatotype 225–325 (226, 325, 225, 325, 225)

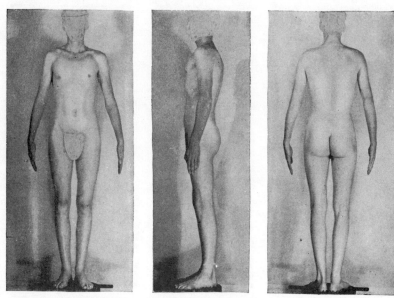

Fig. 28. The somatotype 235–345 (235, 345, 245, 335, 235)

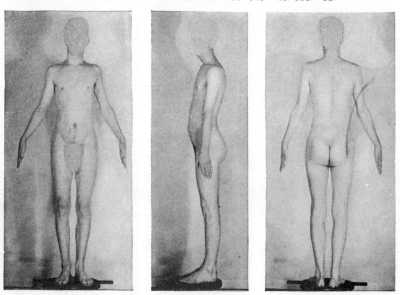

Fig. 29. The somatotype 325–325 (325, 325, 225, 325, 325)

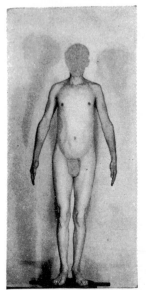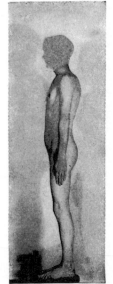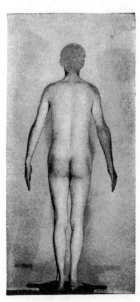

Fig. 30. The somatotype 425–325 (326, 425, 325, 435, 425)

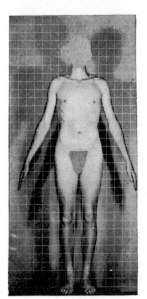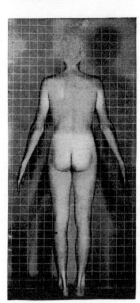

Fig. 31. The somatotype 435–425 (425, 435, 326, 425, 443)

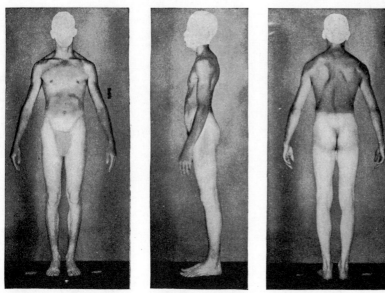

FIG. 32. The somatotype 154–145 (154, 145, 154, 154, 145)

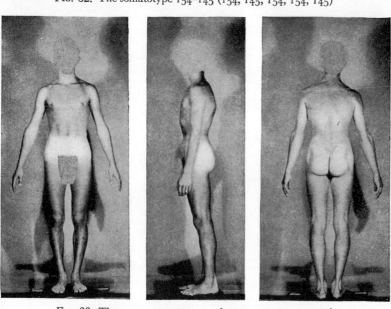

FIG. 33. The somatotype 254–253 (254, 253, 244, 253, 154)

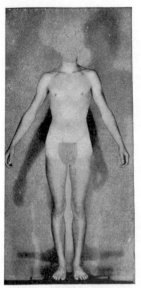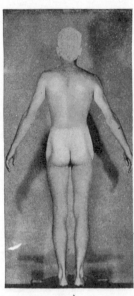

FIG. 34. The somatotype 244–244 (244, 244, 244, 244, 244)

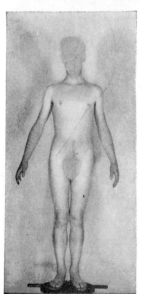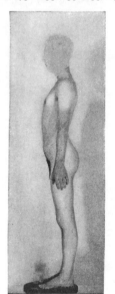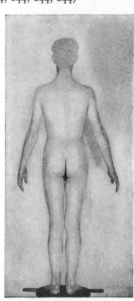

FIG. 35. The somatotype 424–434 (425, 434, 424, 434, 424)

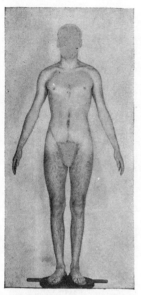

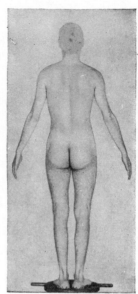

FIG. 36. The somatotype 254–344 (353, 254, 244, 254, 345). This physique shows a striking dysplasia between regions I and V, i.e., between the head and neck, and the legs. Total dysplasia = 20.

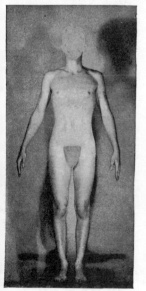

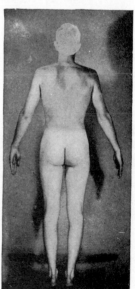

FIG. 37. The somatotype 344–344 (334, 353, 344, 344, 444)

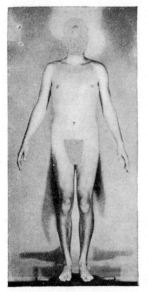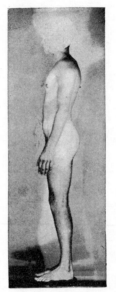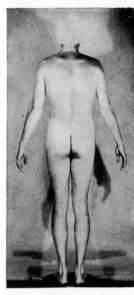

FIG. 38. The somatotype 354–344 (354, 353, 344, 353, 345)

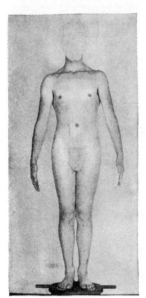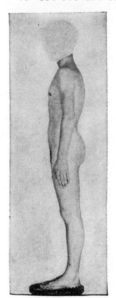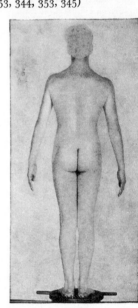

FIG. 39. The somatotype 444–453 (444, 354, 344, 453, 543)

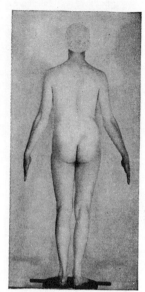

Fig. 40. The somatotype 524–425 (425, 524, 524, 524, 425)

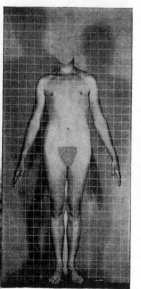
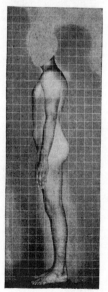
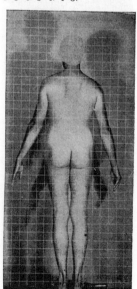

Fig. 41. The somatotype 534–534 (524, 533, 534, 534, 534)

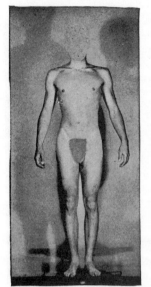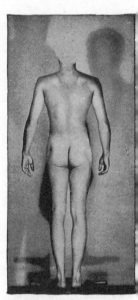

FIG. 42. The somatotype 163–254 (254, 163, 163, 163, 254)

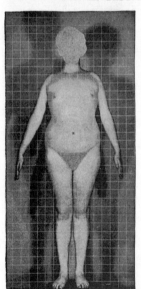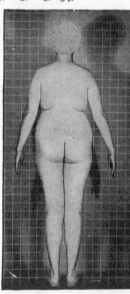

FIG. 43. The somatotype 613–712 (613, 712, 613, 712, 613). Note the high gynandro-morphy.

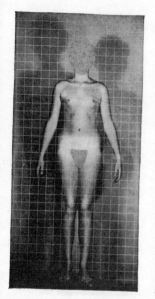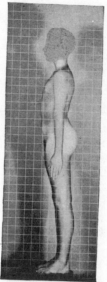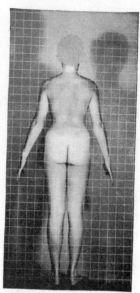

FIG. 44. The somatotype 523–514 (514, 523, 514, 523, 523)

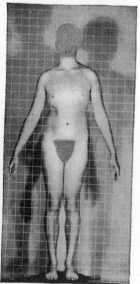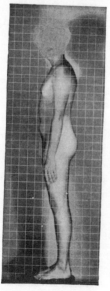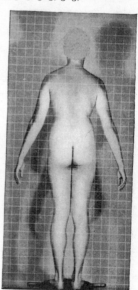

FIG. 45. The somatotype 523–523 (523, 523, 523, 523, 523)

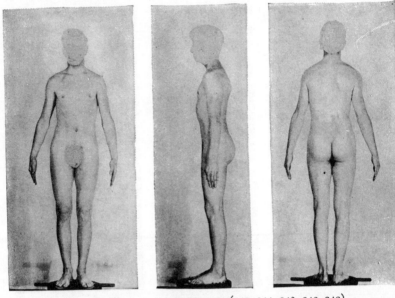

FIG. 46. The somatotype 343–343 (343, 344, 343, 343, 343)

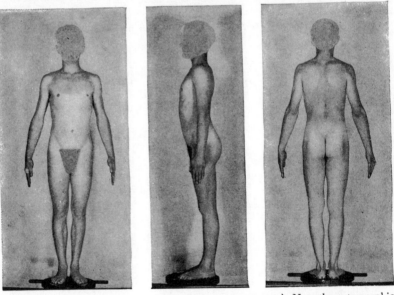

FIG. 47. The somatotype 443–443 (453, 442, 443, 443, 434). Note the ectomorphic dysplasia in the legs.

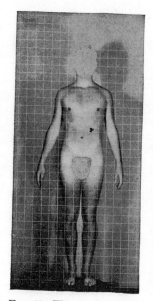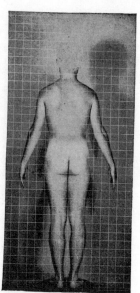

FIG. 48. The somatotype 443-442 (442, 442, 434, 443, 442). Note the ectomorphic dysplasia in the arms.

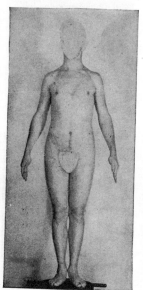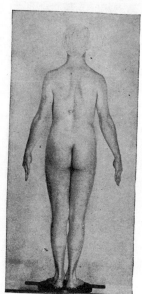

FIG. 49. The somatotype 543-532 (452, 532, 533, 543, 533). There is a marked mesomorphic dysplasia in the head and neck.

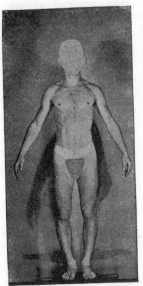

FIG. 50. The somatotype 162–162 (162, 253, 162, 162, 162)

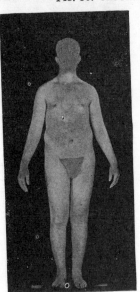

FIG. 51. The somatotype 612–612 (522, 613, 612, 612, 612). This is an excessively rare somatotype.

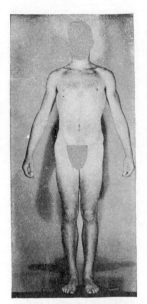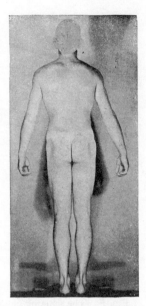

Fig. 52. The somatotype 172–262 (262, 172, 172, 172, 263)

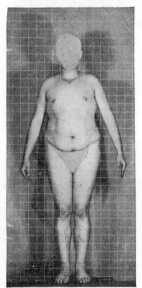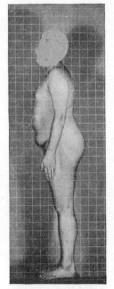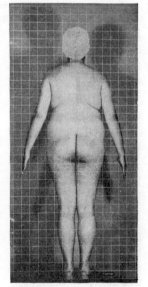

Fig. 53. The somatotype 712–712 (712, 712, 613, 712, 712). Note the ectomorphic dysplasia in the arms.

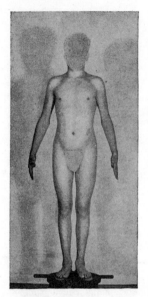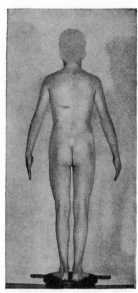

Fig. 54. The somatotype 442–443 (451, 442, 442, 443, 434). The disparity in ecto-morphy between region I (head and neck) and region V (legs) is three degrees. Such a dysplasia is rare among white American college students, although this particular dysplasia appears to be common among schizophrenic psychotics (see p. 239).

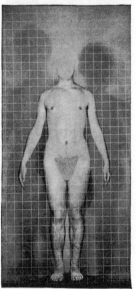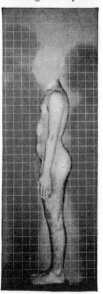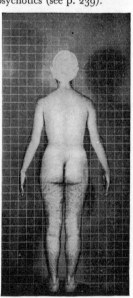

Fig. 55. The somatotype 522–523 (524, 522, 523, 522, 621). This physique shows a con-verse dysplasia to that of Figure 58. Here the high ectomorphy is in the first region.

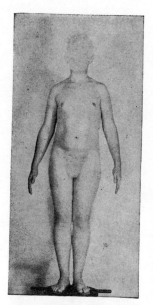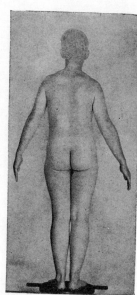

FIG. 56. The somatotype 622–622 (533, 622, 622, 622, 621)

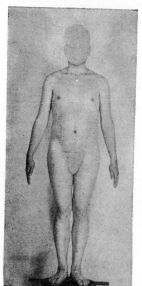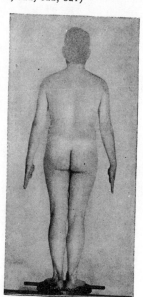

FIG. 57. The somatotype 632–542 (632, 632, 542, 632, 542)

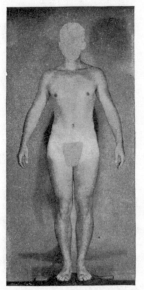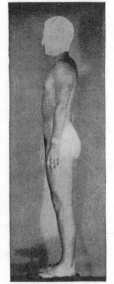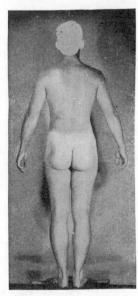

FIG. 58. The somatotype 362–262 (262, 262, 362, 362, 362)

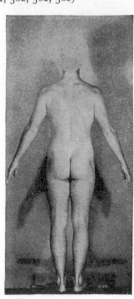

FIG. 59. The somatotype 452–452 (452, 451, 443, 452, 451)

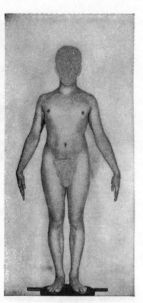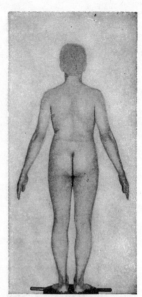

FIG. 60. The somatotype 542-532 (542, 532, 543, 541, 532)

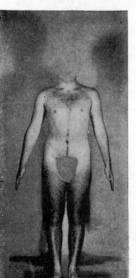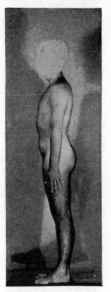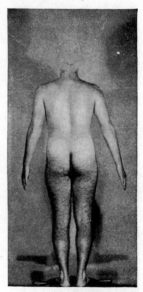

FIG. 61. The somatotype 542-541 (542, 541, 542, 541, 542)

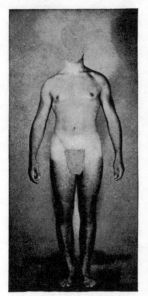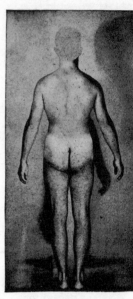

FIG. 62. The somatotype 171–262 (262, 171, 171, 171, 262)

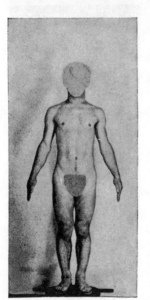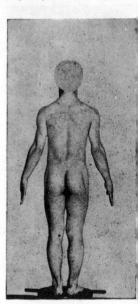

FIG. 63. The somatotype 271–171 (271, 171, 171, 271, 271)

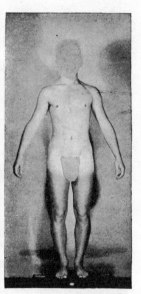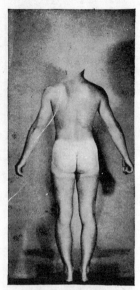

FIG. 64. The somatotype 261–262 (261, 162, 252, 261, 261)

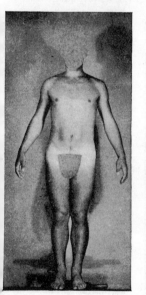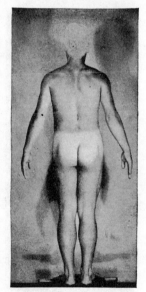

FIG. 65. The somatotype 371–362 (362, 271, 362, 371, 371)

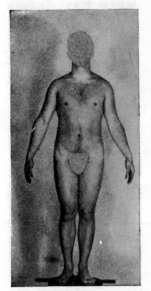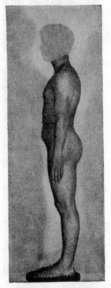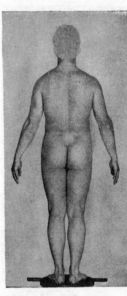

Fig. 66. The somatotype 461–461 (461, 461, 461, 461, 461)

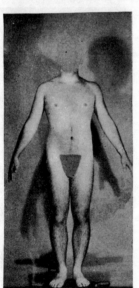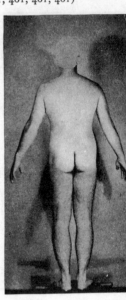

Fig. 67. The somatotype 551–541 (551, 551, 541, 541, 551)

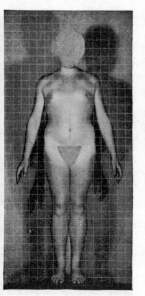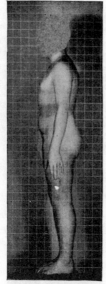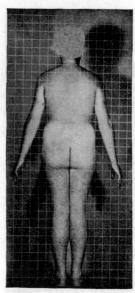

Fig. 68. The somatotype 631–632 (631, 631, 622, 632, 631)

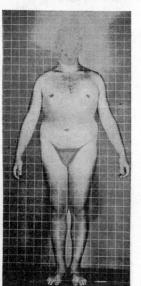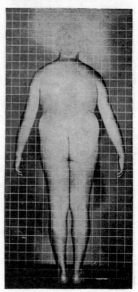

Fig. 69. The somatotype 721–631 (721, 721, 632, 721, 631)

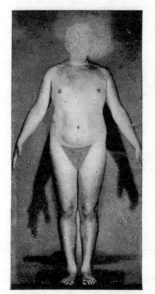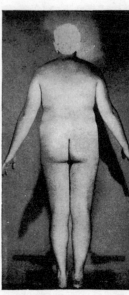

FIG. 70. The somatotype 641–731 (641, 731, 731, 641, 641)

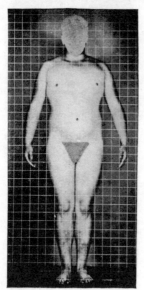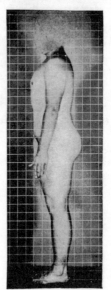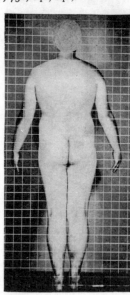

FIG. 71. The somatotype 731–641 (731, 731, 641, 641, 731)

The following plates (Figs. 72-79) show two slightly different somatotypes at various ages. The 451 (Figs. 72-75) shows a rather uniform increase in fullness with advancing age. This increase is typical of those somatotypes in which the second component is dominant. The 541 (Figs. 76-79) shows a more localized increase in fullness in the abdominal trunk with advancing age. This localized increase is typical of those somatotypes in which the first component is dominant. The illustration of each somatotype is not of the same individual, unfortunately, because it requires 30 years to obtain such a series on the same person. Nevertheless, somatotyping at the various ages shown can be done with reasonable certainty.

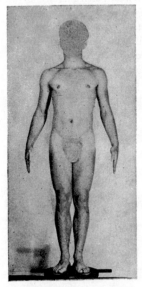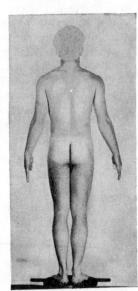

Fig. 72. A 451 at age 17

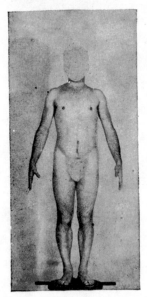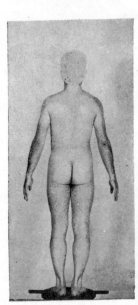

Fig. 73. A 451 at age 26

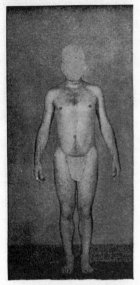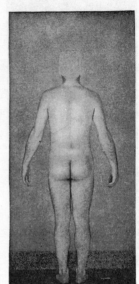

FIG. 74. A 451 at age 28

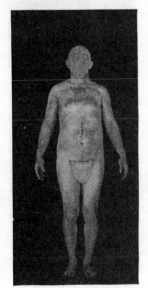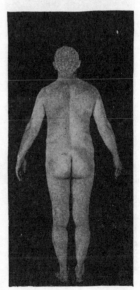

FIG. 75. A 451 at age 45

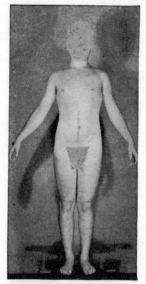  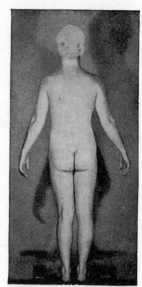

FIG. 76. A 541 at age 18

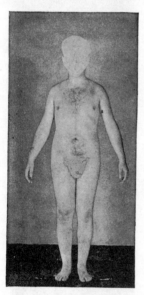  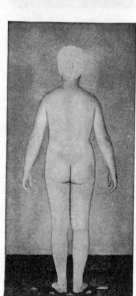

FIG. 77. A 541 at age 27

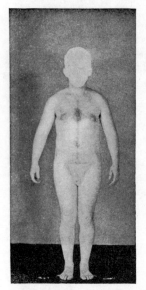

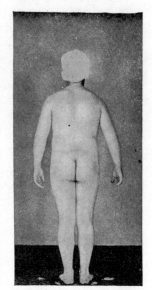

FIG. 78. A 541 at age 33

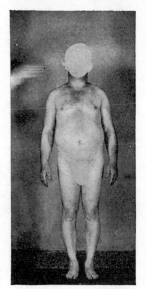

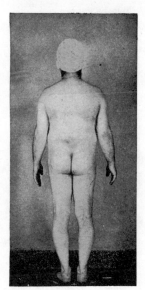

FIG. 79. A 541 at age 43

The following plates (Figs. 80-85) show examples of older physiques rather extreme in each of the three components. These individuals were all about 30 years of age at the time of photographing.

Figures 86-89 show three professional wrestlers and the heaviest man we were able to find in a large eastern city. In the general population it is possible to find extreme variations in obesity and in muscular development which fall slightly outside the range encountered in the college population.

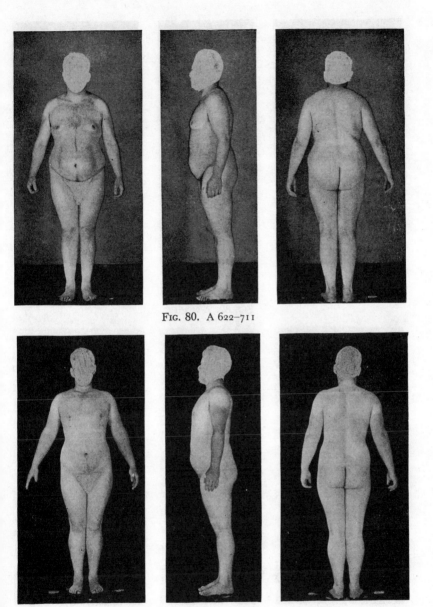

FIG. 80. A 622–711

FIG. 81. A 631–632

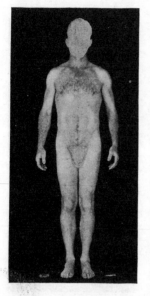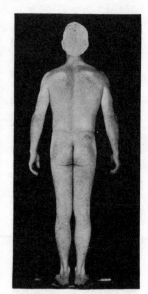

FIG. 82. A 263–172

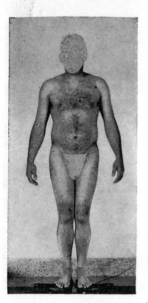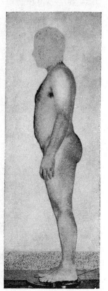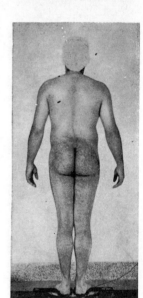

FIG. 83. A 362–362

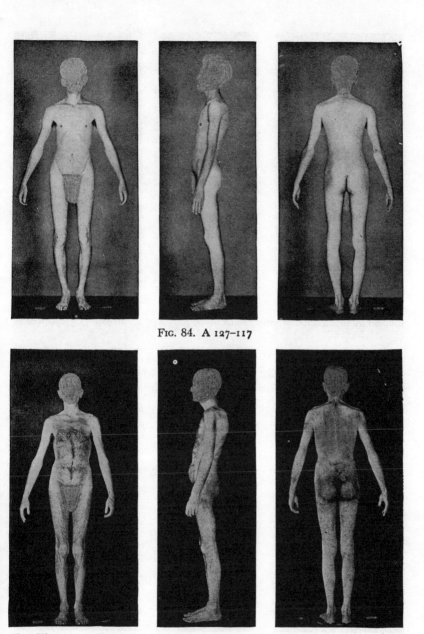

FIG. 84. A 127-117

FIG. 85. A 217-216. Extreme hirsutism sometimes occurs with the third component.

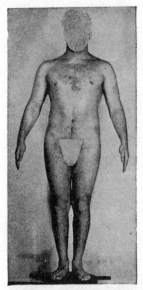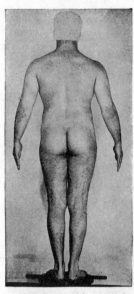

FIG. 86. A professional wrestler, somatotype 371, age 21, height 71.3 in., weight 218 lbs.

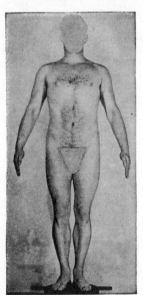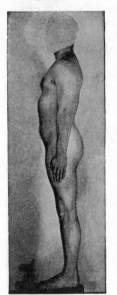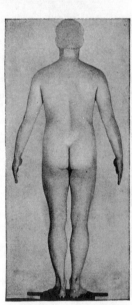

FIG. 87. A professional wrestler, somatotype 362, age 27, height 73.3 in., weight 216 lbs.

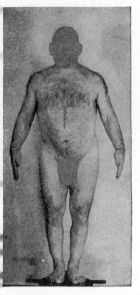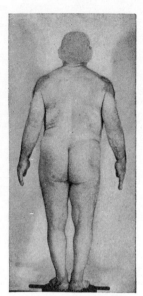

Fig. 88. A professional wrestler, somatotype 461, age 36, height 68.8 in., weight 276 lbs. X-ray photographs show indications of acromegaly.

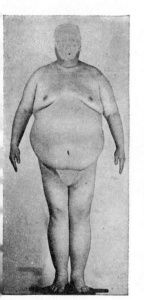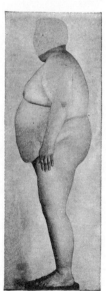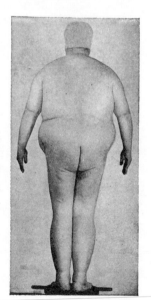

Fig. 89. A 711 in full blossom. Age 42, height 72.8 in., weight 400 lbs.

high, the trunk short, the shoulders relatively narrow, the abdomen full and predominant over the thorax, the arms and legs puny in the distal segments, and the whole appearance, especially in the dorsal view, is strikingly feminine. But there is ordinarily no hypogenitalism or other primary suggestion of the Froehlich condition.

The 4 in the first component is well past the endomorphic mean for men. About 60 per cent of the male population in the colleges are less than endomorphic 4, and somewhat less than 15 per cent are endomorphic 5 or higher (see p. 130). In considering endomorphic 4, then, we are considering men who fall roughly within the most endomorphic two-fifths of the population. With women, the situation is quite different, for women as a group are more endomorphic and less mesomorphic.

THE 345

This rather rare somatotype is usually a tall, slender, "well-built" youth, who in his teens looks more ectomorphic than he is, who tends to put on 10 or 15 pounds in the early twenties, and who grows heavier still at later ages. There is often a conspicuous mesomorphic dysplasia, that is to say, some inconsistent increment of the second component in one region of the body. Thus, unusually wide shoulders are common in the 345, or an unexpectedly massive neck, or face, or both. Occasionally the 345 is seen, with the chest or with the whole trunk of a mesomorphic 5, but with ectomorphic extremities. It is a somatotype which abounds also in other dysplasias and is rarely seen with the same components throughout the body. The beginner in somatotyping will usually mistake the young 345 for the 245 or 235.

THE 435

Like the 345, the 435 is highly dysplastic and relatively rare. Morphologically there is the same contrast with the 345 that is seen between the 235 and 325, but the contrast is not quite so sharply defined. Frequently, in the 435, the first component is relatively concentrated in the trunk, with the third component more conspicuous in the extremities, but sometimes the opposite is the case. This variability accounts in a measure for the great difficulty experienced by a long line of brilliant anatomists and physical anthropologists in their attempts to found a morphological classificatory system solely on specific measurements, or on simple indices alone. Such a classification can never be of the maximum utility, for it does not reach down to basically common factors.

The 435 develops a magnificent "bay window" in middle life. The emergence of the expansive abdomen is a matter of the relative strength of the muscles in the abdominal wall and the strength of the first component. The 216 grows a little pendulous "melon" below the umbilicus, which hangs like a stone in a sack. The 325 can grow a fairly respectable paunch but it is low and tends to bulge in the lower half. The 435, with his stronger abdominal musculature, can distribute the protuberance evenly, and his "bay window" at its best seems to include the lower chest as well as the abdomen. The 425 often balloons out abdominally like a Dutch oven. The physiques of higher endomorphy than 4 do not tend to grow what we call a "bay window"—they tend to assume the spherical form as a whole.

THE FOURS IN ECTOMORPHY

154	244		254	344		354
		334			444	
514	424		524	434		534

THE 154

In the 154 the second component has surpassed the third, and hence this is a distinctly muscular physique, with a secondary element of linearity and brittleness. There is strong muscle relief over the entire body. The head is solid and massive, the neck, although still relatively slender, is muscular and clearly of greater transverse than anteroposterior diameter. The trapezii are well developed, giving the neck a pyramidal appearance in the frontal photograph. All the bones are now on the heavy side. The chest is deep and tapering, and highly predominant over the small, flat, muscular abdomen. The shoulders are broad and relatively massive. This physique could no more develop a "potbelly" than a 117 could win a boxing tournament. The hips are narrow, sometimes extremely narrow, and the pelvis is contracted and steep. For the female 154 (rare) childbirth might be excessively difficult and require Caesarean section. The hands of the 154 are strong, usually with long, muscular fingers. The joints are fairly large. Yet the limbs are still relatively long and slender, and this is by no means a blocky physique. The face is still essentially a sharpened, not a blunt face.

If the 145 can be said to be a slender ectomorph with a strong interference of ruggedness, the 154 is a rugged mesomorph with a strong interference of fragility.

THE 514

The male 514 is extremely rare. This physique is closely related to the 415, but is more eunuchoid (Froehlich), and appears somewhat more massive and less collapsed, because of the lower third component. The head is larger and rounder than that of the 415, the face is more full but not heavier in the bone, the trunk is enclosed in a blanket of subcutaneous fat, and therefore exhibits a slightly less conspicuous weakness in the upper chest and less appearance of lumbar weakness. The abdomen is full, with a distinct anterior bulge over the symphysis, as seen in the lateral picture. The high waist is less narrow, and deeper in the anteroposterior diameter. There are always more or less conspicuous breasts. The arms and legs are shorter than those of the 415, and are less conspicuously fragile. The upper arms and thighs show the distinct beginnings of "hamming." The lower legs may be blanketed with subcutaneous fat, even to the ankles.

THE 244

The 244 carries the second and third components in balance. This is the first physique we have considered (except the rare 515) which does not have a dominant component. When not dysplastic, this is often taken as the ideal slender male body. The 244 appears in bathing trunks, and otherwise adorned, on the advertising pages of magazines perhaps more often than any other male physique. The face and body are strong and masculine but lightly built. There are no morphological peculiarities to mark this physique as departing from good conservative masculine taste. The face is lean and alert, the neck is neither long nor short nor overly slender. The shoulders are broad, the waist narrow and low, the chest clearly predominant over the abdomen, and the arms and legs are neither long nor short, but slender and well muscled. The trunk is moderately long but never extremely long. The hips are typically narrow. The 244 is usually of moderate height but is sometimes very tall. With a second component of 4 and a first of 2, the bones tend to disappear under smooth and well-molded muscling. There are no sharp angles, but there is no conspicuous softness and the gynandromorphic index is usually low. However, there are many dysplastic variations of this somatotype, and not more than one 244 in twenty would do for the discriminating advertiser.

THE 424

This is another of the feminoid somatotypes, and, as would be expected, it is much commoner in women than in men. But the 424 is not conspicuously weak, like the 325. He has a round face with soft, small features and a small mouth, and almost invariably he has a rosy color. Almost all of this group blush easily. The subcutaneous capillaries appear to be unusually sensitive to vasodilator control. Similarly, nearly all of this group speak with delicate voice control, and with a voice that is notably sensitive to emotional influence.

The 424 generally has endomorphic shoulders, i.e., shoulders that are rather high and square and soft, and that do not protrude laterally much beyond the line of the trunk. The chest is relatively full, and seems plump, as if inflated from within instead of being controlled by external muscles. There is usually the beginning of breast formation. The waist is high, although not extremely so, and it is not pinched in so markedly as is the rule with the extreme ectomorphs. The abdomen is full and predominant over the rather full chest, but there is rarely any local suprapubic protuberance. This local bulging over the symphysis is caused by a roll of abdominal fat—a characteristic of the somatotypes that are 5 or higher in the first component. The 424 has wide hips, a trunk which appears distinctly feminine in the dorsal view, and frail, soft arms and legs, but the limbs lack the highly fragile appearance of ectomorphic 5, and they do not appear to be too long in the distal segments.

The 424 is rarely eunuchoid, or Froehlich.

THE 334

The 334 is the commonest somatotype yet considered (see p. 268), and is one of the most prevalent of the entire series. It constitutes about 5 per cent of the male college population. Like the 244, this is one of the "normals," but with a second component of only 3, and with so much soft endomorphy for a light muscular equipment to carry, the 334 oftens falls on the periphery of the unusual somatotypes, especially when he happens to have a high gynandromorphic index, as is frequently the case. In this physique endomorphic softness and mesomorphic hardness balance each other, against a predominant moderate ectomorphic fragility. The face is smaller and softer than the face of the 244, the neck lacks muscular molding, the chest is flatter in its upper third, the shoulders narrower, the shoulder girdle less erect, the trunk usually a little shorter than that of the 244, the waist a little higher, and the somewhat more plump abdomen is deeper and about equal in proportions to the chest. The arms are slender, with softness appearing over the deltoids, and the legs have a soft appearance and a slight rounding of the upper thighs which marks a distinct contrast with the legs of a 244. No sharp muscular relief is seen at any point in the body, and there is no frank endomorphic predominance in any region.

Dysplasias are conspicuously abundant, especially those which produce a high gynandromorphy. There are 334's who look distinctly feminine, and others who (with dysplastic faces) carry a sharply masculine appearance.

THE 254

The 254 lacks the harsh muscle and bone relief of the 154. He usually has a larger head and face, blunter, heavier features, and softer contours of the whole body. He looks older than he is, as do almost all the mesomorphs. Even in the teens, there are hard, set lines in the face, often with deep furrowing of the forehead, and with straight lines running downward from about the level of the lower third of the nose and out over the corners of the mouth. These facial lines are a hallmark of a high second component. The mesomorphic skin is thick, extremely rich in connective tissue, and closely tied down to the subcutaneous tissues below it. Like thick leather, it cannot form fine wrinkles, but only long, permanent creases.

The 254 has broad shoulders, a chest highly predominant over the abdomen, and hence a singularly athletic appearance. This physique approximates the traditional athletic figure much more closely than does the heavy, massive, and blocky form of the mesomorphic 6's and 7's. Usually the 254 has arms or legs which are disproportionately long.

THE 524

The rare 524 has the highly feminine tendency of the 514, but is a much stronger physique. The head, face, and features are larger and rounder, the posture is usually more erect, the chest is not so conspicuously narrow, and it is inclined to be rather full and plump, even in the upper third. The shoulders have a distinctly endomorphic set and project little laterally beyond the line of the body, the waist is still high, and the plump, round abdomen predominates distinctly over the similarly plump but somewhat smaller chest. There is usually a distinct early suprapubic bulge. The hips are wide, and dorsally the figure appears almost entirely feminine. The trunk is generally short, but not markedly so. The "hamming" of the upper arms in the deltoid area is distinct, and the same tendency in the thighs (as revealed by an increased LTU_1 measurement) has set in strongly. These two early "hamming" characteristics, and the early blunting of the angle between chin and neck, are consistently associated with 5 in the first component.

THE 344

The 344 is the most frequently occurring somatotype (the mode) in the male college population. This is the "average" young man. The physique resembles the 244, but is heavier, rounder, and softer, and lacks the distinctly lean or lithe characteristic of the latter. The features typically lack the sharp, clean-cut character of the features of the 244. The face and head are heavier and tend to be rounder. The neck does not show the sharp muscle molding that is prized by sculptors. The shoulders are on the broad side, the chest is fairly full and tapering, the waist is rather narrow, and the abdomen is shapely and small as compared with the chest. There is a smooth and slightly rounded finish to the entire body, even throughout the arms and legs, which is altogether foreign to the somatotypes of low first component. Yet this is withal a well-molded physique, of excellent muscular tone and marked cleanness of line. In the competition between the first and second components, muscular elasticity clearly has the upper hand.

In the colleges sampled thus far the 344 is commoner than the 443, but only slightly so. Each of these somatotypes constitutes about 5½ per cent of the distribution. In the general population it may well be that the 443 is somewhat commoner than the 344.

THE 434

With the 434 we leave behind all thought of any frank eunuchoid, or Froehlich, tendency. This physique is one of the middle group of "normals," but it has come into that group from the Froehlich direction, and upon close examination one sees some suggestion of all the feminoid traits of its family. The posture is erect and the general outline is inconspicuous, but a distinct tendency to roundness and softness pervades the body. The face is rounded, tending to be fat, and the features do not often have sharp definition. Typically, no muscle lines at all are seen in the neck; the chest is plump, and in more than half the instances there is a distinct beginning of breast formation. The shoulders are of medium breadth, but the hips are distinctly broad, which usually gives the shoulders a relatively narrow appearance. The waist is moderately high, and in the dorsal picture the body carries a suggestion of the hourglass effect. The abdomen is full but not protuberant, and the abdominal trunk appears to dominate over the thorax. The thighs are inclined to be rather plump, but without "hamming," and both lower legs and forearms seem a little weak as compared with the upper segments of these respective limbs.

The 434 is a decidedly dysplastic somatotype, and sometimes appears with excessively wide hips, with highly endomorphic legs, with a collapsed chest of low second component, with a protuberant abdomen, etc.

THE 444

The 444 is at the central point among the somatotypes, but in terms of frequency of occurrence 4 is past the mean in all three components (see Fig. 13, p. 130). This is a rather common physique, and is possibly the most dysplastic of the somatotypes. It is a difficult thing to find a 444 who is consistent in all five regions of the body.

The outstanding characteristic of the 4 in the first component is sleekness. All endomorphic 4's are sleek. They groom well, they are relaxed, they are well filled out all over, their hair combs easily and lies smoothly over a well-rounded head, they have rosy color and good complexion, they are supple, and they have an easy carriage and a smooth walk. Usually they have soft, pleasing skin. There are no sharp angularities of body, and usually none of manner. Smoothness is the dominant note.

The 444 is unique in that in one sense he has all three components dominant. There is the relaxed smoothness of a moderately strong first component, the strength and erectness and good molding of a well-represented second component, and also much of the linearity, delicacy, and sensitivity of ectomorphy. When all these traits are well blended in a physique, the result is usually a distinguished appearance, particularly when the 444 is tall, as he frequently is. But dysplasias are the rule, and there are several common dysplasias. One of the commonest is that of a massive head and face (453 or 543) with a thick neck, and slender, ectomorphic legs.

When not dysplastic, this somatotype has a fairly large, well-rounded head, rather prominent, well-formed features which are not sharp but a shade on the heavy side, and a facial expression which is relaxed rather than tense or keen. The neck is of moderate length and thickness, without sharp muscle relief. The shoulders are medium broad, the trunk a little on the heavy side, with soft contours, the waist neither conspicuously high nor low, and the abdomen and thorax are about equally proportioned. There is no abdominal bulging, but there is the definite suggestion of fullness, and the promise of a future portly trunk. The portliness will be general, over the whole body, not local and abdominal. The limbs are well proportioned to the trunk, and if anything appear a little on the slender side. There is no "hamming," but there is a slight plumpness of thighs and upper arms.

THE 354

There are seven somatotypes whose total component values add up to 12. These are the 345, 435, 444, 354, 534, 453, and 543. All, except the 444, are scarce, and all are extremely dysplastic. It seems a little as though nature has undertaken all she can handle when she attempts to hold in balance so many strong components, diverging in three directions. Loss of balance somewhere in the body appears more or less inevitable under such circumstances. At any rate, it is difficult to find a perfectly consistent example of any of these somatotypes.

The 354 is a heavy and athletic physique, which is totally lacking in the sharp corners and detailed muscle relief found in the 154. The head and face are distinctly massive, though by no means comparable to the huge heads of the extreme endomorphs. No bony relief is ordinarily seen in the face, and no muscle relief in the neck, which also is distinctly on the thick or heavy side. The broad shoulders and massive chest predominate over the comparatively slender lower trunk, but the abdomen is by no means small. It is fairly thick in both diameters, but being heavily muscled it appears relatively slender and firmly molded. The hips seem comparatively narrow because of the wide shoulders, but they are not actually narrow. The limbs are strongly built, with considerable slenderness in the distal segments, and they are well rounded but far from endomorphic in the proximal segments. The 354 is often tall.

The problem of the relation between psychological conflict and the dysplasias is one of which we know little as yet, for we have never before had a technique for measuring either conflict or dysplasia. With the standardization of a method of computing dysplasia, the problem of psychological conflict might be brought into a clearer focus. If so, it would not be surprising to discover that such personalities as the 354 are prone to develop profound and dramatic conflicts.

The 354 has a powerful physique, with what the prize fighters call a "glass jaw." This is characteristic of all three of the somatotypes that are 5 in the second and 4 in the third component. Such people have great strength, but also great vulnerability, and they are not up to the toughness of the other mesomorphic 5's. The 354 is typically a big fellow who looks strong, and may look much tougher than he really is. Whether or not such a physical make-up produces characteristic psychological reverberations in the ordinary course of life is at least an interesting question, but such questions cannot be answered until we can study systematically both the physical and psychological sides of the personality.

THE 534

This is usually a fairly tall physique, which grows fat early and, if not dietetically guarded, tends to develop an enormous front. With the second component at 3, the enlargement takes place fairly evenly throughout the whole trunk, and the "bay window" extends over the entire front. When the 534 is extremely fat, the peculiar contrast between the huge body mass and the long ectomorphic-4 extremities is a striking phenomenon which once observed will not easily be forgotten. After a person has once begun to think systematically in terms of component variation, and has mastered the general appearance of the common somatotypes in their youthful bud, the accurate recognition even of the rarities in their full later blossom becomes an easy and almost subconscious matter. There can be no excuse for failing to recognize a 534 in full blossom. Nothing could be confused with it but the 524, and this is a relatively slumped physique, with a low, protuberant abdomen which may become enormous and unwieldy.

By way of digression, it might be pointed out here that there is no somatotype which should not easily be recognized when seen in middle age, if the main characteristics of the youthful bud are well mastered. Moreover, the experienced eye should at once measure the state of nutrition of a physique, and should be able to tell about how far a physique is above or below the usual weight for its age and its somatotype. The recognition of the different somatotypes is fully as easy as the recognition of the seventy or eighty commonest birds, if one will go about the matter with a naturalistic point of view and will make a hobby of using the eyes. In order to do this, it might be necessary only to overcome the prudery of the averted eye, which is deeply ingrained in modern society as a moral principle, but which has long since outlived its useful function—if it ever had one.

But let us return to the 534. This physique has a fairly large, soft face, which often presents the triangular ectomorphic shape. The features are soft and relaxed, usually with flabby lips and sleepy eyes. The neck seems too small for the large body and for the rather large head, and no muscularity is seen in the neck. The chest is plump and full, except in the upper third, which is generally flattened anteriorly. There are usually small breasts. The shoulders are not narrow, but they seem rather narrow, for the trunk as a whole is wider in comparison with the shoulders than is usually the case. The rather high waist seems to be just about in the middle of the trunk, and seems to divide it like an hourglass into two approximately equal halves. The wide hips and the wide feminine curves of the thighs blend with the curves of the chest walls above to complete the hourglass effect. There is always a definite, although usually a small, suprapubic abdominal protuberance, as though there were a pocket there into which some small object had been stuffed. The early "hamming" of the upper arms and of the upper thighs is distinct. The arms and legs seem a little too long for the trunk, which itself is a little short to carry so much weight. The forearms and lower legs are relatively weak.

THE THREES IN ECTOMORPHY

163	253	263	343		353	453
				443		
613	523	623	433		533	543

THE 163

The 163 is an extremely masculine somatotype. The bony structure is heavier and more massive than in the 154, and the tense, strained appearance of the face, which is so characteristic of the endomorphic 1's who are less than 6 in the second component, is replaced by an appearance of strength and of heavy security. There is nothing for the mesomorphic 6's to be afraid of, and their faces seem to show it. Squareness predominates in the face, and in the individual features. The jaw is square and large. The highly muscular neck is distinctly broader than deep. It is the transverse diameter that predominates. The chest is broad, with wide shoulders, but there is a distinct flatness anteriorly in the upper third of the chest. The waist is narrow, but less narrow than those of the 154 and 145, so that some of the taper of the chest is gone. The whole trunk is much broader than deep. All the transverse diameters predominate markedly over the anteroposterior diameters. The abdomen is flat, and the waist is typically so low that the abdomen appears dwarfed and contracted as compared with the broad chest above it. Over the whole body sharp muscular detail is seen, and there is no softening of contours. Usually the veins of the hands and arms stand out. The hips are relatively narrow, and this

physique presents the complete antithesis to gynandromorphy. The legs seem knotty, rather than brittle and weak, although the lower legs and forearms are comparatively delicate.
There is a certain pinched look about all the endomorphic
1's. They look as though they needed to fill out, but they
will not fill out.

THE 613

The 613 is an overwhelmingly endomorphic physique.
The head has a distinct tendency toward roundness, but the
face is hypoplastic, usually with a sharply receding jaw and
a delicate chin, so that the whole lower face appears to fall
away as if it were melting. The neck is likely to be long,
and if so it appears extremely slender, with no trace of
muscular molding. This is a pipestem neck. The angle between the jaw and neck is partially erased by adipose accumulation, and when the chin is sharply receding, this angle
disappears altogether. The upper chest shows the ectomorphic
flattening in front, but apart from that the chest as a whole
is almost globular—the widest point appears to fall at about
the level of the nipples, rather than higher. The shoulders
are narrow and highly endomorphic (nonprojecting). The
waist is extremely high, and though the mass of the chest is
great, that of the abdomen considerably exceeds it. The abdomen is both wide and deep, and there is a good roll of
fat above the symphysis pubis. Breast formation is distinct.
Perhaps the most striking hallmark of the 6's and 7's in the
first component is the fact that the widest transverse diameter of the body below the waist (TB$_3$) usually falls well
above the iliac crests instead of over the trochanters, as is
the case with most of the other somatotypes.

The 613 often has a collapsed spine, that is to say, a sharp
lumbar lordosis, which gives the relatively short body an
even shorter appearance. When this characteristic is present,
there is a compensatory high kyphosis causing the neck to
project forward at a sharp angle. The upper arms show the

characteristic "ham" formation of extreme endomorphy, as do the thighs, and both arms and legs seem long in the 613. A common dysplasia in this somatotype is that of ectomorphic 4 in the arms or legs or both. The forearms and lower legs then appear excessively frail and stiltlike, and they are indeed weak to handle so great a weight. There is a strong tendency in this somatotype for the condition known popularly as knock-knees to develop, and the 613 usually cannot easily bring his heels together when standing up. We have one instance of a 613 with legs that are ectomorphic 5.

In all the extreme endomorphs, the genitalia are small or underdeveloped.

THE 253

The 253 is one of the commonest of the strongly masculine somatotypes. It comprises about 3 per cent of the male college population. It resembles the 163, but all the contours are softened and the body, although muscular, is less powerful than that of the mesomorphic 6. In the face and head, muscular and bony strength predominate over a secondary ectomorphic fragility, with a slight, diffuse endomorphic softening. The jaw is strong but more pointed than square. In the muscular neck, the transverse diameter predominates markedly. The shoulders are broad and the chest is strongly muscled, although the ectomorphic anterior flattening of the upper third is nearly always present. The waist is relatively narrow, and low, but a little less narrow and not quite so low as in the 163. The chest predominates clearly over the abdomen, although not so markedly as in the 163. The limbs are muscular, well proportioned, but seem a little brittle in the extremities.

THE 523

The 523 is a frank endomorph, but he is sharply set apart from his close relative the 613, in that the former does not belong among the extremes. The difference between the 5 and the 6 in any component is for this reason an important one. The 6's are conspicuous extremes. The 5's are not. The 613 and especially the 712 often experience great difficulty in locomotion. It is not uncommon for the 712 to give up walking altogether in early middle life. But the 523 is a normal, usually good-natured fat man who has no trace of masculine hardness or toughness, and is likely to be sensitive and somewhat effeminate. The 523's are also inclined to be mentally gifted. In a study of the scholarship records of 1,700 male students who had been somatotyped at the University of Wisconsin, we found that the 523's stood second among the somatotypes, but in this series there were only seven instances of 523's. The 225's were first, and a small group of ten 126's were third. It was of interest to note that of the ten somatotypes that stood first in this informal study, seven were at 2 or 3 in the second component.

The 523 has a round, rather large head, with a soft round face which always has a weak chin. Usually the face carries a suggestion of the ectomorphic triangular shape in the frontal view. The distance between the ears is considerably greater at the pinnae than at the lobes. That is to say, FB_1 dominates clearly over FB_2. The mouth is relaxed and inclined to be shapeless. The lips usually gape open. The neck, although not approaching the pipestem neck characteristic of the 613, is a little too slender for this massive physique and lacks muscular relief. This neck is usually of medium length. The trunk presents a striking hourglass effect, but as compared with the 613, the chest is better constructed to cope with the round, fat abdomen. There is a slight ectomorphic flattening of the upper chest, the shoulders are narrow, and the breasts are budding. There is an ectomorphic stoop to the shoulders, as seen in profile. The abdomen is both long and deep, yet the trunk as a whole is rather short. At the age of 18 there is always a sharp constriction at the waist, which, of course, is high. In later years the constriction tends to widen out, but it never entirely disappears, even in extreme obesity. This is an unfailing point of differentiation in mid-life between the endomorphs who are low in the second component, and those who are higher. In the latter the whole trunk inflates like an expanding football, erasing the waist completely, while in the former the high waist always remains clearly marked, if only by a sharp fold of fat. There is a small roll of fat over the symphysis. The upper arms and thighs show distinct but not extreme "hamming." The distal segments of arms and legs are comparatively weak, but there is not the glaring weakness of the 613.

THE 263

The rare 263 is a massive, powerful, highly masculine physique, which also carries a considerable degree of ectomorphic fragility, usually in the extremities. It is often a dysplastic somatotype, revealing extreme strength of structure at some points and marked weakness at others. A muscular, powerful neck, and extremely wide shoulders are common variants. Sometimes the legs are unusually long, thus causing the trunk to appear relatively short. The forearms may be disproportionately slender and brittle. The 263 is generally tall, and appears distinctly more massive than the 163. The sharp, almost ragged muscular relief of the latter is not seen in this physique. The endomorphic 2 is almost always uniformly distributed throughout the body, and there is usually no sign of local endomorphy at any point.

There need be no question about the identification of mesomorphic 6 if it is actually present. When there is doubt, the safe rule is that one is looking at mesomorphic 5 rather than 6.

The 263 has a powerful, massive facial skeleton. The face dominates clearly over the cranium, especially in the profile picture. The features are relatively large, and strong muscle lines are conspicuous, although individual variation in the shape of the features is great. The nose may be long or short, but it is always strongly built. The upper face may predominate over the lower, or conversely. The forehead may be sharply receding or high, and the jaw prognathous or receding. The so-called long Nordic "horse-face" is common among the mesomorphic 6's. The only constant feature is massiveness of bone and muscle, and departure in some fashion from the soft, spherical form.

The chest is broad and highly predominant over the relatively contracted, flat abdomen. The upper chest is inclined to be flat, and there is often a considerable ectomorphic stoop in the shoulders. The trunk is generally long, sometimes very long, although this characteristic tends to be concealed in the 263, by the relatively long legs and arms. There is usually a distinct brittleness at the wrists and ankles.

THE 623

This rare physique may in general be described as a much taller and stronger 613. The 623 is often over six feet tall, and may become enormous in later life, although this could be controlled to some extent by diet. When the second component is relatively low, it appears to be an easy matter to control the full blossoming of a high endomorphy by a sternly regulated diet.

Like mesomorphic 6, the full endomorphic 6 is easily recognized if it is present. The 623 has a large head and face, with weak bony structure and weak muscles. The jaw is usually hypoplastic, and all the features are flaccidly relaxed. The neck lacks the pipestem appearance of the 613, and may be fairly massive. The chest is somewhat flattened in the upper anterior third, and is otherwise rounded and "pneumatic" appearing. The shoulders are relatively narrow. The waist is high, with the full abdomen strongly predominant over the relatively full chest. The greatest transverse breadth of the lower body is found at or above the iliac crests, which themselves are high. There is strong "hamming" of the upper arms and thighs, but the forearms and lower legs are long. The forearms are invariably slender, but the lower legs may be encased in a blanket of fat, which gives them a shapelessness common but by no means constant in high endomorphy.

THE 343

This strongly masculine somatotype is among the three or four commonest male physiques, and is another representative of the "average" male body. The 343 is usually of medium size and medium height, and he carries no morphological traits which set him apart or mark him as different from the main body of mankind. He is a trifle more slender than the "average man," a little less fragile in the extremities, and just a shade more strongly built.

In the face, muscular and bony strength predominates, but the face and head are of medium size and of variable shape. The jaw is inclined to be strong, on a small or medium scale. It does not compare with the massive mesomorphic jaws, but it differs still more sharply from the fragile hypoplastic structure of the ectomorphs, and from the softened and blanketed framework of the endomorphs. The neck looks strong, because the muscular structure is well outlined, but there is no sharp relief. The shoulders are on the broad side, with the chest well supported, although there is nearly always a slight flattening of the upper anterior third. The waist is slightly on the slender side, with the abdomen well under muscular control, and the chest clearly predominates over the abdomen. The trunk is rather long in comparison with the limbs, and there is no sharp muscular relief, and no angularity anywhere in the body. The waist is moderately low, and ordinarily the gynandromorphic index is low, although among a good handful of photographs of 343's a half dozen exceptions may be found. Both arms and legs seem moderately slender, well proportioned, and smoothly molded. This is not a very dysplastic somatotype. Many examples are found showing little variation throughout the five regions of the body. Physically at least, this somatotype belongs distinctly to the normal, middle group.

When a medium-sized, well-poised young man is found who gives no impression either of leanness or sleekness, on the one hand, or of fragile linearity or blockiness, on the other, he is probably a 343.

THE 433

The 433 also belongs to the middle ranges of human physique, and passes as the man on the street. But this is a different kind of man on the street from the 343, for the 433 is distinctly feminine in general impression, whereas the 343 is distinctly masculine. The 433 carries a strong feminine suggestion, although not necessarily in any sense an effeminate suggestion, for we are speaking morphologically and not psychologically. Actually the complexities of human life are such that the 433 is inclined often to react in a manner to overcompensate for the gynandromorphy of his physique, and to simulate characteristics of toughness. In referring to the 433 a colleague once said, "Yes, I know the 433. He is the little soft-faced fellow who smokes fat cigars and spits on the sidewalk."

The 433 has round, chubby cheeks with a high color, soft hands and soft bodily contours, and a general distribution of curves which faintly suggest the female physique. The features are a little smaller than those of the 343, and the face is much rounder. The neck is soft, and is a little smaller in the transverse diameter. The shoulders are narrower, and the chest a little more flattened in the upper third, though as a whole the chest is more rounded and "pneumatic." The waistline is moderately high, with the abdomen clearly predominant over the chest, and there is a feminine hourglass appearance to the trunk when seen dorsally. There is distinct endomorphic inflation of the upper arms in the deltoid region, and in the upper thighs, although this could hardly be called "hamming." The proximal segments of both arms and legs predominate over the distal segments, which appear rather weak. The distribution of secondary hair is usually strongly feminine, as is the case in all somatotypes where the first component is stronger than the second. A common dysplasia in the 433 involves extremely wide hips.

THE 443

In general appearance the 443 resembles the 343 much more than he resembles the 433. A second component of 4 shapes the body and fixes the skeletal framework in so distinctly masculine a mold that the first component of 4 introduces little of the feminine influence conspicuous in the 433. The 443 is a heavier, rounder, and somewhat softer 343, rather than a stronger and harder 433.

The face is more massive than that of the 343, with the features a little more blunt. The mouth is inclined to be rather large, and somewhat relaxed. The lips often seem full and flabby. In all the mesomorphic somatotypes, including the 443, there is a strong tendency toward acne, and there are often small pockmarks or large pores in the face—the scars of old acne infection. This susceptibility of the mesomorphic skin to staphylococcus invasion is less marked in the lean mesomorphs of extremely low endomorphy. The neck of the 443 may seem somewhat on the full side. The shoulders are moderately broad, like the shoulders of a 343, but they may not seem so broad at first glance, for the chest is more full and round. The waist is slightly lower than the mean between the 343 and 433, and the chest predominates over the abdomen. The waist is distinctly less narrow than that of the 343, and therefore little athletic taper is seen in the chest. There is no local bulging of the abdomen at any point, but there is an even fullness, and in later life the entire trunk will seem to expand almost evenly as the waistline increases. The 443 in full blossom, unless he sternly controls his diet, becomes heavy bodied, or even barrel bodied. But he is muscular, and does not become flabby-fat.

An endomorphy of 4, under the encouragement of gluttony, is capable of remarkable blossoming.

The 443 is one of the most common somatotypes, perhaps the most common for the population at large. With the 343 and 344, it makes up the middle range of masculine physiques. These three somatotypes constitute nearly a sixth of the total male population. The 443 has what may be called a chunky physique, in contrast with the heavy mesomorphs, who are blocky.

THE 353

The 353, commonest of the mesomorphic 5 physiques, presents in some ways a strong contrast with his close relative, the 253. With the increment of one degree of endomorphy, the peculiarly strained appearance of the 253 is lost, and there is a general smoothness and evenness of contour, and a relaxation of the whole body. In contrast with the 335, which in a more distant way may also be regarded as a relative, the 353 is not typically dysplastic.

The body of the 353 is powerful and highly muscular, but falls short of the extremely massive mesomorphic 6's. In youth the 353 belongs distinctly in the slender class. He is probably well the most common high school and college athlete, since the 6's are rare.

The head and face are fairly massive, with the facial skeleton prominent. The nose is likely to be large, with a strong bridge. The jaw is prominent, long, and usually slightly pointed. The supraorbital structure is strong, lifting the eyebrows. The face as a whole is generally long. Muscle lines predominate, but are softened and relaxed by a diffuse endomorphic influence. The neck is likely to be rather long, and muscular, with soft muscle relief. The shoulders are wide, and predominate over the waist, which is muscular rather than conspicuously narrow. The chest is clearly greater than the abdomen, but the latter is also inclined to an even, muscular fullness. The trunk is distinctly long, but so are the limbs. It is what is generally called a well-proportioned physique. There is no "hamming" and little sign of any special endomorphic fullness over the deltoids or at the level of LTU$_1$. A soft muscular relief is typically seen throughout the upper arm. The forearms and lower legs are long, muscular, and slender.

THE 533

This is the commonest of the endomorphic 5's. It comprises about 2½ per cent of the male population. All the highly endomorphic physiques can be differentiated from one another with greater ease than can those showing the other two predominances, because in the endomorphs the third component manifestations that are present are amplified and rendered especially conspicuous. An ectomorphic increment, say a lengthening of a few inches, would be more conspicuous in a basketball than the same increment would be in a golf club. Thus, the differences of appearance between the 533, 532, and 534 are dramatic and unmistakable.

The 533 has a massive head, with a large face, but the features are not prominent and the bony skeleton is light. When the facial bones of the 533 are seen in an X-ray photograph, they appear slender, and one has the impression of looking at an ectomorphic face covered by a shadowy veil. All the features of the face are relaxed, although they do not present the flaccid appearance of those endomorphs who are excessively low in the second component. The mouth tends to be shapeless, and the lips may protrude. The neck is relatively slender, as compared to the massive chest and large head. It is without molding, and looks rather like a small, round stovepipe. The chest seems to be under moderate pneumatic pressure, except in the upper anterior third. The anteroposterior diameters tend to approach the transverse diameters, both in the chest and in the abdomen. The shoulders are rather narrow, the breasts are budding, and the waist seems to be just about in the middle of the trunk. It

is a high waist, which gives the body a distinct hourglass
effect, with rounding curves both above and below. The
transverse diameter of the trunk at the iliac crests tends to
equal that over the trochanters. Endomorphic inflation at
the deltoids and in the upper thighs is marked, although far
from extreme. The arms and legs are moderately long, and
are slender in the distal extremities.

THE 453

The 453 and 543 belong to the group of somatotypes carrying a total component value of 12. These are complex physiques, extremely rich in dysplasias and subject to many
variations of pattern. One gets the impression that these personalities are psychologically as well as morphologically complicated, and that strongly conflicting drives frequently produce manifestations of internal tension and distress which
are currently labeled "functional," or neurotic. But we have
as yet made no formal studies of this matter.

The 453 usually has a massive face which predominates
conspicuously over the cranial mass of the head. The face is
both long and deep, usually with a large projecting nose and
a heavy jaw which is pointed, rather than square. There is
no sharp relief, however, in the face, and the appearance
about the mouth, cheeks, and eyes is one of relaxation rather
than of tension. The eyebrows are usually high and arched,
and there is typically a healthy-looking fullness in the cheeks.
The mouth is full and muscular. The face of the 453 is invariably what is called an open, candid face. This is true, at
least, of a sample of about sixty 453's of whom we have standardized photographs. The neck is rather thick, in both anteroposterior and transverse diameters, and it is round rather
than sharply muscular in appearance. The chest is broad and
full, the transverse diameters predominating markedly. The
abdomen is full and rounded, but well under muscular control, and the low waistline gives the great chest the appearance of disproportionate predominance over the really rather

massive abdomen. The ectomorphic flattening of the upper chest is present, but is slight and seems insignificant. The outstanding feature of this somatotype is the large, deep chest. The arms and legs are inclined to be rather long, with distinct ectomorphic fragility in the distal segments.

One of the commonest dysplasias in the 453 is one which produces wide hips and a high gynandromorphic index.

THE 543

The 543 is to be distinguished from the 453 principally by its high waistline and the much greater abdominal mass. The face is a little smaller as compared with the cranial structure, and the features are less pronounced. It is a still more relaxed and softer face than that of the 453. The eyebrows are inclined to be lower, and the chin and nose less prominent. The neck is smaller in the transverse diameter, but fully as large in the anteroposterior diameter. The chest is still a large one, but distinctly less predominant than in the 453. It is a rounder chest. The waistline is if anything slightly above the center of the trunk, with a strongly swelling abdomen below and a similarly expanding chest above. With a 4 in the second component, any conspicuous breast formation is rare unless a strong first component dysplasia is present in the second region (upper trunk). The back is typically well formed, with a fairly low lumbar curve which suggests strength in the trunk. Yet the trunk as a whole presents a strongly feminine appearance, with wide and curving hips, and a definite hourglass effect. There is a complete loss of muscle molding in the upper arm, and there is endomorphic expansion of this area, although it could hardly be called "ham" formation. The "hamming" tendency is seen, however, in the upper thighs, and the LTU_1 measurement can usually be depended upon alone to establish the differential diagnosis between the combinations of the 4-5 and 5-4 in the first two components.

The trunk of the 543 is shorter than that of the 453, and

the distal segments of the arms have a distinctly more fragile
appearance. The 453 is frequently tall, the 543 more rarely so.

THE TWOS IN ECTOMORPHY

162	172	252	262	352		362	452
					442		
612	712	522	622	532		632	542

THE 162

The difference in appearance between the 162 and the
163 is clear. The 162 suggests strength, with little weakening at the extremities of the arms and legs. This physique
foreshadows the blockiness of the 261 and of the mesomorphic
7's. The 163, however, seems to tend the other way, and
strongly suggests in its extremities the fragility and angularity of the ectomorphs. The 162 is hard all over and is
built to stand punishment, but with the first component at
1 he usually lacks the resiliency and the sustained endurance
of the professional heavyweight athletes. The latter are
usually 271's, 261's, or 361's. The 162 remains lean throughout life, as do all the endomorphic 1's, except perhaps the
171. The professional athletes, on the other hand, tend to
grow fat and heavy during their postathletic years, although
they do not, of course, take on endomorphic contours. Their
muscles, which often become hypertrophied, tend to infil-
trate with fat, and they grow heavy all over. A first component of 2 will easily permit this kind of fattening, but
the endomorphic 1 remains lean.

The head of the 162 is typically of moderate size, and with
the third component so low there is a conspicuous lack of
angular projection in the face. The head is essentially cubical. The nose usually seems rather short and blunt. The jaw
is square, with the mouth usually straight and firm. There
are hard muscular lines throughout the face, but the tight-
drawn characteristic of the 163 is not seen. A conspicuous
feature is the typically wide neck. The transverse diameter

of the neck frequently approaches, though it does not quite equal, the greatest width of the head. It sometimes does equal FB_2. The anteroposterior diameter of the neck is relatively small. The trapezius muscles are sharply pyramided. The shoulders are relatively broad, but the chest is not so massive as several of those we have considered. It is relatively a flat chest, in which the transverse diameters sharply predominate over the anteroposterior diameters. With the extreme muscularity of the entire trunk, the abdomen is flattened and contracted, although less so than in the 163. The trunk presents detailed muscle molding, like that of a Greek statue. The waist is low, and the hips are narrow. The legs and arms are relatively slender but strongly muscled. There is a slight slendering, rather than a weakening, of the wrists and ankles. This is a physique excessively low in gynandromorphy.

THE 612

This great rarity differs from the 613 in that the ectomorphic characteristics are far less conspicuous. The head is usually large, but is sometimes strikingly small with a somewhat elongated oval face in which the bones are small and the structure weak. The neck seems relatively small, and the anteroposterior diameter is likely to exceed the transverse diameter, but the neck of the 612 is never long, and may be extremely short. The whole chest is almost oval, and the sharp flattening of the upper chest seen in the 613 is not present here. The shoulders are relatively narrow, and the trunk as a whole suggests a large, fat figure 8 with little constriction at the center. The inner surfaces of the thighs are in contact all the way to the knees, and the figure 8 includes the entire body from neck to knees. The anteroposterior diameters at the level of the nipples, waist, and symphysis are all nearly equal, and may indeed be identical. The waist is extremely high, and there is usually a sharp, high lordotic curve. The hips are wide and the widest point below the waist is generally well above the iliac crests. In the lateral photograph the upper arms are strongly of the inverted triangle or "ham" shape, as are the thighs. The arms are not long, but the forearms are weak. The arms hang loosely and nervelessly, like useless flippers. There is usually weakening at the knees, producing a lateral spread of the lower legs (knock-knees). Compared to the 613, the legs are short. Compared to the 621, they are long. The whole body shows an extreme flaccidity, which is perhaps seen best in the arms.

The 612 is so rare that we have seen only a half dozen or so clear examples. None of these was in any way eunuchoid, or Froehlich, though we have seen three or four of the almost equally rare 613's who were distinctly Froehlich.

THE 172

The 172 is probably the masculine ideal which, in heroic moments, rides in the romantic imagination of both men and women. As an ideal, it carries supreme strength and masculine ruggedness with no trace of softness or weakness, yet it also carries a secondary note of ectomorphic linearity and sharpness of outline and feature. This is the legendary ideal of nearly all combative and dominating peoples. The perfect hero for the serial action-thriller of the cinema or of the newspaper cartoon is the 172. "Tarzan," "Dick Tracy," "Smilin' Jack," "Li'l Abner," "Superman" and so on, all are fine 172's. These are the current heroes.

The 172 has a broad, square face, with extremely powerful, square jaw, and with firm, sharp, straight muscle lines. The mouth is firm and straight, and usually large. The nose is long and straight, with a strong high bridge. The facial mass predominates strongly over the cranial mass, and the head as a whole is large, although never extremely large. The head gives the impression of being almost cubical. The neck is broad, with an extremely wide transverse diameter which often equals the FB_2 measurement. The anteroposterior diameter less markedly exceeds the average. There is strong muscle relief in the neck, which is well supported by pyramiding trapezii. The shoulders are extremely wide, and the upper chest is broad. The shoulder girdle is erect, high, and almost level. The chest is also fairly deep, but the transverse diameters predominate strongly. The waist is slender but not extremely so. It is powerfully muscled—the rectus muscles and the muscle attachments along Poupart's ligament stand out sharply. The waist is low, the abdomen relatively insignificant, and the lumbar curve of the back is low and sharp, since it involves the sharply defined, muscular buttocks. The trunk is long, with a broad athletic taper to the chest. The arms are rather long, and heavily muscled throughout, the ATL_1 measurement approaches ATU. The wrists are broad. The legs are long, powerfully muscled, but the lower legs may seem slender for so massive a physique.

Most actual examples of the rare 172 are distinctly dysplastic. Typically he has most of his third component concentrated in one or two areas, and seems poorly proportioned and muscle-bound, with enormous bones. He always carries the suggestion of acromegaly, and frequently develops that condition. He is almost always slow spoken and mild mannered, and he is not often intellectually inclined.

THE 712

The 712 is the excessively endomorphic physique with the weak back and the long legs. It is a rare somatotype, but it is so conspicuous that nearly everybody knows one or two. The body is literally swamped with first component, and the extremely weak second is barely able to carry it around. Locomotion is difficult, and everything "shimmies," or wiggles up and down, when the 712 walks. This somatotype is much more common in the female than in the male, and it is not uncommon for the female 712 in middle life to give up locomotion altogether and to become chair-ridden, if the family or government can afford it. Otherwise, a strict diet is necessary. The legs and arms are too long and too poorly muscled. To complicate the difficulty, the thighs tend to become enormous, and there is a lateral spreading of the lower legs, producing knock-knees. The female is occasionally unable to bring her thighs backward and forward past one another, and then has to progress with a sidelong leaping waddle, like an auk.

This physique carries a large head and face, but not the huge head of the 711, or 721. The head as a whole is almost round, but there is always some ovalness in the face, and the bony skeleton is excessively weak. Often the chin is extremely weak. The features are soft and sodden, as if no muscles were present. Depending upon the strength of the third component in the first region (head and neck), the neck may be surprisingly small, and relatively slender and round, like the neck of the 612. The shoulders are actually broad, but relative to the enormous abdomen below they are narrow. The posterior axillary folds run straight up and down, or they may even converge a little from below upward. This is a hallmark of excessively low second component, and also of dominance of the first over the second. In the physiques carrying strong predominance of the second component over the first, the posterior axillary folds diverge from below upward, at a wide angle, and thereby add to the so-called athletic taper. The arms hang loosely, like rubber arms that are inflated under low pressure, and they resemble hams in the upper segments. The forearms are small, slender and weak.

In the 712 the maximum breadth below the waist (TB$_3$) is found over the iliac crests, and it usually exceeds the total outside breadth of the shoulders. It exceeds TB$_1$ by a wide margin. The waist is extremely high, and though the chest is actually large and approaches a sphere, it is dwarfed by the enormous abdomen. The trunk as a whole presents the outline of a huge figure 8, of which the lower segment is both deeper and wider than the upper segment. There is always a heavy fold of fat over the symphysis, and another fold which runs inward and upward from the waistline under the scapulae across the back, on either side. In extreme obesity, these two folds meet at the mid-line of the back and form part of the circumference of what may be almost a perfect circle. The diametrically opposite part of this circumference, as seen photographically, is the line of shadow at the lower fold of the buttocks (subgluteal fold). It is only in the 712 that the fat folds of the back are seen prominently at an early age.

THE 252

The 252 is nearly always a little fellow, of short stature. He is short, lean, and strong. These little 252's sometimes look slender at first glance, but they are far from ectomorphic. They can train down to a low weight, however, and many of the featherweight and lightweight boxers are 252's. The 252 is usually fast on his feet and, with his lightness and predominant muscularity, is adept at athletic games and contests which involve dodging and quick shift of balance, combined with endurance and toughness. There is no fragility in this somatotype. This is the hard-chunky or slender-chunky, physique.

The head is of moderate size, with the face predominant over the cranium. The face is of strong architecture, like the 253, but lacks the suggestion of brittleness and tenseness and the angularity of the 253. The first region (head and neck) in the 252 tends to look more endomorphic than it is. It tends toward a round general outline, but upon close inspection, it is not round but compact, bony and muscular, with a square chin. The neck is rather short and muscular, with prominent trapezii. The shoulders are broad in comparison with the body, the waist is low and narrow, and the athletic taper of the chest is pronounced. This is usually a beautifully balanced physique, with a long trunk, deep chest, narrow, muscular abdomen, and a perfect diffusion of the soft endomorphic element throughout the body. It is one of the least dysplastic of physiques, perhaps in part due to its characteristically small, compact size. The slender, muscular arms and legs seem short.

THE 522

Like the 252, the 522 is nearly always short. In youth, the latter looks short, pudgy, and soft. Later he tends to grow fat through the middle, and may have a heavy, pendulous abdomen.

The head of the 522 looks too large, with the cranial mass usually dominating over the facial structure. The features are heavy in a flabby or often in a coarse sense. The eyes generally appear to be too large. The mouth is relaxed or flaccid. The neck is poorly supported by the trapezius muscles, giving it the suggestion of a stovepipe. The rather large chest is of distinctly endomorphic, spherical shape, but the waistline is high and the abdomen predominates. With so low a third component, the trunk as a whole seems relatively compact, and the 522 does not in general outline appear to be so weak a physique as is the case with mesomorphic 2 when the third component is higher. The lumbar curve of the back is rather high, and usually sharp. The 522 shoulders do not appear narrow, though they are relatively narrow when compared with the wide hips. The entire body is covered with a soft endomorphic blanket, which obscures all muscle relief. The rather short, weak arms hang flaccidly, and the legs typically appear stumpy and shapeless.

THE 262

The 262 is a powerful, massive, and usually a rather tall physique. It is by far the commonest of the mesomorphic 6's. There is the same muscular predominance that is seen in the 252, and the same suppleness and general smoothness of contour, but the 262 belongs among the big people, and the 252 among the little people. The former is an extremely rugged, conspicuous physical personality. The latter is an inconspicuous but tough little fellow.

The 262 has a large head in which the facial mass is markedly predominant. The jaw is heavy, but lacks the square prominence of the jaw of the 172. All the features reflect great strength, and this is a strength entirely free from the slightly brittle suggestion which emanates from the 172. There are no corners in the 262 physique, and no weaknesses. The face is usually both broad and long, but length predominates over breadth. The nose is of variable length, but is always heavy and strong at the bridge. The FB_2 measurement tends to approach and sometimes to equal the FB_1 measurement. It is a broad, heavily muscled neck, with the transverse diameter strongly predominant. Often the neck is long. The shoulders are broad, but not extremely so, and the rather thick, heavily muscled middle body tends to detract from the broad appearance of the shoulders. The chest is deep in both its upper and lower segments, but the transverse diameters predominate conspicuously over the anteroposterior diameters. On the trunk of the 172 the outlines of nearly all the muscles can easily be traced, but the 262 is of softer contour and most of the muscle detail is lost, although there is no localized dominance of the first component at any point in the body. Everywhere the surface contour is determined by muscle molding, not by subcutaneous fat-deposit. The waist is rather low, and the chest is strongly predominant over the abdomen. Both arms and legs are long and heavily muscled, with no ectomorphic brittleness in the distal segments.

THE 622

The 622 and 632 are the least rare of the endomorphic 6's. In the 622 the collapsed weakness of the 612 is absent, and there is a fairly good tone and uprightness to the body. This is usually a rather tall physique. The large head has a distinct spherical suggestion, but there is often a trace of ectomorphic triangularity in the face. The features are much stronger than those of the 612. The flaccidity of expression may be entirely absent. The jaw is usually a little hypoplastic, the nose, rather small for the large head, and the ears are quite likely to show an ectomorphic lateral projection of the upper part (pinna). The neck is much stronger than the pipestem neck of the 612, but equally less massive than the short, thick neck of the 621. The trunk as a whole presents the figure-8 effect of high endomorphy, and typically forms what is perhaps the most perfect figure 8 of all. The waistline is nearly always just about in the exact center of the trunk. The abdomen and chest are both large. The shoulders are broad. The extremely high first component, with its tendency to sphericity, is able more than to compensate for the second component weakness when the third component is not higher than the second. The shoulders of the 623 tend to be somewhat narrow, and those of the 613 are extremely narrow, but the shoulders of the 622 are broad, and his trunk as a whole has a symmetry and balance not present in the other endomorphic 6's which we have considered. The abdomen of the 622 is full and round, but usually does not extend beyond the projection of the chest, and there are no traces of the great folds of fat which are seen in the 712. The arms and legs are long, and with so poor a musculature they seem a little more ectomorphic than might be expected. The arms hang rather flaccidly.

THE 352

This somatotype falls at a point intermediate between the chunky group and what we call the blocky group. The latter are the massive, hard physiques which are ectomorphic 1. The 352 is a rugged physique whose height may range from very tall to very short. With so strong a second component, the first tends to be well and diffusely distributed, and there is no sign, in youth, of any endomorphic protuberance of the abdomen or other local endomorphic concentration. Muscularity predominates strongly over the spherical tendency. Yet all over the body there is a distinctly well-rounded appearance and the promise of a heavy body during the middle decades of life.

The head is massive, with strong predominance of the facial skeleton. The features entirely lack the sharpness or clean-cut characteristic of the 253, and they are much stronger. This is a face that can stand the physical punishment of the boxing ring. The mouth is usually large, with thick, heavy, muscular lips which contrast sharply both with the shapeless, flaccid lips of endomorphy and with the thin, sensitive lips of ectomorphy. The jaw is wide and strong. The neck is rather full, with transverse predominance, but there is nearly always some initial blurring or straightening of the angle between the chin and the neck. The shoulders are wide and the chest is more full than that of the 252 or 253. The ectomorphic anterior flattening of the upper third is nearly gone. The waistline is higher than that of the 252, but is still relatively low, and the waist is thick and muscular. The trunk as a whole is massive, and usually rather long, with the thorax strongly predominant. The hips are on the narrow side, but there are frequent variants with wide hips. The arms and legs are strong enough to be called sturdy, with good rounding, but with no first component accumulations in the proximal segments.

THE 532

The 532 is an entirely different physique from the soft endomorphs which we have considered. The 3 in the second component gives the 532 enough toughness and firmness of structure to identify him with the average run of males. The 532 is merely a rotund or stocky fellow who usually has great energy and a tendency to put on weight easily.

The head is large and round, with a large face having a heaviness or coarseness of feature. The eyes tend to be large and the nose broad. The shape of the nose is highly variable. The mouth has extremely full lips, often projecting or sucking lips, and it is a large, shapeless mouth. The neck is

much stronger than that of the 522, especially in the transverse diameter. The chest is rounded and fairly full but the
lower segment of the trunk predominates. In the dorsal picture the trunk presents a strongly feminine appearance, but
in this case it is the upper part of the figure 8 that is deepest
or longest. The hips are nearly as wide as the shoulders. The
abdomen has a rotund fullness, especially over the symphysis,
but there are no folds of fat. In the 532 the trunk as a whole
is relatively long, for the arms and legs are rather short.
The thighs are in contact all the way to the knees, and there
is a pronounced endomorphic inflation of both thighs and
upper arms. The forearms are relatively slender, but the
helpless flaccidity of the arm of the 522 is entirely absent.

The 532's are prone to eat gluttonously and to grow enormously heavy. Frequently they are heavy smokers. For some
reason a physique with a strong combination of the first two
components against the third can tolerate large quantities of
nicotine. We have encountered a half dozen 532's who
among them smoke enough pipe tobacco to paralyze as many
ectomorphs, but they appear to thrive under the heavy dosage
of this drug and in some manner they seem to incorporate
its effect into their regular physiological economy. There
is no doubt that this serves in a measure to keep their weight
down. When an endomorphic mesomorph or a mesomorphic
endomorph suddenly stops tobacco after extensive use of it,
his weight tends to shoot up quickly to a higher level.

THE 442

The 442 is chubby. No other descriptive term fits him quite
so well. Like all moderately endomorphic people, he has
round, chubby cheeks and a ruddy pink color which in cold
weather blossoms out to a brilliant red. He is stocky but
not fat, sturdy but not blocky, and all his features tend to
be blunt or "rubbery." There are no sharp corners and
there is nothing about the 442 that appears easy to break.
He can be picked up and dropped. He is usually a little

below average height. In youth he generally has and expresses tremendous energy, but if too well fed or too successful in the middle decades he is immoderately prone to grow fat and sodden. The female 442 is a magnificent PPJ (pyknic[1] practical joke). In early youth she is highly active, and is generally a "pep" girl. Before marriage she remains extraordinarily slender, like the bud of a late-blossoming tree. The unpracticed eye does not perceive the latent first component. After marriage the joke is sprung.

The head of the 442 is of intermediate size, and rather rounded. The face has a squarish appearance, but it is a squareness without corners. The features are rather small, but blunt and solid. The neck is strong and well filled out but not large. The shoulders are rather high, and square and strong. They are not wide shoulders. The chest is well developed and well supported. There is little athletic taper, for the waist is rather thick. The waist is a little low. The hips are of moderate breadth. The trunk is fairly long, of excellent straight posture, and all the contours are rounded and even. There is no perceptible muscle detail, but there is no endomorphic accumulation or bulging. The legs and arms are of moderate length, are well muscled and of soft contour. There are many dysplasias in the 442, though the striking dysplasias are found mainly among the ectomorphic somatotypes. The most common dysplasia in the 442 is a great variation in gynandromorphy.

THE 362

The 362 is a massive, powerful, big fellow who closely resembles the 262 in general characteristics, but is more rare and much heavier. The head is larger and the face is conspicuously lacking in the sharp detail of the 262. The features are heavy, more relaxed, often sodden. The mouth is

[1] This illustrates a legitimate use of the term *pyknic* (Greek word for compact, solid). These individuals are compactly and solidly built. The term "pyknic" does not imply endomorphic softness.

large, with thick lips which are frequently hypotonic. The neck is thick. The chest is rounder than that of the 262, and somewhat more massive. The waist is thicker, so much so that the taper of the chest is largely gone. The trunk is long, and as a whole it is an exceedingly massive, powerful trunk, strongly suggesting the blocky 361. The trunk is strong in both transverse and anteroposterior diameters, but the former predominate. The hips are wider than the hips of the 262, but they are still relatively narrow when compared with the wide shoulders. The limbs are long and are strongly muscled throughout, but there is unmistakable endomorphic suggestion in the upper thighs.

The 362 is ideally adapted for professional athletics, but tends to put on weight too fast and is always bothered with the problem of "training." If he gets too much to eat, he can expand to an astonishing weight in middle life, but it will be a general expansion all over the body, not a local abdominal blowout.

THE 632

This is one of the largest physiques. The 632 is tall, broad, and deep. He is often very tall. Of seven men weighing over 300 pounds whom we have examined within the past several years, three were 632's. The 731 is inclined to be still larger, but he is excessively rare.

The head is well rounded, with a face both long and broad. The second component is strong enough to give the face a good deal of strength, and more firmness and appearance of character than is seen in the face of a 622. The jaw is strongly formed but not prominent. The mouth seldom shows the overrelaxed, suckling appearance so common in some of the endomorphs of low third component. The neck is broad and deep. The shoulders are unusually broad, and so is the entire trunk. Also, the trunk is deep, throughout both the thoracic and abdominal segments. The greatest transverse breadth below the waist is over the iliac crests, and this measurement exceeds TB_1, though it does not equal or challenge the outside breadth of the shoulders. The waist is broad, and it falls fairly high on the long trunk. The abdomen and chest are of about equal anteroposterior depth, and both are relatively enormous. The whole body is deeply swathed in an endomorphic blanket, but there are no folds of fat above the symphysis or across the back. These folds are a hallmark of 7 in the first component. There is, however, a marked abdominal protuberance above the symphysis. Arms and legs are long and fairly well muscled, and the upper segments show conspicuous "hamming."

THE 452

The 452 is the commonest of the overwhelmingly massive physiques, or of the physiques totaling 9 or more in the first two components. These are solid, heavy people, of great strength and energy.

The head and face are distinctly of the square or cubical sort, and are above average size. The bones of the face are strong and prominent. The jaw is assertively square, although not often prognathous. All the features are strong, but the sharp, clean outline of the more ectomorphic faces is absent. There is a softening endomorphic suggestion about the cheeks, and the mouth and lips may be full. The neck is strong, fairly long, and the transverse diameter predominates. The upper anterior third of the chest usually shows a greater or less degree of ectomorphic flattening, but the chest as a whole is broad and fairly deep, and the shoulders are often very broad. The trunk is conspicuously long, and the waist is low, but the waist is not narrow, and the abdomen is both broad and fairly deep. Compared to the wide shoulders, the hips are narrow, but the TB_3 measurement falls just about at the mean for the male distribution. TB_3 is always found over the trochanters, in the 452. The arms and legs are long. Often the 452 has extremely long arms, and a nearly constant feature of this somatotype is a marked heaviness of bone which shows up strongly in the forearms, wrists, and ankles. The upper segments of the arms and legs are well rounded and softened, but there is no "hamming." Muscularity strongly predominates in this physique as a whole, and the contrast to the 542, while one of the most difficult somatotype differentiations to master, is still as sharply defined for the practiced eye as the difference, to a novice, between a robin and a jay.

THE 542

The 542 is softer, rounder, and of much smaller bone than the 452. Also he is of different shape. He has a relatively high waist instead of a low one, and abdominal preponderance instead of a thoracic preponderance, inflated upper arms and thighs, budding breasts, relatively wide hips with fat buttocks, small forearms as compared with the soft upper arms, and fat, relatively "pneumatic" thighs which in the lateral photograph show a pronounced tendency toward the formation of hams.

The head of the 542 is pronouncedly round, with only a suggestion of the essential squareness of the face of a 452. All the facial features are smaller, and less prominent, although the nose is often rather sharp and projecting. The slight facial triangularity which typically accompanies ectomorphic 2 is usually seen in the face of the 542. The neck is usually short, and is smaller in the transverse diameter than the neck of the 452. The shoulders are high, with a tendency toward endomorphic squareness, and there is a rounding and softening of the chest which marks a sharp contrast to the 452. The shoulders of the 542 are soft, and while far from narrow are not conspicuously wide. The hips are wide, although the widest transverse measurement is generally over the trochanters rather than up at the iliac crests. There is invariably some slight endomorphic bulging over the symphysis. The trunk as a whole is long, but not so conspicuously long as that of the 452. The limbs are shorter, and distinctly weaker. As a rule, the 542 is rather short of stature. The 452 is of medium height.

THE ONES IN ECTOMORPHY

171	261	271	361	371	451		461
						551	
711	621	721	631	731	541		641

THE 171

The 171 represents the full flower of uncomplicated meso-morphy. There is no weakening in this physique at any point. The example pictured in Fig. 1B (p. 5) is that of an 18-year-old youth who has been in school most of his life, and presumably has not especially trained or overdeveloped his muscles. Under training these muscles of the 171 can be made to stand out and to bulge more conspicuously, just as the belly of the 711 will expand and prosper under the stimulus of overfeeding.

The head as a whole is of distinctly cubical appearance, and of moderate size. It is small when compared with the huge endomorphic heads, and large when compared with the ectomorphs. There is little linear projection of any of the facial features, and the jaw is so strong and so square that the cubical appearance of the head tends to be well main-tained in the lower face. There is no ectomorphic tenseness in this face, and no trace of the flabbiness and overrelaxation of endomorphy. The neck is broad and muscular, with the transverse diameter markedly predominant.

The chest is full, well tapered, and conspicuously muscu-lar, with the transverse diameters strongly predominant over the anteroposterior measurements. The trunk as a whole has a relatively flat appearance. The shoulders are broad, but they are by no means the broadest shoulders to be en-countered. Actually the shoulders of the 711 are a trifle broader than those of the 171. It is when both transverse and anteroposterior diameters are considered that the sharp anthropometric differences are found. The waist is rugged and muscular, but fairly narrow, and it is not unusually low. This is because of the presence of the massive muscles of the pelvic girdle, and also because of the increased mass of the bones and connective tissue making up the pelvic girdle. There is also a roll of muscle over the iliac crests. The trunk is long, with a low lumbar curve. The shoulders do not present the high, square appearance of endomorphic shoulders, but are sloping, owing to the pyramiding of the trapezius muscles and of other muscles entering into the shoulder girdle. The hips are relatively narrow when compared with the shoulders, but they are by no means narrow hips. The pelvic bones and muscles are too heavy for narrowness. The arms and legs are heavily muscled, with great strength in the forearms and in the calves. There is no ectomorphic fragility at the wrists or ankles. This is a powerful physique, but not a very heavy one.

THE 711

In the 711 the first component is at high tide, and neither muscularity nor ectomorphic interference shows through at any point. It is as though the whole body were "pneumatic" and gently and evenly inflated at low pressure. The body walls may be thought of as thinner or less resistant at the center of the body, and progressively a little more resistant as the peripheries are approached from the center. There is thus a general tapering at the extremities, a growing inflation as the limbs join the body, and a tremendous inflation in the mid-section of the body.

The most conspicuous characteristic of high endomorphy is the great increase in the anteroposterior diameters of the body. In the extreme cases the front-to-back measurements nearly equal (occasionally surpass) the transverse measurements at the center of the body. As the first component increases, the great visceral mass increases and presses outward upon the thoracic and abdominal walls. The amount of "give" is limited laterally by the ribs and posteriorly by the vertebral column. Expansion takes place mainly by pushing the sternum forward, and thereby raises the ribs to a more horizontal position, as they are in the newborn infant. In the 711 the ribs are nearly horizontal. In the 117 they form an acute angle with the sternum, falling sharply forward and downward from their attachments at the vertebrae and permitting the sternum to fall inward toward the back and flatten the body.

The 711 has a huge head. His head circumference taken just above the ears is usually equal to about 35 per cent of his height. The face is large and broad, but the features tend to blend with the general plan of roundness, and they project but little. The facial skeleton is rather small, but the overlying blanket of soft tissue and fat is heavy. The mouth is usually sodden and shapeless. The whole face is completely relaxed. The neck is extremely short, as externally perceived, and the head may sit upon the torso like a pumpkin on a barrel. The anteroposterior diameter of the neck equals or surpasses the transverse diameter.

The shoulders are broad, high, soft, and "pneumatic." The enormous chest increases sharply in the anteroposterior diameter from above downward, but not in the transverse diameter. At the base, the front-back diameter may nearly equal the transverse diameter. The waist is high, and the abdomen is almost a sphere, even in the 18-year-old 711. There is a great roll of fat over the symphysis, and usually another across the back, beneath the scapulae. The abdomen is so large and predominant in this physique that the rest of the body seems merely attached to the abdomen, like an anterior and caudal appendage. The great chest appears attached to the abdomen like an inverted funnel.

The arms are relatively small and hang flaccidly, with great inflation of the upper segments. The legs carry out the "pneumatic" picture and are enormously inflated in the upper segments. In the lateral photograph the thigh suggests an inverted pyramid. The soft endomorphic blanket covers both the wrists and the ankles. The wrist measurement (ATL_2) just about equals that of the 171, but the ankle measurement (LT_2) clearly exceeds that of the latter physique. Yet when the bones of the highly endomorphic wrist and ankle are seen in an X-ray photograph, they are far smaller and more fragile than those of the highly mesomorphic extremities.

THE 261

This is one of the blocky physiques. The 261 is easily distinguished from the 171 by the far smoother contours of the body, and especially by the head and face, which lack the harsh cubical quality of the 171. The head is slightly larger than that of the 171, and there is no suggestion either of the trace of ectomorphic interference seen in the 262 or of the harsh squareness of the 171. Nothing appears fragile, and the face suggests the resilience and toughness of high-grade solid rubber. All the features seem small. A pug nose is the rule in this somatotype, and the mouth is firm and strong. The neck is short, massive, and broad, with the transverse diameter much the stronger. The trunk is long and extremely muscular, with wide, powerful shoulders, a rather low waist, and the chest markedly predominant over the abdomen. The 261 may look more athletic than the 171, for the latter is often "muscle-bound," especially about the pelvis. The arms and legs are short and marked by muscles that extend visibly all the way to the wrists and ankles. There is no trace of weakening or of fragility at any point throughout the entire physique. Yet there is no harshness of contour at any point.

In the ectomorphic 1's there is relatively little dysplasia, especially when the second component is high. Where the mesomorphic structures predominate so overwhelmingly, the first component that is present tends to be distributed diffusely and fairly evenly throughout the body, giving an evenness and suppleness of contour which is rightly associated with great strength and endurance. If the third component is at 1, there is not enough of it to cause much ectomorphic dysplasia at any point.

THE 621

The 621 is a physique quite different from the 711. The latter represents what is really a biological orgy of first component expression, in which all restraint is thrown to the winds. But the 621 has a secondarily dominant second component, and it is enough to give shape, control, and a certain buoyancy to the endomorphic body. Mesomorphic 2 can carry endomorphic 6, and with a little dietary help may keep it remarkably under control, but there is little that mesomorphic 1 can do with endomorphic 7.

The head of the 621 is round and large, like the head of the 711, but not so enormous. The features have a solider quality. The neck is short, and both wide and deep. The trunk is distinctly longer than in the 711. The shoulders are relatively wide, more sloping, and firmer. They lack the flaccidity of those of the 711. The chest shows the same progressive expansion of the front-back diameter from above downward, as shown by the 711, but in the 621 this phenomenon is far less conspicuous. The chest is large, and the abdomen is still larger, but the body lacks the suggestion of overwhelming inflation that is seen in the 711. The abdomen protrudes anteriorly beyond the chest, but only slightly so. There is a protuberance over the symphysis, but no suggestion of a fold of fat.

The 621 has a relatively long body, and short arms and legs which show no trace of ectomorphic weakening at the wrists or ankles. We sometimes call this physique the soft-chunky somatotype. The 621's are inclined to exhibit great energy.

THE 271

The rather rare 271 is the Hercules of human beings. This is the highest flower of ruggedness and muscular strength, supported by a slight and diffuse endomorphy which takes away the harshness and jaggedness of the 171 without adding a visible increment of softness or endomorphic accumulation at any point in the body. In the later decades, the 271's tend to grow heavy, but it is a general even heaviness, never a local inflation. Endomorphic 2, spread diffusely throughout the great muscular system of a mesomorphic 7, naturally indicates a greater absolute accumulation of weight in later life than does endomorphic 2 appearing in the lean and fragile structure of an ectomorphic 7.

The 271 closely resembles the 171 in general outline, but the sharply cubical suggestion of the head and face is softened, as though the cube now had rounded corners and had been polished down a little. The softening extends throughout the body, which is a little heavier and thicker than the 171 but otherwise almost a duplicate of the latter. The head of the 271 is larger than that of the 171, the abdomen is a little more full, the waist is broader and deeper, and the sharp muscular detail is absent all over the body.

THE 721

The 721 belongs in the series with the 631, 541, 451, 361 and 271, in contrast with the 712, which seems to be a continuation of the series including the 217, 316, 415, 514, and 613. The 712 is a weak, partially collapsed physique which is completely overwhelmed with the first component, and carries a strong Froehlich tendency. The 721 is an enormous, rather erect and active physique, with a fairly long trunk and broad shoulders and a muscular equipment strong enough to carry around the great load of endomorphic 7 with astonishing efficiency. Yet nowhere in the 721 is there any visible muscularity. The only evidence of second component is in the general erectness of the body, and in the absence of any signs of collapse at the thoracic girdle or middle trunk.

The head of the 721 is large, like that of the 711, but is inclined to be less spherical. It is deeper from top to bottom, if the face is included. The jaw is stronger, and there is a suggestion of firmness about the mouth. The neck is inclined to be a little longer. The phrase pumpkin-on-a-barrel never applies to the 721. The shoulders are broad. The huge and seemingly expanding chest appears to push them out. In the 271 or 171, by way of contrast, it seems as though the massive, muscular shoulders had seized the chest and were pulling it outward. In the endomorphic 7's the arms and shoulders are relatively insignificant appendages, like those attached to rubber dolls. In the 711 the chest seems to be something like an antechamber leading to and opening into the enormous abdomen which altogether overshadows it in size and importance. In the 721 the chest seriously challenges the abdomen, although it may not quite equal the latter in size. The great folds of fat regularly seen in the 711 and 712 are not seen in the 721. The 721, like the other endomorphic 7's, carries the strong suggestion of being a hollow rubber figure which is under pneumatic inflation, but in this physique the rubber in the center of the figure seems to be of better and stronger quality than it is in the 711, and more resistant to the pressure from within. The pressure seems to be a little higher, forcing out the shoulders and giving more erectness to the limbs and to the body as a whole.

THE 361

The 361 is a massive and extremely powerful physique, although it does not look massive in comparison with the 721. This physique is closely similar to the 261, but is heavier and rounder without being weaker. The head is large, and some of the cubical characteristics of extreme mesomorphy have been lost in the rounding and filling out which accompanies an increment of a full degree of endomorphy. But the face is still strongly mesomorphic, with a massive bony skeleton and great muscular strength clearly predominant. The mouth is strong, straight, and firm. The jaw is square and wide. It is a face which appears as though a well-delivered blow would glance off without doing any particular damage. The trunk is long, the shoulders are broad, the thoracic girdle is powerful and erect, and the chest is deep and mobile. There is a distinctly greater fullness of the abdomen than is seen in the 261, and there is relatively little lateral constriction at the waist. The waist is a little higher than that of the 261. The buttocks are well filled out, but small and sharply defined. The hips are still relatively narrow. The arms and legs are well proportioned to the long trunk, and they are distinctly sturdy, with no trace of weakness at the extremities. The thighs are full, but still entirely under the control of muscular shaping. There is no "hamming."

The 361 is strongly inclined to professional athletics, but, once out of his teens, he has a hard time keeping down his weight. These great muscles which are diffused with an endomorphic 3, seem as thirsty for fat as a sponge for water, and the 361 passes over to a heavy, stolid, barrel-bodied middle age. Nevertheless, he can fight off fat either by constant strenuous exercise or by stringent dieting, if he strongly desires to do so. All the mesomorphic physiques carry predilection for muscular exercise, and this is their natural way of holding the first component in check. The difficulty is that if a mesomorph orders his life around his desire for exercise, that is about all he will ever get done.

THE 631

The 631 departs quite sharply from the "pneumatic" softness of the physiques which are overwhelmed by the first component. This is primarily a soft and endomorphic body, but it is secondarily an erect and well-molded body. Mesomorphic 3 carries enough muscular strength and skeletal firmness to give any physique an upright posture and erect carriage. As the second component progresses beyond 3, the result is primarily a strengthening and fixing of a general pattern which is already established in lesser mesomorphic dominance.

The 631 has a large head which departs from the sphericity of the 711 even more than does the head of the 721. In the face of the 631 the jaw may be prominent and fairly strong and there is a distinct set to the features which is not seen in the 621. The neck is longer, and the whole body is usually much taller than that of the 621. The shoulders are of moderate breadth, and the relatively wide, deep chest no longer shows the steady progression of front-back diameter from above downward. That is to say, the chest of the 631 does not, like the chest of the 711, give the impression of an inverted funnel leading downward to an enormous abdomen, but it seems to be a segment of the body in its own right. The anteroposterior diameter of this chest remains about the same from the nipple level to the level of the xiphoid process, and the abdomen does not project beyond the anterior projection of the chest. However, the waistline is high, the hips are broad, and the abdominal mass predominates over the thoracic mass. There is a soft protuberance above the symphysis. The arms are rather long and well shaped, with distinct muscular shaping in the forearms. In the thighs the legs show the characteristic "ham" formation of endomorphic 6, but a trace of muscular molding is seen about the patellae and in the calves. The ankles and wrists are thick.

THE 371

The 371, 731, 461, 641, and 551 are all excessively rare physiques which combine a total strength of 10 in the first two components against the minimum of 1 in the third. This is the fringe of the human distribution and it demonstrates a lower incompatibility between the first two components than exists between the second and third, or between the first and third. All these physiques are extremely massive, and they all exhibit as little of the third component as nature has seen fit to produce. A detailed description of them would be superfluous, since each is but an extension or exaggeration of a trend which is already much in evidence in one or more of the various ectomorphic 1 physiques which we have considered.

The 371 looks like a still heavier and more massive 271. The height over the cube root of weight falls at about 12.1. The extreme muscularity, brawny shoulders, relatively constricted waist, predominance of chest over abdomen, and tremendous strength of arms and legs in the extremities, all distinguish him clearly from the rare 461.

THE 731

The 731 looks like a taller, wider, and stronger 721. This is the heaviest and most massive of all physiques. The 731 carries the broadest shoulders, the deepest and widest chest, and the thickest arms and legs to be seen in human flesh. The most conspicuous characteristic is the enormous chest, which balances and matches the equally enormous abdomen.

THE 451

The 451 is a massive, compact physique, of short stature, and usually of tremendous energy. It is a body built for an active, strenuous life. The endomorphic 4 supports the predominant mesomorphic 5 to produce a highly efficient machine as long as the first component is kept in check by vigorous activity, but given an opportunity, the endomorphic 4 will produce a laying-on of fat which rises like the tide and soon swamps the athletic outline of the physique. This endomorphic swamping is a much more conspicuous and dramatic phenomenon when the first two components are of nearly equal strength than when the first predominates. In the latter case, the endomorphic blossom comes early, usually before adolescence, and it reaches its height before the individual has attained physical maturity. With a low second component to carry it, such a blossoming cannot go far, and these physiques do not change much after adolescence. The 711 and the 325 look much the same at 40 as at

18, except that the latter will probably grow a "bay window."
But the 443, the 442, and the 452 are among what we call
the "pyknic practical jokes" (see p. 199). In their case, the
relatively strong second component holds the endomorphic
tendency in check during early life, and gives the impression
to the inexperienced eye that athletic slenderness is permanently predominant. Actually it is predominant only as
long as a vigorously active life is maintained, or a rigid diet
established. Under ordinary circumstances, especially after
marriage, the first component suddenly asserts itself and for
a time seems to run rampant. These people can sometimes
gain 30 or 40 pounds within a year. Likewise they can lose
this weight relatively easily, if they are willing to diet
rigidly, but usually they are not. Whenever somatotyping is
mentioned publicly, someone almost invariably comes forth
to recite "I was very slender at twenty, but look at me now."
When one looks he sees a barrellike fat body, together with
a pudginess about the face and in the neck, and relatively
small extremities. Very often these physiques are 442 or 443,
but occasionally a 451 turns up as a PPJ.

The 451 has a fairly large head—slightly more cubical
than spherical—strong, blunted features, a rather massive
neck, a long trunk with wide shoulders and a well-supported,
muscular chest, a wide, rather low waist which marks the
boundary of a well-filled but muscular abdomen, rather narrow hips, and short, heavily muscled arms and legs.

THE 541

Several colleagues have felt that one of the most difficult
distinctions to make is that between the 451 and the 541.
Actually it is not too difficult, if clear examples of the two
physiques are seen side by side. The 541 might be classed as
a PPJ, but from the beginning he is frankly dominated
by the first component. The head is larger and more spherical, the features are less pronounced and usually broader,
the mouth is inclined to have thick, relaxed protruding lips,

the neck is less strong transversely, the angle between chin and neck may be almost erased in the lateral picture, the trunk as a whole is heavier and shorter than in the 451, with a distinctly higher waistline and a much larger and fuller abdomen, and the limbs are even shorter than those of the 451. There is distinct endomorphic inflation in the upper segments of the arms and thighs, and the muscling of the forearms and calves is weaker. The 541 is of extremely short stature.

Both the 451 and the 541 are rare, and it is excessively rare to find a clear, nondysplastic example of either. We do not find extreme dysplasias in these somatotypes, but the commonest occurrence is a physique which falls about halfway between the 451 and the 541, showing characteristics of each in different parts of the body. There are, of course, many more intermediate physiques than there are clear examples of any of the somatotypes.

THE 461

The rare 461 at 18 has about the same height over cube root of weight as the 371 (12.1). He is distinctly rounder and heavier than the 361 without lacking any of the muscular and bony strength of the latter, and without showing any of the characteristics of endomorphic 5. This physique tends to grow heavy in mid-life. The features of the face are extremely heavy and massive. They are what are called coarse features. Both the 461 and the 371 seem to show a tendency toward acromegaly.

THE 641

This physique resembles the 631, retaining the characteristics of 6 in the first component, but is heavier, more erect, and taller. The 641 has broader shoulders and a deeper, more massive chest, and stronger muscling in the extremities. The facial features are heavier and stronger than those of the 631, and the neck is more massive. Yet the body as a

whole is overwhelmed with the first component. The height
over cube root of weight (11.7) is about the same as that of
the 712.

THE 551

The 551 falls at a point intermediate between the 461 and
641. All five of these excessively rare somatotypes which
combine a component total of 10 in the first two components
against 1 in the third have conspicuously massive features
which lack any trace of fragility or delicacy. As one observ-
antly walks the streets of a metropolitan center like New
York City, the impression grows strong that in the general
population there is a more frequent occurrence of all these
heavy physiques than is found on the college campuses. In
the colleges these five somatotypes combined make up a little
less than ½ of 1 per cent of the male population. They
probably do not constitute more than 1/10 of 1 per cent
of the female college population.

CHAPTER VII

TOWARD A CONSTITUTIONAL
PSYCHOLOGY

WE SHALL now raise certain problems whose solution hinges in part upon the development of an adequate method for classifying human physiques. These questions relate to heredity, endocrinology, temperament, psychoses, crime, immunology, and the like. Into some of these problems we have already gained a measure of insight; into others we have scarcely been able to penetrate at all. Concerning none of them can the last word be spoken at this time, but the thesis here presented is that when a definitive answer is made to these problems it will be an answer which does not ignore differences in physical constitution.

It is perhaps pointless merely to set down a list of potential projects for research without indicating what are reasonable working hypotheses and what might be the estimated outcome. Because a scientist depends for his hypotheses partly upon intangibles, and since the best means of discovering their worth is to expose hypotheses to scrutiny and test, the following pages contain many suggestions which only the patience of future inquiries can vindicate or refute. They are, for the most part, ideas garnered in the course of a decade of research on human beings, with a plan of constitutional classification in mind.

Most of the problems referred to in these sections have arisen from several broad fields of observation rather than from specific circumscribed experiments. Five such general fields might be mentioned: (1) Clinical observation in the routine course of hospital life. (2) Nursery school studies, observations in a children's hospital, and especially the study of several small groups of delinquent children. (3) Special group studies, mainly of psychotic patients in mental hospitals. (4) Studies of college students, particularly the intensive study of a group of 200 midwestern college students who had been somatotyped. (5) Observations made during the course of the constitutional analysis of persons who have presented themselves for treatment or advice. Space does not permit a thorough documentation and a complete marshaling of the evidence obtained in these various investigations. Instead, we shall outline only in broad strokes the constitutional study of personality as it appears to us at present, and leave the details for another volume.

THE PROBLEM OF NORMS

The first major problem in any such study as this is the establishment of norms. We need to know what are the distributions of the somatotypes for the general population, for men and women, for college populations, for racial groups, for underprivileged and overprivileged groups, for different age levels, and so on. The norms for 18-year-old male college students may perhaps be regarded as satisfactorily established. Roughly, we consider the distributions appearing in this book as norms for the age level 16-20. We are now attempting to build up a sufficient collection of data from standardized photographs to make it possible to publish similar norms for the age levels 20-25, 25-30, 30-35, 35-40, and 40-45. In most somatotypes, the measurements (except chest and abdominal measurements) vary but little at these different age levels, and the variations which do occur can presumably be determined accurately by somatotyping sufficient samples at different ages. We have already done this with relatively small samples, and have now available an extensive collection of pictures of males who are over 20. But the norms for these later ages are not yet ready for publication.

No satisfactory somatotyping of women has yet been done, and the study of racial variation, although exceedingly interesting, has not been systematically begun. From the samples of noncollege men that we have had available, it appears that the third component is a fraction of a degree lower for the general population than for college students, and that both first and second components are a little higher. For the second component this difference seems to be quite clear, but there is more doubt about the first component.

The problem of establishing norms for what has been called racial variation offers some singular complexities. Physical anthropologists have used head measurements and the subjective estimate of pigmentation as a means of trying to classify the human species into a number of alleged racial types. These measurements have been confined almost uniformly to what we have called region I, and all the classifications have rested upon the variation of isolated measurements rather than upon any basic organizational conception of even this one region, considered as a related unit. The outcome of this work has been a confused series of anatomical concepts containing all the pitfalls of the old typological bugaboo.

Starting with a few supposedly original types such as Nordic, Mediterranean, Alpine and Armenoid, physical anthropologists have become deeply involved in a struggle to describe all the morphological variations (of the head and face) which they encounter, in terms of mixtures of these types. Despite the brilliant work of the anthropologists themselves, such an effort is likely to end in verbal chaos, for the presumed primary types, instead of referring back to basic, scalable components, refer only to specific mixtures of components which have been found to occur at particular periods of time and in particular places. That is to say, the presumed primary racial types are actually names referring only to the prevalence, at a particular time and place, of certain component mixtures. To try to describe a physique as a mixture of Alpine and Nordic and Mediterranean is like describing it as a mixture of 542, 145, and 534. Such a description does not refer back to elements which can be isolated in description and gauged in terms of scales. The process is like referring to chemical compounds not as combinations of chemical elements but as mixtures of other equally complex chemical compounds. The problem of building a descriptive science rests heavily upon the perception and utilization of the most elemental descriptive units available, and if a scientist fails to select such units, it is extremely difficult for other related disciplines to make use of his work.

Armed with a technique for somatotyping we are in a position to lay hold on the problem of racial norms. For example, we could accept tentatively one of the conventional racial classifications and proceed to discover how the members of the race are distributed among the somatotypes. Perhaps there are discoverable correlations between basic somatotype and the isolated indices of the racial anthropologist. For races such as Orientals and Negroes it seems probable that different anthropometric norms from those presented in this book will have to be established for the somatotypes themselves. It is possible that new somatotypes may be discovered among these other races, and that some of the somatotypes common in our own racial group may be rare or even absent in other racial groups.

Quite probably there are a number of so-called racial characteristics, both morphological and pigmentational, which vary more or less independently of the basic somatotypes, and which can be measured within the present groupings of somatotype. In one sense the somatotype classification may constitute a sort of warp for which detailed racial description may in time provide a woof. But this may not be possible until racial anthropology can be restated in terms of a set of components of its own.

Almost the same problem confronts us in attempting to relate clinical medicine to morphology. Physicians have for centuries confronted the fact that there are relations between physique and susceptibility to disease, such as peptic ulcer, tuberculosis, gallbladder disease, poliomyelitis, apoplexy. But apparently driven by the same motivation which led the physical anthropologists to describe a type of physique common in the Alps as the "Alpine type," medical scientists have for the most part been content with such concepts as ulcer type, apoplectic type, gallbladder type, and the like (see p. 245). These supposed types they have defined only in terms of a few isolated and often independently varying linear measurements.

The relations between hereditary racial characteristics and morphology, and between immunity or susceptibility and morphology, present problems of great importance to human society, but before much light can be thrown on such problems it will be necessary to devote a certain amount of patience and care to the establishment of norms, and therefore perhaps to the redefinition of the concept of racial constitution and of clinical constitution in terms of patterns of components which are more elemental than accidental time-place associations, on the one hand, or than arbitrary caliper measurements, on the other.

The racial observations which we have already made in terms of constitutional study, are perhaps not yet worthy of mention, for we have too few cases to establish any racial norms at all. There are one or two interesting indications, however. In a series of about 400 northern Negroes whom we have photographed and somatotyped, there is a clear tendency for the distribution to spread out and away from the middle range of somatotypes, and to reach all three extremes with marked frequency. Extremely endomorphic, extremely mesomorphic, and extremely ectomorphic Negroes are proportionately more common, in this small sample, than in the white population. The same phenomenon appears in a series of about 300 Jewish college students. Among the Negroes it is the extreme second component that is most prominent, and among the Jews it is the first, but a dominant third component is also prevalent in both groups.

THE QUESTION OF THE PERMANENCE OF THE SOMATOTYPE

The question as to whether or not the somatotype can be modified during the lifetime of an individual can be answered with finality only after a few hundred physiques have been followed closely throughout the whole of a lifetime, and photographed at regular intervals. This, of course, we have not yet done, but it has been possible to follow the development of several hundred individuals over a period of about a dozen years, and while many have shown sharp fluctuations in weight, we have discovered no case in which there has been a convincing change in the somatotype. In order for the somatotype to change, the skeleton must change, as well as the shape of the head, the bony structure of the face, the neck, wrists, ankles, calves, and forearms, and the relations of stature to measurements made at places where fat does not accumulate. The deposit or removal of fat does not change the somatotype, for it does not change significantly any of the measurements except those where the fat is deposited. Such changes need never cause a body to be confused with another somatotype, for all the somatotypes differ in many ways other than in the tendency to lay on or not to lay on fat.

A 444 is not changed by nutritional disturbances to a 443, or to anything else. He only becomes a fat or a lean 444, or perhaps an extremely fat or an emaciated and wasted 444. We have examples of both extremes. It can be said that the case has yet to occur in which a nutritional disturbance has caused a physique either to become unrecognizable or to simulate another somatotype strongly enough to cause any justifiable confusion. It is true that an extremely thin ectomorphic 4 looks at first glance as though he might be ectomorphic 5, but closer inspection shows at once that the wrists and ankles are far too heavy in the bone, all the bones are too strong and thick for ectomorphic 5, the shape of forearm and leg is wrong, the predominance of distal over proximal length in the arms and legs is missing. Furthermore, the facial structure, neck structure, the thoracic and pelvic girdles, the proportions and line of the trunk and back, the shoulders, all the joints, indeed almost every structure in every region of the body says eloquently that this physique has no claim to ectomorphic 5, but is merely underweight. Two-thirds or more of the measurements tell the same story. Not only do the scale values for the different components remain the same for the total physique, but if adequate anthroposcopy is carried through, the index of dysplasia remains invariant in the face of nutritional disturbances.

In acromegaly the skeleton does change, and the measurements and whole appearance of an acromegalic may in some parts of the body simulate extreme mesomorphy. But this rare pathological condition is easy to recognize, and in addition, acromegalics are always highly mesomorphic, usually extremely mesomorphic, to start with. Acromegaly can be usually recognized under anthroposcopy by the fact that the muscular element throughout the body has not kept pace with the great overgrowth of bone. The paralytic or muscle-wasting diseases can also be recognized readily enough by inspection. These two kinds of conditions constitute the only known exceptions to the rule that the somatotypes remain easily recognizable throughout adult life.

We have records of some remarkable nutritional variations within some of the somatotype groups. It will probably be possible eventually to publish norms of maximum nutritional variation for all the common somatotypes, and to include the anthropometric limits within which all such variation occurs, but this will constitute an interesting task for a good statistical staff.

Here is a case in point. We have at hand the pictures of two men, both 533. Both are 69 inches tall. One is 43 years old, and the other 41. There is a weight difference of 35 pounds. According to our weight-prediction curve for the

533 (which is not yet ready for publication), one is 30 pounds overweight and the other is 5 pounds underweight. We also have pictures of these two men in bathing suits, taken about twenty years ago. In these pictures the two physiques look almost exactly alike. Constitutionally, they still look enough alike to be of necessity of the same somatotype, but one has a portly waistline and the other still looks in the trunk about as he did twenty years ago, except for a generalized increase in fullness. Only measurements on the middle trunk now show any particular discrepancy between the two physiques, and there is no other somatotype into which the group of measurements taken on the fat 533 will fit. If this latter individual should gain another 30 pounds, and if the other should lose 30 pounds, it still would be unnecessary to somatotype either of them as anything other than a 533. It should be added, however, that in somatotyping physiques which show an obvious nutritional disturbance, we do not feel that the data are satisfactory, or the somatotype scientifically certain, unless we have access to the previous physical history of the individual. With these data available, and trustworthy, the sharper the deviation from the normal nutritional pattern the easier and more certain is the somatotyping.

We have investigated over forty cases of what we call the PPJ (pyknic practical joke) where an individual who has suddenly grown much heavier, usually during the twenties or early thirties, although occasionally as late as 40, has retained bathing-suit pictures of himself in his pristine slenderness. These people are nearly always 4 in the first component, with a fairly strong second component which usually just barely exceeds the first, and which temporarily holds the latter in check and prevents it from "blossoming." The third component is typically either 2 or 3. In all these instances it has been easy to demonstrate that the somatotype has remained constant. The inexperienced observer of the human body easily confuses youthful slenderness with the third component, but this factor will no more mislead an experienced student of physical constitution than the long neck of a goose will induce an old hunter to mistake it for a heron. Similarly, a superficial student of these methods tends to confuse the first component with manifest fat. But endomorphs are not necessarily fat, and this component like the other two components is expressed in the skeleton, in the muscle and connective tissue, in the skin and subcutaneous tissue, in the circulatory system (capillary bed), in the relative relaxation of the entire body, in the shape of the shoulders and the shoulder girdle, in the shapes and relative sizes of the chest and abdomen, in the shape and proportions of the pelvic girdle, in the architecture of the limbs, and indeed in every tissue of the body. In gauging the first component, one is indirectly estimating, among other things, the potentiality for putting on fat, and this ability is perhaps the most dramatic characteristic of the endomorph, but it must be remembered that the first component is one of three correlated variables, and in looking at any anatomical part one must necessarily think in terms of all three components.

The somatotyping of young children is a much more difficult matter than that of adults. If an individual is past 30, the somatotype can ordinarily be read like a newspaper headline, but our evidence appears to indicate that what is at 30 so boldly manifest was in the beginning written just as clearly, although in finer print. We have not yet attempted any systematic somatotyping of young children, and have not yet taken standardized pictures of them, but we have been able to watch a group of upward of a hundred change from infancy to adolescence. There is evidence for the hypothesis that the somatotype can be accurately measured at age 6, and that it can be approximately predicted almost from birth, but both suppositions remain to be tested. Similarly, it seems probable that the physical constitution at the morphological level is rather rigidly determined before birth, and that it cannot be perceptibly changed during the course of a lifetime. At least it can be said that no case, where reasonably satisfactory pictures are available, presents evidence of a change in the physical constitution taking place during the course of life. Of course, our methods of study are still so new that such negative evidence can hardly be regarded as conclusive. In the course of thirty years it will be possible to settle this matter with certainty, merely by keeping accurate photographic records of an extensive series of cases. In the meantime, the burden of proof belongs to those who maintain that physique is largely a matter of nutrition and training.

Another bit of indirect support for the hypothesis that the somatotype does not change is perhaps to be derived from the fact that in our several series of pictures of men in older age groups, we have found nearly the same distributions of somatotypes that occur at college age. The same somatotypes are common and the same ones are rare, and about equally so, at 40 as at 18. The step of actually following an extensive series of individuals from 18 to 40 we have not yet taken. But since we have seen no case of a change in the somatotype, and since we know that the same distributions hold at these two ages, the evidence remains strong that, in adult life at least, no change occurs in the somatotype.

To look ahead for one short paragraph, and to anticipate the material of another volume in this series, we have found that the modifiability of the manifest aspects of *temperament* is another matter. By constructing and applying a simple scale for measuring the relative strengths of motivational drives, we have not only found that analogous elemental components appear to express themselves in temperament almost as clearly as in physical constitution, but we have been able to measure three elemental components with some reliability. At the motivational level, we call these components *viscerotonia* (first component), *somatotonia* (second component), and *cerebrotonia* (third component) (see p. 236). Provided our techniques of measuring the motivational components are accurate, there is little question that some change in externally manifest motivation takes place in response to educational and environmental influence. At least certain changes take place in *what we measure* as the motivational components.

THE PROBLEM OF CONSTITUTIONAL WEIGHT STANDARDS AND THE PREDICTION OF THE INDIVIDUAL'S PHYSICAL FUTURE

We do a great unkindness to those trusting people who still believe in the divinity of the printed word when we allow the usual publications of height-weight-age norms to go unexplained. It is sorrowful to hear the lament of a 632 who is already 30 pounds underweight, but who reads daily on the printed scales that she is 30 pounds overweight. And the poor 117 who weighs 99 pounds reads with horror that he should weigh 178. This kind of foolishness gives some of our best people inferiority complexes, and then they have to be analyzed or sent to church. For a European male population we are already able to publish differential height-weight standards for the age 16 to 20 (see p. 268). With these norms extended to other ages it will be possible to present a scale of height-weight standards for each different somatotype which will be meaningful to individuals, to doctors, and to insurance companies. Such a scale of norms for children would be of great value in children's medicine and in educational institutions where the development of children is watched. Research of this kind now awaits only the standardization of the somatotyping technique for young children.

The prediction of an individual's future weight and physical development will be possible when we somatotype the individual accurately. If only a little of this kind of attention could be paid to children, much later bewilderment might be saved. We might at least prevent the PPJ from setting her heart upon the career of a professional dancer, and tragedy could be prevented in the lives of young boys if we gave up trying to make athletes of nonathletic somatotypes. One of the most common causes of frustration in the life of the male is this custom of exposing boys promiscuously to the influence of athletic ambition. Possibly not more than five or six boys in a hundred are physically equipped to play a particular athletic game with conspicuous success. It is probably more harmful to the average boy of 8 to encourage him to *want* to be a successful football or baseball player than to encourage him to masturbate. He is fairly certain sooner or later to discover the shortcomings in this latter practice, but he has small defense against the inner tragedy of ill-advised ambition.

We need to dispose the influences to which children are exposed in such a manner that youngsters set their hearts upon values which represent the fulfillment of their own constitutional potentialities. This point of view, which emphasizes the constitutional differences in human beings and advocates differential treatment early in life, is counter to the current educational philosophy which stresses the virtue of socializing and leveling influences—forces which protect the child from differential development and lead him to think and to aspire as the radios and the newspapers and the neighbors are thinking and aspiring. It is not improbable that this kind of nondifferentiating influence is what produces sensitivity to popular styles in one generation and the war ·fever in the next.

THE INFLUENCE OF HEREDITY

We know almost nothing yet concerning the influence of heredity upon somatotypes. Stature and bodily build may be a direct result of heredity[1] carried in the genes or an indirect result of such heredity largely through its influence upon the physiology and chemistry of the body. Or perhaps food or early environmental factors may play a part in the final determination of the somatotype. It seems fairly certain that particular endocrine variations are constant accompaniments

---

[1] Davenport has produced apparently valid evidence that at least three specific genetic factors, and probably a fourth, determine body build.

of at least the more extreme variations in somatotype, but this fact does not answer the question of the influence of heredity, for the remote cause of the endocrine dominances and that of the dominances of bodily components may be identical and may lie far back among the genes. Light on this matter will have to await the establishment of a research bureau which can pursue a systematic constitutional study over more than one human generation, and can standardize methods of constitutional inquiry which will describe human beings in terms of combinations of scalable components.

There are many interesting points upon which such a study of constitutional heredity might shed light. For example, is there a tendency for congested urban stocks to return toward the means in the various components and to breed out the variants and rarities? Is there a tendency for isolated in-breeding stocks to fall within a narrow range of somatotypes, and possibly to produce certain rare somatotypes in greater numbers? Are there actually some somatotypes possible, under these conditions, that did not occur in the college population we have studied? Is there a tendency, when there is a wide choice, for certain somatotypes to mate with one another, and do families enjoying sustained economic and social security therefore tend to become hyperevolute, as Viola thought, and does this tendency set up a cycle which goes over into degeneracy? For the production of desired component mixtures are there optimum matings of people who do not themselves represent these somatotypes? Can disease propensities be bred out by the application of this sort of knowledge? By using a simple descriptive technique which accurately defines constitutional dominances can we then determine just what is the heredity of cancer, and thereby wipe out this disease?

Still further questions are these. Is there any sound biological justification for promiscuous human reproduction? Can we by standardizing constitutional methods of study find out what kind of women produce children most easily, and what kind of children they produce? Is there a large element in the female population which reproduces both badly and with difficulty? Is there another element which reproduces both well and easily? Is there any constitutional factor which renders it necessary for all the somatotypes to reproduce in order for people to be happy? It may not be a difficult thing to find an answer to some of these questions. Conceivably we could study the offspring of parents showing all the gradations of fecundity and of constitutional morphology. We could construct a scale of ease of reproduction or of difficulty of reproduction. There are women for whom the process of parturition is pleasant and exciting, others for whom it is a horror. Almost every obstetrical intern comes to recognize these differences intuitionally. We need but to keep systematic records in such matters.

In general, the extremes in each component have a difficult time with parturition. Then should women who are as high as 6 in some component have children? Or should the women who enjoy it most have the offspring? Furthermore, are the "easy" children the most gifted and valuable ones, are they the least gifted, or is there no relationship? It may be that certain important variations are born only of women for whom childbirth is difficult.

What is the effect of the age of parents upon children? There is good evidence that later born children tend to excel, in certain mental abilities, those born earlier. Why is this? Do the younger ones have somatotypes different from the older ones? Should at least one parent always be well along in physical maturity to ensure the best chance for gifted children?

For a long time now there has been talk of a eugenics program, but it seems possible that we have hitherto attacked the problem from the wrong end. We have talked only in terms of suppressing the unfit and of eliminating or sterilizing a fringe of unfortunates. But for many reasons it does not seem wise to subject an unhappy minority to harsh treatment. May it not be more desirable to tackle the problems at the other end and to discover what parentage produces the best children? It is still difficult to agree on what we shall mean by "best," yet not so difficult or so dangerous as to decide on what is "worst." Furthermore, from the standpoint of the practical administration of social controls, encouragement at one end might succeed where discouragement at the other end fails. A lesson might be drawn from the handling of mules.

The problems of heredity are among the most important problems in human life. A commonplace thought indeed, but for some reason men have feared to face the meaning of heredity. But apart from our reluctance to stand up to the issue there are other impediments. We have lacked a systematic scheme against which to think or to keep accurate records. There has been no acceptable descriptive language. The problem now is, have we here in this present approach to constitutional study a method with which to tackle the socially significant problems of heredity? If so, we can proceed, perhaps, to build a psychology which need not turn away from life for its research.

THE INFLUENCE OF ENDOCRINE FUNCTION

The question of the relation of endocrine secretions to the development of the body is one in whose service much brilliant and fascinating research has been sacrificed. Actually, we know little about the problem, and a principal reason for our present confusion is that all the work that has been done, however careful and accurate it may be on the side of chemical analysis, has been extremely superficial and pointless as regards constitutional classification. No studies of the endocrines have yet been carried out on individuals who have been formally somatotyped, although we have (by inspection) informally somatotyped several groups of clinical patients on whom endocrine data were available. There is no question but that the mesomorphic ectomorphs are almost uniformly endowed with active thyroids, that mesomorphic endomorphs have sluggish thyroids, that in acromegalics and in other mesomorphs there is relatively active secretion by the anterior lobe of the pituitary and by the adrenal cortex, and that the ectomorphic endomorphs and endomorphic ectomorphs (including the cases of Froehlich syndrome) tend to lack secretions from the posterior lobe of the pituitary, and the males lack gonadal (interstitial) secretion. All this is common knowledge.[2] Also, it is common knowledge that many attempts to correct pathological conditions associated with endocrine patternings have resulted in baffling complications, and in only temporary good results. Some good endocrinologists appear to assume that the endocrine conditions "cause" the observed variations in physical constitution, and the study of the physical constitution itself has been almost totally ignored.

If now the problem of describing endocrine dominances and weaknesses, and of experimenting with endocrine therapeutics, can be approached from a constitutional point of view, perhaps endocrinology can be provided with a key to an understanding of the many puzzling contradictions that have been encountered. An obstacle with which the medical profession has always had to contend is the human desire to explain things in terms of a single cause. What can be caused by a given glandular secretion may be one thing in one type of body, but something quite different in a member of another somatotype. Hence, the search for single causes must give way to analysis in terms of correlated variables.

The Italian anthropologists, a generation ago, knew that at least some of the ectomorphs were hyperthyroid. Di Giovanni and Viola called their microsplanchic the hyperthyroid type. This correlation is of great interest, but we need to be concerned with what lies behind the hyperthyroid characteristic. Does the thyroid gland determine the constitution, or

[2] For an excellent popular summary of the main facts in the field of endocrinology, see Hoskins, R. G. *The Tides of Life*, New York, Norton, 1933.

is the hyperthyroidism merely one item in a general constitutional pattern, and is the problem of the interbalancing of the internal secretions and of the relative dominances of different endocrine elements in the body rather a reflection than a cause of a deeper and more general balancing of constitutional components? When the third component predominates in a physique, the epiphyses of the long bones are seen to remain open longer than when one of the other components predominates, and the shanks and forearms grow to a relatively greater length. Similarly, when the third component is dominant, and the second is stronger than the first, the thyroid gland appears to be overactive. Also, when the third component is dominant, with the first component low, the gut remains extremely small, and relatively short. It hardly seems likely, however, that either the epiphyses of the long bones, or the thyroid gland, or the gut constitutes an elemental cause of this general state of affairs. It seems more probable that behind the whole pattern of these observable phenomena a deeper constitutional factor may be at work. Glands probably determine personality only in the same sense that the long bones and the short ones, and the gut and the muscles and the skin, and the rest of the structures of the body determine personality. It seems a more reasonable hypothesis that the physique as a whole consists of a patterned organization of elemental components which all together produce the observed aspects of the individual personality.

The exact relation of the somatotypes to glandular dominances can be ascertained, within the limits of accuracy of endocrine analysis, as rapidly as an extensive series of individuals can be studied. But like many other research projects associated with this work, such studies can probably best be carried out as incidental enterprises associated with regular clinical routines. The best answer to the question of the relation between constitutional pattern and endocrine pattern can probably be obtained from a constitutional study of the individuals who, in the ordinary course of events, present themselves at a general clinic.

On a few specific points our studies can already shed light. For example, it appears certain that different standards of normality are needed for the interpretation of basal metabolic rates. Normal persons who are mesomorphic ectomorphs show an average BMR reading at least twenty points higher than normal individuals of the same age who are predominantly mesomorphic endomorphs. For the 235 the normal or zero point in these readings should be probably twenty points higher than for the 532.

The rate of physiological sexual maturation presents a problem which can be studied profitably by constitutional methods, at least in females. Dominance of the third component appears to predetermine a late appearance of the menses. The ectomorphs, at least the mesomorphic ectomorphs, mature slowly. But the earliest to mature are neither the extreme endomorphs nor the extreme mesomorphs. These earliest ones are almost always rather large children, strong in *both* of the first two components and low in the third. The highly endomorphic girl with low mesomorphy often menstruates late. The same is true of extreme mesomorphs, although the extremely mesomorphic female is rare. Apparently the third component tends to postpone sexual maturation, and a modest predominance of either of the first two components tends to hasten it. On the other hand, a strong predominance of either of the first two components alone tends, in the female, to suppress sexual development altogether. We do not know the role of the endocrine variations which accompany these phenomena.

About thirty years ago someone advanced the hypothesis[3] that ectomorphic man, or *homo concavus* as he has been called, is by origin a dweller of the coastal regions of the world, where the iodine supply is high and where thyroid activity is presumably greater. Similarly, the endomorphs

[3] We have not been able to trace the source of this notion.

and mesomorphs, or combinations of these two variants (*homo convexus*), have been thought to come from inland environments where iodine is lacking and where thyroid activity is therefore lower. The endomorphic Teuton has been cited as an example of the latter type, and the lean Yankee or lean Englishman as an example of *homo concavus*. This notion illustrates how closely in men's minds the idea of thyroid overactivity is associated with the third component.

THE RELATION OF PHYSICAL CONSTITUTION TO TEMPERAMENT

The second volume of these studies will be directed toward the problem of the relation of constitution to psychological manifestations. Here the matter need only be mentioned. The hypothesis to be proposed is that personality, broadly conceived, is the product of the play of a complex pattern of environmental pressures upon a living organism that carries an innately determined constitutional patterning. This is no novel conception, but it is often lost to view. Looking as ever for a short cut, men have alternately denied the influence first of environment, and then of constitutional heredity. Either all must be heredity or all must be environment. Such a "monotheism" constitutes an obvious impediment to our thinking. Greek philosophers were well aware of this pitfall, and they named it the *enantiodroma* of life, or the problem of the opposites.

Assuming, then, that the pattern of personality at the level of temperament is bound in some fashion to the constitutional pattern, how may we proceed? First we must devise techniques and procedures by which we can get at the significant psychological variables. Then we can proceed empirically to discover what relations obtain between the psychological and the constitutional pattern. If the functional interdependence of our variables is close and demonstrable, we may end by describing all aspects of the individual—physical and psychological—in terms of these functional relations and thereby obviate the need for any dichotomy which separates the psychological from the physical.

We have, as a matter of fact, found such a clear relation between physique and behavior, and between organic constitution and the mental outlook, that it seems almost fatuous to attempt to draw a line between what is organic and what is functional in the human personality. It could, indeed, be argued that no such line can be drawn. On the other hand, it is convenient to study the aspects of the individual in terms of different levels—not levels, however, that are conceived as fixed and independent of one another. At the first level is the physique, laid down by heredity and relatively constant throughout life. At this level we study anatomy and morphology. At the next level we attack problems relating to the chemistry and physics of the body. Here we study physiological functions: nervous mechanisms, endocrine secretions, visceral reactions, and so on. We study these as they are related to one another and to the pattern of bodily constitution. At still another level we study what may be called psychological motivation or temperament. It is at this level that we find, among other things, the motivational components viscerotonia, somatotonia, and cerebrotonia, to which we have already referred. These are components of behavior defined operationally in terms of concrete tests and experimental procedures, and our problem is to discover their interrelations and their functional dependence upon the components of physical constitution and upon physiological function. But, as already pointed out, these and related topics are the subject of another volume.

Here, however, we may list a few of the distinguishing characteristics of the three temperamental components, viscerotonia, somatotonia and cerebrotonia, as they appear in their most dramatic manifestations. As with the three morphological components, the extreme variants are rare and most people combine in their temperaments various mixtures of these traits.

The extreme *viscerotonic* temperament is characterized, among other things, by a general relaxation of the body as a whole. The viscerotonic is a "comfortable" person. He loves comfort: soft furniture, a soft bed, luxurious surroundings. He also radiates comfort. He participates easily in social gatherings and makes people feel at home. He exhibits an extraversion of affect by showing a warm interest in many people and a genuine tolerance of their personalities. Whatever his feelings he expresses them easily. His joys and sorrows he communicates to others. Food is of great importance in the life of the viscerotonic and his fondness for fine food and ceremonious eating is backed by a good digestion and an ability to dispose of large quantities of "roughage."

In the extreme *somatotonic* we encounter an active, energetic person—a person addicted to exercise and relatively immune to fatigue. He walks assertively, talks noisily, behaves aggressively. He stands and sits with an upright posture and in youth presents the general appearance of a maturity beyond his years. He is concerned mostly with affairs of the present and meets his problems with some form of activity. His is an extraversion of action rather than of affect.

The extreme *cerebrotonic* is an "introvert." He is under strong inhibitory control as regards expression of feeling— he is unable to "let go." His history usually reveals a series of functional complaints: allergies, skin troubles, chronic fatigue, insomnia. He is sensitive to noise and distractions. He is not at home in social gatherings and he shrinks from crowds. He meets his troubles by seeking solitude.

These abbreviated characterizations are samples selected from a much more extensive list. At the level of temperament they are analogous to the check lists of morphological aspects listed on p. 37. They serve to identify the components of temperament just as the morphological check lists identify the components of physique. And as with the morphological components, the components of temperament can be gauged on 7-point scales in such a way that a component-description of the individual is possible. The components of temperament correlate with the components of physique, but not in any one-to-one fashion.

An observation regarding intelligence is perhaps in order at this point. Viola and his followers regarded dominance of the third component (microsplanchny) as a hyperevolute characteristic, and they believed that the microsplanchnics excel in intelligence. The difficulty with a conception of this sort lies in the problem of defining intelligence. If intelligence should be defined purely in terms of conscious sensitivities and perceptual acuities, there is probably truth in such a supposition, but if adaptability and individual success in a society be taken as criteria of intelligence, then it is certain that superior intelligence does not lie in strong dominance of the third component, and probably not in strong dominance of any component but rather in certain balances and ratios among the components. This may in part explain the complete failure of the hundreds of efforts that have been made to establish relationships between intelligence, on the one hand, and physical "types," on the other. Always the mistake has been made of dealing with but one component of physique at a time, and of trying to relate one component (or one type-tendency) to the various criteria studied. Such a mistake seems necessarily to predetermine failure, for neither physiques nor personalities are built one component at a time. Endomorphy, for example, isolated from the other components means practically nothing, even in a morphological and anthropometric sense, let alone in terms of its psychological implications. An endomorphy of 5, associated with mesomorphic 1 and ectomorphic 4 (the somatotype 514), produces a long-legged, round-shouldered, completely soft and effeminate boy who has underdeveloped genitalia and falls in the range or at the edge of what the medical scientists call the Froehlich category. But an endomorphy of 5 associated with mesomorphic 4 and ectomorphic 1 (the 541) produces a ruddy, powerful, active, barrel-bodied boy who is usually full of bounding energy and is likely to become president of something. Our criteria of intelligence have been so mixed and confused, and so lacking in any basic component orientation, that intelligence tests would probably show little difference between the 514 and the 541. Yet the two patterns of personality are profoundly different at the level of temperament.

The point we are here stressing is that in 'correlating some aspect of human behavior (clinical, psychological, physiological, or what not) with somatotype we need, in general, to consider the entire range of somatotypes rather than the variation of a single component. It is quite possible for a trait of personality, for example, to correlate highly with somatotype and yet show zero correlation with one of the three components taken alone. If we imagine the somatotypes plotted on a plane surface, as shown in Fig. 18, the problem of correlation can be envisaged as the plotting of the measure of the trait in question along the verticals perpendicular to the plane surface. If the value of the trait is the same for members of all somatotypes, if all points along the verticals are equidistant from the plane, there is no correlation. If these points are not equidistant from the plane, there is correlation. The actual statistical methods for gauging the amount of correlation should be worked out to meet the requirements of the particular problem in hand.

THE RELATION OF CONSTITUTION TO MENTAL DISORDER

Kretschmer's important contribution to constitutional theory grew out of the study of institutionalized psychotics. He found that manic-depressives were "pyknic" and that schizophrenic patients were predominantly "asthenic." But the morphological side of his work was not adequately developed. He did not mean by pyknic precisely what we mean by dominance of the first component. He placed in that category all the large and massive physiques, including what we call endomorphs but also including the mesomorphic endomorphs and many of the endomorphic mesomorphs. In short, Kretschmer's "pyknics" were really the whole range of somatotypes conspicuously low in the third component, except for the extreme mesomorphs. The latter were his "athletics," and this category also included most of the ectomorphic mesomorphs. His "asthenics" were the extreme ectomorphs plus most of the mesomorphic ectomorphs. He had a fourth group, which he called the "dysplastics," and of these there were two principal subgroups—the "eunuchoid asthenics" and the "eunuchoid pyknics." The latter two groups were, of course, what we call the endomorphic ectomorphs and the ectomorphic endomorphs, respectively. In short, Kretschmer was really working with three groups each of which included many conflicting somatotypes, and with a "wastebasket" category consisting of those physiques which are extremely low in the second component. With such a classification, it is astonishing that he was able to establish any statistical relation at all.

During the past year, we have photographed about 3,000 young schizophrenic psychotics and about 300 manic-depressives in the state hospital system of one of the eastern states. This material is now being examined and will eventually be published as a separate monograph, but three indications are so strikingly apparent that their premature mention can do no harm. First, the dysplasias in the schizophrenic groups are far more conspicuous and striking than is any tendency for schizophrenia to be confined to a particular range of somatotypes. The mean dysplasia for schizophrenes is sharply higher than that for college students or for the general population. Second, certain specific dysplasias are conspicuously frequent among the so-called hebephrenic and catatonic schizophrenes. Three dysplasias are especially noteworthy. These are (1) a marked weakness of the second component in the second (thoracic) region, (2) strength of the third component in the fifth (legs) region, and (3) a high gynandromorphic index, g, in many somatotypes which ordinarily do not carry a high g. Third, there are striking constitutional differences between the patients manifesting what is conventionally called paranoid dementia praecox and the hebephrenic and catatonic groups. The so-called paranoid dementia praecox patients are distinctly higher in the second component. They are more massive and stronger, although it is not clear that they are higher in the first component. They resemble the manic-depressive patients more closely than they resemble the hebephrenic and catatonic patients. The latter two groups are very similar, and may be constitutionally indistinguishable. These generalizations represent preliminary impressions which have been derived from the anthroposcopic sorting of about half the series. It should be added that Kretschmer's original thesis maintaining that the dementia praecox patients are overwhelmingly ectomorphic seems to be supported in part. The hebephrenic and catatonic patients are highly ectomorphic as a group, although they are not always ectomorphic. It seems to be certain component patterns and dysplasias, rather than ectomorphy in general, that carry the schizophrenic tendency. The paranoid patients are probably higher in the second component than in the third. The manic-depressives seem not to be dominantly endomorphic, but may be more mesomorphic than endomorphic. Among them are many endomorphic mesomorphs and many mesomorphic endomorphs.

Freud's theory of regression places the responsibility for mental disintegration squarely upon early childhood experience. He believes that in the face of conflict the mind tends to fall back to an earlier developmental level at which frustrational influences prevented normal "assimilation of experience." The point to which a mind returns under such conditions is determined largely by the existence of some fixational complex of unassimilated experience. Thus, paranoia (in the ordinary nonpsychotic sense of that term) represents a return to the homosexual (preadolescent) stage of development, while dementia praecox means that the mind has gone all the way back to an infantile stage. Jung holds what is really a somewhat similar theory of regression. He speaks of regression to various levels of the "personal unconscious" and even to the "racial unconscious," which lies behind consciousness like a reservoir of cumulative wisdom, deep in some sort of germinally transmissible matrix and which can be got at (Jung thinks) only by the method of interpretive dream analysis. Freud and Jung thus employ essentially the same general analytic principle. They attempt to penetrate to the origins of the "complex" of unassimilated experience which grew out of an inadequate response to conflict.

But was this original failure to respond adaptively to conflict due primarily to external environmental pressures, as the Freudians assume, or was it due to more basic constitutional factors in the individual himself? By pointing to specific early experiences which seem to have been associated with mental conflict, the psychoanalysts have not necessarily proved that the difficulty was due fundamentally to these events. Their argument is like that of one who would blame the match for the damage done by the firecracker. We need to find out *who* these people are that regress, that is to say, who they are in terms of constitutional make-up. Not that analytic treatment is useless, but perhaps it remains a mere palliative, and a blind one, until its patients themselves can be described in language that is uniform and scientifically meaningful. This task is difficult but not impossible. If analysts, using whatever method they fancy, can reciprocate with constitutional study in a research program which will keep track of individuals as well, for example, as the medical profession now keeps track of its syphilitic patients, it may not be impossible to make headway in analytic psychology even in one generation.

THE PROBLEM OF THE RELATION BETWEEN MENTAL CONFLICT AND DYSPLASIA

The problem of dysplasia, or the uneven manifestation of components in the different regions of the body, is one of first importance. It is possible to catalogue the dysplasias accurately (see p. 71) and to determine the frequency of occurrence of each dysplastic combination. Not only can we measure dysplasias in terms of the three basic components— endomorphy, mesomorphy, and ectomorphy—but also in terms of secondary variations such as gynandromorphy. The person with a high g component can be regarded as dysplastic in the sense that his primary and secondary sexual characteristics are not in perfect agreement.

These gynandromorphic dysplasias are the most spectacular and probably the most common. In some regions of the body in the 316's, 415's, 514's, and 613's are seen almost equal mixtures of masculine and feminine bodily characteristics. Now, what sort of "dysplasias," if any, occur at the level of temperament? Are there physiological misanthropic mixtures which parallel the morphological dysplasias? Our own observations, based upon the use of techniques to be described in another volume, indicate that motivational inconsistencies are common. There appear to be disproportions and inequalities in behavioral expression which show up in various panels of conscious activity. In particular, there appear to be cases of what we might call gynandropsychic incompatibility, that is to say, incompatibility between masculine and feminine motivational impulses.

It may be well to raise here the question, what is psychological conflict? This term "conflict" has been used by many writers in two different senses. Under one meaning, conflict may refer to the natural and inevitable striving of elemental tendencies for dominance within the personality. In this sense conflict is analogous to a principle of equilibrium among forces—a principle which pervades all of nature. Man is then a product of conflict in the same sense that a tree is an outgrowth from the soil in which its roots are held and nourished. The term "conflict" is also in common use in a pathological sense, in which it refers to incompatible drives, needs, or motivations. This type of conflict may be regarded as analogous to the structural dysplasias. Conflict, in this sense, may be a thing to be got rid of, through psychoanalysis or some other curative device, but some forms of it may serve as an important catalyst in society. It is perhaps unwise to limit the term "conflict" to this restricted meaning, for it renders difficult the teaching of a normal psychology of persons in whom normal conflicts (interacting forces) are present.

In the pathological cases it is not conflict itself that represents the pathology. The pathology lies in the *pattern* of the forces which impinge against one another. We need to distinguish from a normal state of conflict those conditions in which alien or incompatible patterns of forces strive for dominance. Such a condition may be called a *dyspsychic* state of affairs.

Now, what relations, if any, exist between the morphological dysplasias and the common dyspsychic patterns which seem to underlie psychopathology? This problem opens a new field of inquiry, for as yet we have had no systematic classification of morphological and psychological variation. Nevertheless, the conviction is here expressed that when Kretschmer and Naccarati and their associates observed relations between bodily build and psychological variation they may have been close to matters of greater importance than appears on the surface.

THE RELATION OF CONSTITUTION TO CLINICAL STUDY AND TO IMMUNITY

Sir William Osler once said that the difference between a great physician and a good one lay in the ability of the former to diagnose the patient as well as the disease. As a doctor grows wiser in his practice he comes to recognize certain disease entities at a glance and others "by the patient's knock on the door." Any experienced physician carries at his finger tips a wealth of insight into a variety of constitutional patterning. He knows at once that this patient is probably a case of high blood pressure, that this other one undoubtedly has a functional complaint, and that the woman in the waiting room is an excellent candidate for gallbladder disease. If asked how he knows these things, the physician may either evade the question with some vague reference to experience or he may attempt to designate certain constitutional characteristics of the patient, generally in a language lacking a clear frame of reference.

As the study of disease has grown more complex and specialized, medical diagnosis has tended to become routinized and formalized in a manner which neglects the constitutional factor. The physician recording a medical history tends to assume the specific task of discovering the nature of the pathology, if any, and he therefore encroaches with the utmost caution upon the domain of the patient's personality. To discover too much about the personality might, in a mechanized and impersonal society, be regarded as taking liberties. Such inquiries, the young physician is taught, can be left to the specialist in these matters, probably to the psychiatrist. But psychiatrists will perhaps be the last to concern themselves with constitutional study. The psychiatric house is itself in disorder, and the state of this specialty is such that therapy and palliation still predominate over diagnosis.

Constitutional study represents, in a sense, a movement away from specialization, both in medicine and in social studies. Consequently, in utilizing constitutional studies as an aid to medicine, we must protect them from a too-close identification with any of the established specialties.

A major field for the application of this method of study undoubtedly lies in the relation between physical constitution and what Dr. George Draper calls the immunity panel of personality, or its degree of natural resistance to particular diseases. Draper himself has long been a pioneer in constitutional work, and he has used both anthropometric and anthroposcopic methods in his clinical observations at the New York Presbyterian Hospital. He is perhaps best known for his work on the differentiation between a "gallbladder type" of physique and an "ulcer type," and for his studies of infantile paralysis. He demonstrated that gallbladder patients are usually of thick, stocky build, while ulcer patients tend toward linear development and represent something of a physical opposite to the gallbladder type.

Constitutional studies of a clinical nature are best carried out cumulatively, and we have for a number of years been concerned with the observation and photography of several different clinical entities. Some clinical diseases are unquestionably related both to physical build and to constitutional characteristics of a motivational nature. We are not yet ready to publish data in this field, but some of the clearer indications may perhaps be mentioned without creating false impressions. We have confirmed Draper's observations on gallbladder and ulcer patients. Victims of both duodenal and gastric ulcer tend to be low in the first component, the latter lower than the former. The 244 is one of the most common somatotypes among the peptic ulcer fraternity, in spite of the fact that this is not one of the commonest physiques in the general population. Gynandromorphy is conspicuously absent in cases of gastric ulcer. This latter finding is so consistent that it is almost possible to predict the location of the lesion from a careful examination of the physique. In a series of 80 ulcer cases arranged in descending order of the g-index, the lesion was found to move from far out in the duodenum steadily inward toward the stomach, as the g-index decreased. When the g-index is at its minimum, the lesion is likely to be found in the stomach itself, usually in the lesser curvature, near the pylorus. There are also certain dysplasias which appear to characterize victims of peptic ulcer, notably one which involves a disproportionately increased second component in the first region (head and neck).

Victims of gallbladder disease, about four-fifths of whom are women, are conspicuously of endomorphic predominance, with the second component stronger than the third. That is to say, they are usually mesomorphic endomorphs.

The poliomyelitis cases who become afflicted with the paralytic complications of the disease are principally endomorphic mesomorphs or mesomorphic endomorphs, although, as Draper and Dupertius have pointed out, a number of secondary factors appear to be consistently associated with this disease.[4]

Cancer is a disease of many varieties and is a condition upon which we have not yet been able to focus a systematic constitutional study. There appears to be a remarkable immunity to all forms of cancer among the mesomorphic ectomorphs who are below 4 in the second component, and, indeed, cancer is apparently rare in all the pronounced ectomorphs. The frequency of most forms of cancer appears to rise with the second component. It is often assumed that cancer is related to constitutional heredity, but since there has never been available a comprehensive classification of constitutional variation, nobody seems to have made an effort to determine *how* it is related to heredity. Nevertheless, the prospect of throwing light on the problem of cancer by constitutional methods of study seems excellent.

There is some evidence that the cancer scourge common to the male—carcinoma of the stomach—follows the same tendency as gastric ulcer. Either it does not occur or it is extremely rare in the presence of normal strength in the g-index. In women peptic ulcers are rare, and carcinoma of the stomach is extremely rare. When peptic ulcer does occur in the female, it is almost always in the presence of a high g-index, that is to say, a high masculine component. Pos-

[4] Draper, G., and Dupertuis, C. W. The nature of the human factor in infantile paralysis. *J. Clin. Invest.*, 1939, 18, 87-100.

sibly the female element in the male provides specific protection against these two conditions. Cancer of the breast is common in women, and not particularly rare in men, but the few cases of the latter condition that we have observed have occurred in men with a fairly high g-index, i.e., in men having a high feminine component.

Syphilis is an interesting disease about which we know remarkably little from the constitutional point of view. In 1899 Näcke published a study demonstrating that tabes dorsalis is a characteristic end result of tertiary syphilis in the "long-thins," while general paresis occurs principally in the "short-thicks." This observation has been widely confirmed and is taught to medical students as a general fact. But are there other relations between component patterns and the behavior of this disease entity? Are there immunities to the luetic spirochete which follow constitutional patterns? We need only to keep careful constitutional records of a few thousand syphilitic cases and to observe systematically the courses of the disease in these cases in order to answer such questions.

There are hundreds of interesting questions to which the constitutional approach might provide an answer. Where do the monsters come from? The mongoloids? The congenitally defective? The hydrocephalics? What children are susceptible to rickets? We know that some infants require many times as much vitamin D protection as others. Is the same true of the other diseases dependent upon vitamin deficiency? Can we, at last, by a method of constitutional description and record keeping, begin to systematize human differences, and without forgetting the trees can we survey the hereditary forest as it affects disease susceptibilities among the population? This kind of work calls for a close cooperation between several departments of medical and anthropological study. It is necessary, perhaps, that we think against the background of the whole individual, or we soon become confused and drown in a sea of statistical crosscurrents.

THE PROBLEM OF DIFFERENTIAL FOOD NEEDS

We need to know how to feed the somatotypes. Here is a chance to test the ancient adage that what is one man's meat is another's poison. In the ordinary course of constitutional study we have picked up a number of preliminary clues. It is clear that the ectomorph needs to eat oftener than the endomorph or the mesomorph, and that the mesomorphic ectomorph requires more food per unit of body weight than is needed by other somatotypes. These mesomorphic ectomorphs seem especially to need protein in larger quantity. This may be true even in the later decades of life. When the first component predominates there is usually a fairly strong craving for sweets. Does this represent a biological need of some sort? Should carbohydrates be limited when the first component is high, or should these people follow their own inner impulse? Questions of this sort can be answered only after careful and systematic research. It is possible that the endomorph ought to eat large quantities of carbohydrates and little if anything else. On the other hand, we know that some individuals can subsist flourishingly on meat alone, but in constitutional terms, who are these people? Is it only ectomorphs or mesomorphic ectomorphs who find in meat an all-sufficient diet?

The endomorphic physique carries a longer and much heavier intestine than does the ectomorphic physique (see p. 33). Does this mean that for endomorphs and ectomorphs there ought to be two quite different diets? Can we by systematizing constitutional studies discover a more rational plan for the differential feeding of these two variations of constitution? Will such feeding exert a direct effect upon disease immunity and upon general resistance to infection? Ought people with a long, thick, endomorphic gut be more herbivorous than those lacking in such equipment? Then what about the rationale of the recent popularity of "rabbit food," or "roughage"? Should only endomorphs eat roughage, and does the heavier gut of that physique require great bulk and indigestible debris for its proper function, somewhat as the mesomorphic physique requires physical exercise? Then are lettuce, bran, spinach, burdock, cucumbers and the like rather an insult and a cause of functional disturbance when fed into the more delicate, sensitive, and naturally carnivorous ectomorphic gut? Such matters are of some dietary interest.

Is it possible that most of the human race, except perhaps the extreme ectomorphs, could live a vegetarian life? We need a kind of research into these matters which is not altogether confined to laboratories, but which can be carried on in the ordinary run of human contacts, especially in connection with such an institution as a large clinic. By systematic methods of constitutional study we might discover in one or two generations just who are the natural vegetarians, and what is the effect of vegetarianism. In ordinary clinical work we collect enough fragments of knowledge about people to make up a highly respectable body of science, but we are foiled by the difficulty of keeping records of it systematically, and every time a first-rate diagnostician dies the wealth of a lifetime of observation dies with him. This is due at least partly to the fact that there has been available no accepted system of anthropological classification to serve as the foundation for record keeping.

THE PROBLEM OF DIFFERENTIAL DRESS AND DIFFERENTIAL FURNITURE FOR CONSTITUTIONALLY DIFFERENT PERSONALITIES

Here are recorded some observations relating to the individuality of certain somatotypes. These statements are meant to be more suggestive than conclusive. They constitute generalizations drawn from a variety of data, and exceptions are undoubtedly numerous.[5]

[5] Observation of the differential habits and tastes of persons of different bodily constitution has now been carried on systematically for a period of some ten years. This has been done, in an extensive way, by a method of keeping cumulative records in notebooks and also, in an intensive way,

It is a reasonable hypothesis that men should no more dress alike than they should think alike. In a world devoted to the full development of human personalities rather than to quantity production, the 117 would probably no more wear the same cut of clothes as the 711 than the two would use the same weight standards. The extreme ectomorph appears, for example, to need a high stiff collar which protects and supports his ectomorphic neck. The endomorph and the mesomorph apparently need no collar at all. The individual with a highly developed torso has an understandable urge to display his body. Exhibitionism, the ectomorphic moralist calls it. But it is probably as natural as the frequent desire of some other individual to write and publish a poem. Magnificent mesomorphic bodies are things of beauty and they deserve, perhaps, to be exhibited. It is a misfortune, however, that the first component seems to carry the same predilection for nakedness and for bodily display, and it is certainly a great misfortune that this fondness seems to vary inversely with the t-index. The consequence of these two misfortunes is that most of the human bodies seen in places of public display are not too reassuring to the eye. Somato-typing done at public beaches does not yield an optimistic picture of the population.

In general, the people whom Jung labeled extravert crave freedom from clothes and freedom from inhibition and prudery, as they generally interpret it. But those whom Jung would call introvert feel strongly the need of clothes. One of the first things that the person of somatotonic predomi-nance often discovers in an analysis is his suppressed wish to be without clothes. The next step is the rationalization that clothes represent inhibition and prudery, and as a result we have experienced a wave of intrafamilial nudity following

through a method of exhaustive psychological analysis of a group of 200 college students. The problem of the validity of these methods of study will be dealt with in another volume. Here we advance merely a few high lights of observed trends in behavior.

the general dissemination of psychoanalytic doctrines. This new freedom has sometimes been painful to the marital partner who happened to carry a more delicate organic nature than the analyzee. Both a high t-index and a high third component appear to predetermine a strong need of clothing, even in bed.

It is interesting to note that during the past twenty years, in the styles of both street and beach, there has been a sharp swing away from dress adapted to ectomorphic dominance and toward styles suited to endomorphic-mesomorphic dominance. The stiff collar has almost disappeared. The bathing suit has dropped away piece by piece. The severe lines of the coat men used to wear, with its straight four-button front and high lapel, have given way to the rounded, short-fronted model which is ideally cut for the 451 but next to impossible for the 145. The earlier high-waisted "ectomorphic" pants have been replaced by low-waisted, wide-bottomed ones. High shoes can hardly be purchased any more. Even the garter is strongly threatened, and the umbrella has all but disappeared from the American scene. All this amounts to a kind of revolution. It is the substitution of one suppression for another.

If the individual personality is to be allowed adequate expression, furniture makers and housebuilders need not one set of styles to follow, but perhaps four, with subvarieties under each. There might be a middle style for the middle range of somatotypes, an endomorphic style, a mesomorphic style, and an ectomorphic style. The endomorph likes soft, overstuffed furniture, deep abysslike chairs, inner spring mattresses, luxurious general furnishing, and ceremonial eating equipment. The mesomorph craves spacious rooms without the overstuffing, and the ectomorph gravitates toward closed-in places and is content with a hard simplicity of furniture. Ectomorphs need chairs with high, shallow seats which slope backward. They also appear to like stiff mattresses.

Houses on hills or on prominent ground appear to run sharply against the ectomorphic grain. These people carry a deep *claustrophilia*, and they want to be tucked away in hollows, in old orchard corners, and such places. They want small, snug houses with steep roofs and with attics and cellars. The mesomorph wants large houses in open places, and likes his house on a hill. The so-called "modern" type of architecture is highly "mesomorphic." It came with the recent "mesomorphic" revolution. At least, it is an interesting hypothesis to suppose that it did. We need, through the process of constitutional analysis, to ascertain and to record the differential desires of the various somatotypes until the need for four or five or more general types of furniture and housing equipment is understood, even by the people who make these things.

CONSTITUTIONAL FACTORS IN SEXUALITY AND MATING

We should like to penetrate to the nucleus of the question of what lies behind natural sexual attraction. The problem is so complicated by the ramifications of marriage and by the social pressures associated with marriage that it is difficult to get at. Yet nearly every person realizes at times what his ideals are concerning the other sex. The simplest sort of diagnostic analysis usually brings these attitudes into clear relief. If careful records of analytic interviews were to be kept and correlated with constitutional factors, it might be possible to solve the problem of constitutional differentiation in basic sexual need.

There is the popular supposition that opposites attract one another. But opposites in what respect? Do 711's attract 117's? Do the feeble-minded attract the mentally gifted? Do the extremely one-sexed attract the gynandromorphic? Or is it simply that low pigment attracts high pigment? Or is this stereotype a myth? Does the matter depend largely upon the t-index? Are persons of like t-index or of widely different t-index most attractive to one another? Is it the motivational level of temperament that determines sexual attraction—the viscerotonics, do they attract or repel other viscerotonics? Are persons of the same age attracted most powerfully or is there a deep mutual mating attraction between the older and the younger? Do all these things vary with the different somatotypes, and with other constitutional factors? But do they, nevertheless, vary *in patterns*, so that eventual understanding may be possible? These questions are easy to pose, difficult to answer.

It is desirable to reconsider the whole problem of sex differences from a constitutional point of view. We need to know who are the highly sexed individuals, and who experience the most pressing need for sexual companionship. Of course, there may be no relation between these two groups. It is the viscerotonic dominance that correlates with a strong need for companionship, but it is probably not the viscerotonics who carry the most imperative sexual need. The ectomorphs appear to be the individuals who are intermittently overwhelmed by an imperative sexual drive and these people also appear to experience the most intense sexual ecstasy. Theirs are sensitive bodies and they are consequently susceptible to the development of masturbational and perversive practices.

What is the relation between celibacy and mental development? What lies behind the age-old human intuition that the highest levels of mentality can be reached only through celibacy? Is this notion a snare? Does it hold good only for some small range of somatotypes? Is it, indeed, only a subtle rationalization of the homosexual desire?

It has long been known that some personalities come early to their fullest mental maturity. They appear as fully matured soon after adolescence as they ever become. Should such people marry early, if they are going to marry at all? Other personalities do not reach their full maturity until late, and there are possibly a few who are still growing even in old age. When should these last marry, if at all? Such questions cannot be answered offhand, but the first step is to find out who these different kinds of people are so that they can be recognized with accuracy and, far more important, can recognize themselves before it is too late. We ordinarily penalize our late-maturing stock by failing to recognize it as such and by permitting it to fall into snares and traps, especially of a marital nature, which threaten it with tragedy. Late maturation probably distinguishes the human "thoroughbred," if such a term can be used in a democracy. Those maturing late appear to have both quality and durability, that is to say, both a high t-index and a certain prolonged youthfulness of the fiber which prevents early decay. We need to know who they are, and we may find it profitable to protect these personalities from early application of the finalizing influences which ordinary marriage entails.

THE PROBLEM OF CONSTITUTION AS RELATED TO CRIME AND DELINQUENCY

It would be interesting to know just who, in constitutional terms, are the delinquents and young criminals. Psychiatrists frequently call attention to the apparent inner weakness or softness of young delinquents. Dr. Franz Alexander of the Chicago Institute for Psychoanalysis has a phrase for what seems to him to be the dominant type of American criminal. He calls him the type who is "tough on the outside, soft on the inside." He goes on to say: "Briefly this is an individual who upon close investigation shows definite passive, dependent and even feminine traits, which are covered up with a more or less thin surface layer of overt toughness, aggressiveness and bravado. . . . Criminality in such individuals is to be explained as a defense phenomenon, an over-compensatory reaction on the part of the individual, by which he tries to deny and cover up his passive, dependent and feminine tendencies by criminal activities in which he displays an adventurous, enterprising spirit, toughness and aggressiveness."[6]

[6] From a paper entitled "Cultural Factors in Crime," read by Dr. Alexander before a Chicago personality study group in 1937.

Observation of young male delinquents lends support to the general soundness of Dr. Alexander's thesis. Our preliminary studies, carried on chiefly in juvenile courts and institutions in the Chicago area, indicate a distinctly higher gynandromorphy (as well as other dysplasias) in delinquent boys than in nondelinquent boys of the same age.

On the side of motivational temperament the impression gained is usually that the delinquents have a driving somatotonia which is intermittent, poorly sustained, and complicated by a hyperattentional (cerebrotonic) characteristic which is generally strong enough to give the suggestion of furtiveness. In other words, these are often sensitive, cerebrotonic boys, and a high cerebrotonia complicated by a strong somatotonic assertiveness is likely to produce a degree of bravado. But another distinguishing trait remains the one upon which Dr. Alexander has put a finger. In these youngsters there is often a feminine element and a gynandromorphic dysplasia accompanied at the behavior level by an abnormal dependence upon affection and security and upon emotional support from without. In a gynandromorphic (bisexual) boy the need for affection and support is strong but is likely to prove a source of frustration, for people as a rule give their emotional allegiance, not to males who are gynandromorphic, but to those who are strong and masculine. The *man* may prove his strength and attract favorable attention through channels of sublimation, but the *boy* often sees no way except through feats of spectacular daring and of conspicuous heroism. Yet he is effectually blocked from athletic and other masculine fulfillment by the very factor which underlies his need for glory, namely, his admixture of the soft, feminine element. In later years it is precisely this element which may supply the ferment of a maturing mind, but at the beginning it presents a harsh dilemma. The criminal escapade offers at once an identification romanticized on the pattern of Robin Hood and a chance to gain the respect of masculine contemporaries. It gives opportunity for the exercise of power over the victimized persons, often a reward in the form of sexual favor, and finally, something for nothing.

These boys are not necessarily highly gynandromorphic. The feminine aspect may not be pronounced, but we usually find it detectable somewhere. Toughness predominates, but the weakness and the clinging wonder of the little girl-boy still ride behind the forced, hard lines of an overstrained face. In addition, the moderately gynandromorphic male is confronted with a difficult sex problem. These personalities may have a singularly imperative sexual impulse. It is sometimes a weak sexual impulse, but always a highly imperative one. There is a "hair-trigger" characteristic about the sexual drive in these lower range gynandromorphs.

It is apparently from the gynandromorphic groups that most of the "peeping" and sexually exhibitionistic males are recruited. These appear to be men in whom the sexual drive is so intense and imperative, and the threshold of excitement so low, that the impulse detonates by combustion induced at long range.

If a more thorough checking confirms our impression that the young male delinquent usually shows a moderate degree of gynandromorphism, the question remains: Is this also true of the older and more hardened male criminal? Is it true of the chronic criminal? Of the man who is prone to commit some major crime in a wave of intense passion? We do not yet have the answers to these questions.

Is the gynandromorphic trait also a characteristic of the young female offender? Is she generally a person who carries some strong element of masculinity or a "hard core" somewhere in her constitution? No guess can yet be made, but this question could presumably be answered if someone were to undertake a careful, systematic study of female delinquents. Of course, the hypothesis must not be neglected that there may be several different kinds of young criminals. But the various patterns may fall into a systematic relationship once a study is begun. It may prove possible to recognize these cases and to redirect the development of a large proportion of them.

It is not an unreasonable assumption that the gifted personality and the criminal often ride the same early trails. Jung has long insisted that it is only the mind possessing a degree of both male and female qualities that is likely to achieve the highest human perspective and creative expression. But this gynandromorphic admixture appears to introduce a peculiar delicacy and a hair-trigger emotional intensity into the human machinery, and thereby to render the personality vulnerable to some pathological resolution of the universal somatotonic-cerebrotonic conflict. These notions suggest the hypothesis that the criminal act often has its inception in a wave of emotional intensification which accompanies a momentary overwhelming of the cerebrotonic by the somatotonic component of temperament. It may possibly be that the sexual orgasm itself is to be explained in terms of a similar principle, except that the violence of the storm is normally confined to physiological levels and the mental balance is left undisturbed.

As a Freudian, Dr. Alexander feels that early criminality is often related to some still earlier sociosexual frustration which has its origin in the parent-child relationship. This Freudian point of view has much in common with the one adopted here, but it is our belief that constitutional factors predispose toward these frustrations. Consequently, when the Freudians go back to "the unconscious" for their explanatory principles, it would appear that they fall one step short of arriving at territory which can be intelligibly mapped. One step more would take them back to the organic constitution. Concerning the problem of treatment, it must be admitted that the constitutional approach has little or nothing as yet to suggest. Perhaps, therefore, we need to think for a long time almost wholly in terms of diagnosis, and *to postpone the thought of treatment just as long as postponement can reasonably be tolerated.*

The question of the punishment of crime is one of the utmost delicacy. The tragedy of the matter lies in the fact that we have kept few records. We do not know what effect punishment has upon crime, because, for one thing, we do not know *whom* we have punished. The following observations and hypotheses might orient our future inquiries into this topic.

Predominant somatotonia (aggressive strength) apparently requires somatotonic treatment. War seems now inevitable because there are in the world foci where arrogant and unbridled somatotonia has been permitted to go so far that no language but the language of somatotonia can be effective. This is the old notion that he who lives by force understands only force. It may be the same with some types of criminal personality and with some types of children. Possibly there is a specific personality requiring rigid discipline, not only for its own best development, but for the security of its environment. The difficulty, of course, is that we have as yet no adequate techniques for revealing who these people are. One thing appears to be indicated, however: the premature use of force in dealing either with children or with criminals or with nations is an irremediable step. Violence sets up an irreversible chain of reverberations which then must run its course.

It is possible that certain personalities *want* physical punishment, need it, and that such punishment is necessary for their balance and happiness, like exercise for the muscles. But it may be that punishment administered to the wrong personality will change a useful and sensitive citizen into a resolute criminal. Likewise, solitary confinement, to some persons, is a pleasant episode, and to others a severe trauma. There are people who seek isolation, and there are others who find a kind of sexual ecstasy in the physical presence of masses of human beings. In its first chapter crime may be almost always a frantic bid for affection, like the whimpering of a neglected dog. Indeed, we might ask, then, is it best to whip the dog, to give him what he cries out for, or to follow some other prescription? There is no formulary answer. The answer to the problem of punishment will take us back to the elemental foundations of personality, even to morphology and anatomy, where we might discover a key to the patterning of the human constitution.

THE PROBLEM OF THE DIFFERENTIAL EDUCATION OF CHILDREN

Children of different constitutional components probably need different educational influences, just as trees which lean in different directions need to be supported from different angles. Two somewhat opposed educational philosophies are now at work. One point of view conceives of education as an effort to normalize and socialize the individual, to fit him for citizenship and for a successful adaptation to the society in which he is to live. The assumption is that the society into which the child is plunged is normal and healthy and that the chief aim of human life, therefore, is adaptation to it. The other point of view conceives of education as an effort to discover and to develop the peculiar potentialities of the individual, more or less regardless of the immediate social value of the emerging traits. The assumption is that the aim of life is not social adaptation and conformity, but maximum individual development. Most educators would probably applaud both views and affirm that what they are trying to do is combine the two. But these are sharply divergent views and the two alternatives may be highly incompatible. At this point education seems to have reached a first-class dilemma.

Clearly, in recent years we have gone far in the theory of education. Compared to older attitudes our present ones border upon enlightenment, but it might still be claimed that we do not know how to treat children. Perhaps we shall never know how to treat them until we learn to tell them apart. The child dominant in the second component is a different animal from one dominant in the first or the third component. The t-index and g-index add further to the differentiation, as do the many other factors of health and heredity and social environment. Our working hypothesis ought, perhaps, to be that a child built on one pattern needs an education different from that imposed on a child of different constitution. At least, research into this matter might prove interesting.

It is possible that some children need rigid discipline for their best development. This may be true in general of somatotonic children—those given to vigorous assertive characteristics. It may well be that a premature attempt at "reasoning" with somatotonic children is even more baffling and frustrating, and in the end more devastating to character, than is the ruthless whipping of a sensitive cerebrotonic child —one marked by sharp inhibition and hyperattentionality. Perhaps viscerotonic children—those characterized by emotional and social warmth, relaxation, gluttony—need to be handled in groups and "socialized" early in their development, whereas the cerebrotonics may need above everything else to be protected from this influence.

Watch young children in a nursery school. There are often a few vigorous-bodied somatotonics who take the lead in all enterprises, a few round, healthy-looking viscerotonics who join in with excellent fellowship, and a few little pinch-faced cerebrotonics who constitute a watchful and unsocialized periphery. These little cerebrotonics seem to want to stay on the side lines and watch. Their eyes are sharp as needlepoints and nothing seems to escape their quick attention, but they do not want to be pushed into the swim. They are under stern internal check, and they seem to want to see without being seen. Should these children be sent to nursery schools and forced into the social press with a score of other children? Should they be sent to boys' camps and girls' camps? We do not know about these things. Modern educators might want to ponder this problem. It may be that late-maturing personalities need a high degree of privacy and seclusion and protection during the formative years. It is possible that loneliness is as essential to the full development of a creature "mentally inclined" as sociability is essential to a viscerotonic or aggressive self-expression to a somatotonic youth.

This ancient argument will go on forever, education meanwhile swinging back and forth between the poles of "freedom" and "discipline" like the pendulum of a clock. At least, the argument will flourish until we can set to work and lay the foundation for an objective insight into the different kinds of children. Of course, it may turn out that, compared with the importance of environmental factors, the hypotheses proposed above are of minor moment. It would be interesting to know.

THE PROBLEM OF EARLY EMOTIONAL ENTANGLEMENTS

There is no doubt that young children are extremely sensitive to the attitudes and to the wills of adults with whom they are thrown in contact during the early years. Psychoanalysts alarm young mothers with the threat of the Oedipus complex, and the possibility of unhealthful emotional entanglement with the will of a parent is not an empty threat. But what lies behind these unhealthful entanglements? Is it simply that the oppositely sexed parent permits too close an emotional bond to become established and thereby sets a sexual snare for the emerging personality? Our own investigations have proceeded with the bias that behind these problems lie constitutional incompatibilities—not simply one principle of suppression or one formula for conflict. With this hypothesis in mind, we always find such incompatibilities, even as Freudians always find the Oedipus complex. (Perhaps in a field so complex as this the student will always find it possible to come out by the door through which he enters.)

In those instances where an adult has failed to throw off an emotional entanglement with a parent or with a grown child, and such instances are certainly common enough, analysis seems to reveal either that one or both of the principals are feeble-minded or else viciously possessive, or that their patternings of temperament are incompatible. In the latter event trauma occurs under many forms and it is perhaps as likely to happen in connection with one parent as with the other. There are often sexual manifestations and there is often sexual imagery and sexual dreaming in connection therewith, but it is entirely possible that these manifestations are incidental. Again, the generalizations reached depend much upon the investigator's bias.

Our own studies seem to indicate that a common incompatibility between adult and child is represented by a discrepancy between the two personalities with respect to the balance between the second and third motivational components (somatotonia and cerebrotonia). When, through the interplay of personalities, somatotonia becomes repressed in a child, the typical Freudian picture of repression seems to result. This kind of individual, if he carries his repression into adult life, can probably be made normally expressive and self-sufficient by psychoanalysis or, if reasonably intelligent, simply by sympathetic discussion and explanation.

Meanwhile, the opposite or complement to the typical Freudian picture of repression is also common, but it is seldom mentioned by the Freudians. This is the condition in which somatotonia has become abnormally dominant and cerebrotonia repressed. This situation appears more difficult to treat, for the methods of psychoanalysis can reach the patient only through the cerebrotonic aspect of his personality, which is now the repressed aspect. The Freudian bias is deficient in the face of such a problem, for this person does not need to be freed from inhibition. On the contrary, he apparently needs his inhibitory component freed, so that he may become more inhibited and more tentative. But probably there is no way of freeing the inhibitory component except by meeting an overly dominant somatonic component with somatotonic measures. This remedy can be applied by the adult to the child, for the adult has an overwhelming advantage over the child. The adult can establish a relatively benevolent dictatorship and can introduce into the somatotonic personality a disciplinary habit which may last through life. This procedure amounts to strengthening the inhibitory or cerebrotonic component through educational channels.

The foregoing assumptions might be tested in future research. In the meantime, it becomes evident that an important part of our present task lies in the development of methods of diagnosis. If the somatotonic child can be turned into a menace to peace through neglect of early discipline, so also, perhaps, can the cerebrotonic child be warped and made into a conscious focus of frustration and of intense suffering through application of the same discipline which would have civilized the somatotonic youngster. Clearly, before we can wisely recommend differential discipline and advise about the parent-child relationship, we must discover our children and know something of their nature. We need diagnosis. And, presumably, diagnosis could be aided by a study of the growth and development of constitutionally different children. Once adequately begun, this work should proceed on its own momentum.

CONCLUSION

Many problems have now been raised; many hypotheses have been put forth. Evidence is at hand to direct our assumptions in some fields; in others we can make only guesses. Now, in signaling these problems, our purpose was to cite some of the many questions where constitutional study is relevant. Perhaps the picture will be greatly altered as investigations accumulate. Time will tell. Perhaps enthusiasm for a method always leads to enthusiastic convictions. If so, sober research must be the corrective.

Consequently, it is to be hoped that the study whose foundation is here outlined may be pressed forward. The assumptions underlying its method are that human behavior is a function of bodily structure as well as of environmental forces, that a useful description of individuals can be made in terms of physical constitution, physiological function, and behavioral manifestations; and that description at these various levels must be coordinated through a common frame of reference. At each level in the study of the individual we can look for first-order variables or components, and then try to devise objective methods for scaling these variables in order to determine their functional interdependence. Thence we can proceed to investigate second- and third-order aspects in order to complete the description of the living human being.

At the level of morphological description we have isolated some principal variables. We have discovered their intercorrelations in human physiques, and have standardized a method by which individuals may be somatotyped with precision and reliability. Upon this foundation it may be possible to build the superstructure of a science of human behavior.

TABLES FOR SOMATOTYPING

Tables 23 through 40 represent the distributions of the means for the 76 somatotypes against 18 anthropometric criteria, including height over the cube root of weight. These distributions constitute the standardized tables from which we at present calculate somatotypes anthropometrically. They are standardized to the extent that 4,000 cases represent an adequate sampling. This standardization holds good only for 18-year-old boys or, for practical purposes, for boys from 16 to 20, inclusive. We hope later to publish similar standardized tables for later age groups, possibly taken at five-year intervals, and for earlier age groups, perhaps taken at two-year intervals. Likewise we shall presumably standardize the technique in the same manner for the somatotyping of women.

Each of these tables is arranged, for convenience, as a progression of the third component, and it can be seen that every one of the 18 anthropometric criteria correlates highly with that component. Height over the cube root of weight shows a positive correlation with ectomorphy, whereas each of the diameter measurements is negatively correlated with ectomorphy. From such a series of tables it is clear that what the problem of somatotyping amounts to, at the anthropometric level, is essentially the development of an accurate method for measuring ectomorphy, together with the establishment of a number of secondary aids for distinguishing between endomorphy and mesomorphy.

Note: When the observed ratio-index (obtained from a photograph) falls exactly midway between two of the ratio-indices used for entering tables 23 to 40, use the next higher ratio-index. Otherwise use the one nearest the observed value.

Height over the cube root of weight[1] (Table 23), provides a

---

[1] The ratio height over cube root of weight is one commonly used. Its

valuable initial indication of the approximate somatotype for the body as a whole. This is simply one variation of the "ponderal index," or index of bodily mass, which has long been used in attempts at bodily classification. Yet when used alone this is by no means an infallible index, for weight is subject to relatively great fluctuation in the heavier somatotypes, and the value of any index which includes weight must depend upon a knowledge of the state of nutrition of the individual concerned. In dealing with 18-year-old college students, height over the cube root of weight has a relatively high degree of dependability (see p. 98), for sharp nutritional deviations are rare in this group, and also the investigator is dealing with physiques which have not yet developed their full endomorphic blossoming.

In later life, when the bodies have grown heavier and have revealed the full endomorphic blossom, accurate somatotyping is generally much easier, for then the task is like that of recognizing the fully elaborated flower as compared with the earlier recognition of the unfolding bud. But in later life weight itself becomes a less dependable indication, for then it is subject to wider fluctuation than in youth. In an inquiry into the physiological history of 1,000 of the students in our series, we found that in only 32 cases, or about 3 per cent, had the individual at one time weighed 10 pounds more than he weighed at the time of being photographed. This fact indicates that height over the cube root of weight is a relatively reliable measure of the somatotype at 18, but we believe that it becomes somewhat less reliable in the later decades of life. When we standardize the technique for somatotyping at later age levels, we shall probably attach less weight to this criterion than has been the case in the study of 18-year-old subjects.

Table 23a gives, for each somatotype, the range and some of the standard deviations of the ratio-index for height over cube

rationale is that, if the body is assumed to be of constant density, the cube root of weight would yield a value proportional to the length of the side of a cube. equal to the body in volume. Division of this value into an individual's height can therefore be regarded as the division of a length by a length to yield a dimensionless ratio multiplied by a constant. The constant itself is not dimensionless, however. For a discussion of this and other anthropometric indices see McCloy, C. H. Appraising physical status and the selection of measurements. *Univ. Ia. Studies Child Welf.*, 1936, vol. 12, no. 2.

TABLE 23
Ht./Cube Root of Weight

Ratio-index	Somatotypes						
11.2	711						
11.3							
11.4	731						
11.5	721						
11.6							
11.7	641	712					
11.8							
11.9							
12.0	551, 631						
12.1	371, 461						
12.2	621	632					
12.3	271, 541	622					
12.4	361	542					
12.5	171	612	623				
12.6	261, 451	362	613				
12.7		172, 452, 532	543				
12.8		262, 352, 522					
12.9		162, 442	453, 533				
13.0		252	263, 353, 523	534			
13.1			163, 443	354, 524			
13.2			253, 343, 433	444			
13.3				434, 514			
13.4				254, 344, 424			
13.5				154, 244, 334	435, 515		
13.6					345, 425		
13.7					245, 335, 415		
13.8					235, 325		
13.9					145, 225	326	
14.0						236, 316	
14.1						136, 226	
14.2						216	
14.3						126	
14.4							217
14.5							127
14.6							
14.7							
14.8							117

Table 23A

This table shows, for a population of 4,000 men, the number of cases falling within each somatotype, together with their mean heights and weights. The ratio of height to cube root of weight, together with the range and some of the standard deviations of this ratio, is also shown. (Where only a few cases are available, the standard deviations are omitted.)

Somatotype	Incidence per 4000	Incidence per 1000 (approx.)	Mean Height Ins.	Mean Height Cms.	Mean Weight Lbs.	Mean Weight Kgs.	Mean Ht./∛Wt. English	Mean Ht./∛Wt. Metric	Range of Ht./∛Wt. English	Standard Deviation of Ht./∛Wt.
117....	19	5	71.2	(181.0)	112	(50.8)	14.8	(48.8)	14.6–15.3	.13
126....	29	7	71.5	(181.5)	125	(56.7)	14.3	(47.1)	14.0–14.5	.12
127....	20	5	72.2	(183.5)	124	(56.2)	14.5	(48.0)	14.2–14.8	.13
136....	7	2	70.9	(180.0)	128	(58.1)	14.1	(46.6)	13.9–14.3	
145....	22	6	70.3	(178.5)	130	(59.0)	13.9	(45.9)	13.7–14.1	
154....	21	5	69.3	(176.0)	136	(61.7)	13.5	(44.5)	13.3–13.8	
162....	24	6	67.9	(172.5)	147	(66.7)	12.9	(42.6)	12.7–13.1	
163....	17	4	69.6	(177.0)	151	(68.5)	13.1	(43.2)	12.8–13.4	
171....	20	5	68.1	(173.0)	163	(73.9)	12.5	(41.2)	12.3–12.7	
172....	21	5	70.2	(178.5)	169	(76.7)	12.7	(42.0)	12.5–13.0	
216....	11	3	69.3	(176.0)	117	(53.1)	14.2	(46.8)	14.0–14.4	
217....	5	1	70.6	(179.5)	118	(53.5)	14.4	(47.6)	14.3–14.6	
225....	78	20	69.0	(175.5)	123	(55.8)	13.9	(45.9)	13.6–14.1	
226....	101	25	72.0	(183.0)	133	(60.3)	14.1	(46.6)	13.9–14.3	.11
235..:.	181	45	70.2	(178.5)	132	(59.9)	13.8	(45.6)	13.6–14.0	.10
236....	20	5	71.7	(182.0)	135	(61.2)	14.0	(46.3)	13.8–14.1	
244....	167	42	68.6	(174.0)	131	(59.4)	13.5	(44.6)	13.3–13.7	.11
245....	56	14	70.5	(179.0)	137	(62.1)	13.7	(45.2)	13.5–13.8	
252....	33	8	66.1	(168.0)	131	(59.4)	13.0	(43.0)	12.7–13.2	
253....	133	33	68.2	(173.0)	139	(63.0)	13.2	(43.6)	13.0–13.4	.10
254....	63	16	70.5	(179.0)	146	(66.2)	13.4	(44.3)	13.2–13.6	
261....	27	7	66.0	(167.5)	144	(65.3)	12.6	(41.6)	12.4–12.8	
262....	91	23	68.1	(173.0)	151	(68.5)	12.8	(42.3)	12.5–13.0	
263....	25	6	70.4	(179.0)	160	(72.6)	13.0	(42.9)	12.7–13.2	
271....	13	3	66.8	(169.5)	161	(73.0)	12.3	(40.6)	12.2–12.4	
316....	5	1	69.4	(176.5)	123	(55.8)	14.0	(46.2)	13.9–14.2	
325....	84	21	69.3	(176.0)	127	(57.6)	13.8	(45.6)	13.6–14.0	
326....	12	3	71.5	(181.5)	136	(61.7)	13.9	(45.9)	13.7–14.0	
334....	201	50	68.5	(174.0)	131	(59.4)	13.5	(44.6)	13.2–13.8	.12
335....	118	30	70.4	(179.0)	136	(61.7)	13.7	(45.2)	13.5–13.9	.10
343....	189	47	67.8	(172.0)	136	(61.7)	13.2	(43.6)	13.0–13.4	.11
344....	230	58	69.1	(175.5)	138	(62.6)	13.4	(44.2)	13.2–13.6	.08
345....	33	8	71.4	(181.5)	146	(66.2)	13.6	(44.9)	13.4–13.8	
352....	92	23	67.1	(170.5)	144	(65.3)	12.8	(42.3)	12.6–13.1	
353....	197	49	68.8	(175.0)	149	(67.6)	13.0	(42.9)	12.8–13.2	.08
354....	52	13	71.1	(180.5)	160	(72.6)	13.1	(43.3)	12.9–13.2	
361....	24	6	66.5	(169.0)	155	(70.3)	12.4	(41.0)	12.3–12.5	
362....	37	9	68.3	(173.5)	160	(72.6)	12.6	(41.6)	12.5–12.8	
371....	2	0.5	66.8	(169.5)	169	(76.7)	12.1	(40.0)	12.1–12.2	
415....	7	2	69.8	(177.5)	133	(60.3)	13.7	(45.2)	13.5–13.8	
424....	53	13	67.9	(172.5)	131	(59.4)	13.4	(44.2)	13.3–13.6	
425....	30	8	69.7	(177.0)	136	(61.7)	13.6	(44.8)	13.5–13.8	
433....	97	24	67.3	(171.0)	133	(60.3)	13.2	(43.6)	13.0–13.4	
434....	139	35	69.1	(175.5)	141	(64.0)	13.3	(43.9)	13.1–13.4	.09
435....	24	6	70.6	(179.5)	143	(64.9)	13.5	(44.6)	13.3–13.7	
442....	117	29	66.8	(169.5)	140	(63.5)	12.9	(42.5)	12.7–13.1	.09

TABLE 23A (*cont'd*)

So-mato-type	In-ci-dence per 4000	Inci-dence per 1000 (ap-prox.)	Mean Height Ins.	Mean Height Cms.	Mean Weight Lbs.	Mean Weight Kgs.	Mean Ht./∛Wt. Eng-lish	Mean Ht./∛Wt. Metric	Range of Ht./∛Wt. English	Standard Devia-tion of Ht./∛Wt.
443....	225	56	68.3	(173.5)	143	(64.9)	13.1	(43.2)	12.9–13.2	.08
444....	163	41	69.9	(177.5)	149	(67.6)	13.2	(43.6)	13.0–13.4	.09
451....	13	3	65.3	(166.0)	140	(63.5)	12.6	(41.6)	12.4–12.8	
452....	92	23	67.8	(172.0)	153	(69.4)	12.7	(41.9)	12.5–12.8	
453....	40	10	69.8	(177.5)	159	(72.1)	12.9	(42.6)	12.7–13.1	
461....	4	1	67.1	(170.5)	171	(77.6)	12.1	(40.0)	12.0–12.2	
514....	4	1	69.0	(175.5)	140	(63.5)	13.3	(43.9)	13.2–13.3	
515....	1	0.25	70.3	(178.5)	142	(64.4)	13.5	(44.5)	13.5	
522....	15	4	65.4	(166.0)	134	(60.8)	12.8	(42.3)	12.7–13.0	
523....	21	5	66.9	(170.0)	136	(61.7)	13.0	(43.0)	12.9–13.1	
524....	20	5	68.4	(173.5)	144	(65.3)	13.1	(43.2)	12.9–13.3	
532....	71	18	67.0	(170.0)	147	(66.7)	12.7	(42.0)	12.5–12.9	
533....	94	24	68.2	(173.0)	149	(67.6)	12.9	(42.5)	12.7–13.1	.10
534....	49	12	69.4	(176.5)	153	(69.4)	13.0	(42.9)	12.8–13.2	
541....	13	3	65.6	(166.5)	153	(69.4)	12.3	(40.6)	12.2–12.4	
542....	56	14	67.6	(171.5)	162	(73.5)	12.4	(41.0)	12.3–12.6	
543....	31	8	69.0	(175.5)	161	(73.0)	12.7	(42.0)	12.5–12.9	
551....	5	1	66.9	(170.0)	174	(78.9)	12.0	(39.6)	11.9–12.1	
612....	2	0.5	66.9	(170.0)	154	(69.9)	12.5	(41.3)	12.4–12.5	
613....	7	2	68.8	(175.0)	164	(74.4)	12.6	(41.6)	12.4–12.7	
621....	13	3	65.6	(166.5)	156	(70.8)	12.2	(40.3)	12.0–12.3	
622....	21	5	68.2	(173.0)	172	(78.0)	12.3	(40.5)	12.1–12.4	.11
623....	17	4	69.1	(175.5)	170	(77.1)	12.5	(41.2)	12.4–12.7	
631....	16	4	67.5	(171.5)	179	(81.2)	12.0	(39.6)	11.8–12.2	
632....	25	6	69.8	(177.5)	188	(85.3)	12.2	(40.3)	12.0–12.3	.11
641....	3	0.75	67.9	(172.5)	196	(88.9)	11.7	(38.6)	11.7–11.8	
711....	8	2	66.8	(169.5)	213	(96.6)	11.2	(37.0)	10.8–11.4	
712....	11	3	67.8	(172.0)	195	(88.5)	11.7	(38.7)	11.5–11.9	
721....	9	2	68.7	(174.5)	213	(96.6)	11.5	(38.0)	11.3–11.7	
731....	4	1	69.7	(177.0)	228	(103.4)	11.4	(37.7)	11.2–11.6	

root of weight. A similar table could be presented in connection with each of the other tables in this appendix, but space does not permit. In general, the standard deviations for the other ratio-indices are larger than those for height over cube root of weight.

Facial-breadth-one (Table 24) is an approximate, although not an exact correlate of cephalic breadth. Against it the somatotypes show a reasonable distribution. This index falls consistently as the third component increases, but its range is relatively narrow. Because the differentiation on the head and face between bone and muscle, on the one hand, and fat, on the other, is anthropo-metrically difficult, we have not been able to find facial measurements which yield a sharp discrimination between the first

TABLE 24

FB$_1$/Ht.

Ratio-index	Somatotypes						
7.2							117
7.3							127
7.4							
7.5							217
7.6						126	
7.7						136, 216	
7.8						226, 316	
7.9					145, 225	236, 326	
8.0					235, 245		
8.1				154, 244	415, 325, 335		
8.2				424, 344, 334	425, 345		
8.3			163, 253	434, 254, 514	435, 515		
8.4		162	263, 343, 433	354, 444, 524			
8.5		252, 172	353, 523, 443	534			
8.6	171, 261	262, 352, 442	453, 533, 613				
8.7	361, 451	362, 452, 522	543, 623				
8.8	271, 541, 621	532, 612, 622					
8.9	371, 631, 461	542, 632, 712					
9.0	551, 731						
9.1	641, 721						
9.2	711						

and second components. In general, however, the first component carries greater breadth than the second, and with the third held constant, both facial-breadth measurements are distinctly useful in arriving at the somatotype for the first area. FB$_1$ increases with the second component, increases more sharply with the first component, and decreases with the third component.

Facial-breadth-two (Table 25) behaves in nearly the same manner as FB$_1$. Its principal value is that of serving as a check on the reliability of the indication given by the latter. At one time we used four of these facial-breadth measurements, but we now feel that for practical purposes two are sufficient. FB$_2$ has a slightly smaller range than FB$_1$, and falls a little more sharply with increase in the third component. It does not, however, yield

TABLE 25

FB$_2$/Ht.

Ratio-index	Somatotypes					
6.8						117
6.9						217
7.0						127
7.1						226, 216, 126
7.2					145	326, 316, 136
7.3				154	225, 235, 325, 245	236
7.4				244, 254, 334	335, 345, 415	
7.5			163	344, 424, 434	425, 435, 515	
7.6			253, 263, 343	444, 514, 524		
7.7		162, 252	353, 433, 443	354, 534		
7.8		262, 352, 442	523, 533, 613			
7.9	261	172, 362, 452	453, 543			
8.0	171	522, 532, 612	623			
8.1	361, 451	542, 622				
8.2	271, 621	632				
8.3	461, 541, 631	712				
8.4	371, 551, 731					
8.5	641, 721					
8.6	711					

as much differentiation between the first two components. That is to say, endomorphy widens the central area of the face (FB$_1$) distinctly more than does mesomorphy, but in the lower area of the face (FB$_2$) these two components exert much the same anthropometric effect. FB$_2$ approximates the bigonial measurement, which, of course, is sharply increased by a widening of the jaw, and mesomorphy means a widening and strengthening of all bony structures. In the lower area of the face mesomorphy tends to catch up with endomorphy, in an anthropometric sense, and actually does so at the lower values of these two components, but at the higher values even the wide jaw of high mesomorphy is no anthropometric match for the spreading face of the endomorph.

From the point of view of the anthropologist, who is accustomed to numerous and precise measurements made on the head, the two measurements used here are perhaps crude and inadequate. But for the purpose of somatotyping they have proved reasonably adequate.

TABLE 26

NTap/Ht.

Ratio-index	Somatotypes					
5.3						117
5.4						127
5.5					126, 216	217
5.6					226, 316, 326	
5.7					136, 236	
5.8				225		
5.9			334, 424	145, 325, 415		
6.0			154, 244, 434, 514	235, 335, 515		
6.1		433	254, 344, 524	245, 425, 435		
6.2		253, 343	444, 534	345		
6.3	252	163, 443, 523	354			
6.4	162, 442, 522	353, 533				
6.5	172, 262	263, 613				
6.6	171, 261	352, 532, 612	453, 543, 623			
6.7	361, 451	362, 452, 622				
6.8	271, 541, 621	542				
6.9	461, 551, 631	632, 712				
7.0	371					
7.1	641, 721					
7.2	731					
7.3	711					

Neck-thickness-anteroposterior (Table 26) and *neck-thickness-transverse* (Table 27) need to be considered together. Both yield excellent correlation with the third component, and when examined together they discriminate well between the first and second. When the first component is high, or predominant over the second, the two diameters of the neck approach one another. That is to say, the anteroposterior diameter tends to rise and to catch up with the transverse diameter. When the second compo-

TABLE 27

NTt/Ht.

Ratio-Index	Somatotypes						
5.6							117, 217
5.7							
5.8						216, 316	127
5.9					415	126, 226	
6.0				514	225, 325, 515	136, 326	
6.1				424, 524	145, 235, 335, 425	236	
6.2				334	245, 435		
6.3			523	244, 434, 534	345		
6.4			343, 433, 533	154, 344, 444			
6.5			253, 443, 613	254			
6.6		522	163, 353, 623	354			
6.7		532, 612	263, 543				
6.8		252, 442, 622	453				
6.9	621	162, 352, 542					
7.0	631	262, 452, 632, 712					
7.1	261, 541	172, 362					
7.2	171, 361, 451						
7.3	271, 551, 641						
7.4	461, 711						
7.5	371, 721						
7.6	731						

nent is high, or predominant over the first, the transverse diameter increases and leaves the other diameter far behind.

The angle formed by the jaw with the neck as seen in profile, constitutes one of the most dependable indications of the first component to be found in the body. When endomorphy is low, this angle is sharp at the apex. As endomorphy rises, the sharpness of the angle disappears and is replaced by a curving line, which in cases of the endomorphic 7 sometimes becomes almost a straight line from the chin to the sternoclavicular junction. We have at times used scaled gradations of this angle as an aid in the anthroposcopic determination of endomorphy.

The six trunk measurements we shall here consider as a group, although they belong to regions II and IV. Every one of them yields a good correlation with the third component, and when all six are examined together the differentiation between the other two components can be made with certainty for the second and fourth regions. In *trunk-thickness-one* (Table 29) endomorphy

TABLE 28

$TB_1/Ht.$

Ratio-index	Somatotypes						
16.8							117, 217
17.2						216, 316	127
17.6					415	126, 226, 326	
18.0				514	225, 325, 425, 515	136, 236	
18.4				424, 524	145, 235, 245, 335, 435		
18.8			433, 523	244, 334	345		
19.2		522	343, 613	344, 434, 534			
19.6		442, 612	253, 443, 533	154, 254, 444			
20.0		252, 532, 542, 622, 712	163, 353, 543, 623	354			
20.4	541, 621	162, 352, 452, 632	263, 453				
20.8	451, 631	262, 362					
21.2	261, 551	172					
21.6	171, 361, 641, 711						
22.0	271, 721						
22.4	371, 461						
22.8	731						

clearly surpasses mesomorphy anthropometrically, except at the extremely high levels, and in *trunk-breadth-one* (Table 28) this relationship is sharply reversed. In the upper chest, the relative balancing between the two massive components can ordinarily be seen accurately and clearly, for all values of ectomorphy. In *trunk-breadth-two* (Table 30) the spreading tendency of the first component widens the waist transversely as well as anteroposteriorly, while the muscular development of the second component tends to hold in and to constrict the soft tissues of the waist. Therefore, endomorphy surpasses mesomorphy anthropometri·

TABLE 29

TT$_1$/Ht.

Ratio-index	Somatotypes						
9.4							117
9.8							217, 127
10.2					415	126, 216, 136, 226	
10.6				514	145, 225, 235, 245	316, 326, 236	
11.0					154, 244, 334, 424, 524	325, 335, 515	
11.4			163, 343, 433, 523	254, 344, 434, 444	345, 425, 435		
11.8		162, 252, 442	253, 263, 353, 443, 533, 613	354, 534			
12.2	171, 261	172, 262, 352, 362, 452, 522, 532	453, 543, 623				
12.6	271, 361, 451, 541	542, 612, 622					
13.0	371, 461, 551, 621	632					
13.4	631	712					
13.8	641, 711						
14.2	721						
14.6	731						

cally in this measurement, but the contrast between these two influences is brought out far more sharply and dramatically in *trunk-thickness-two* (Table 34). In this diameter, a high endomorphy produces such remarkable expansion that this measurement may be more than double the mean found in extreme ectomorphy, and the 171 is found at a point anthropometrically only about one-third of the way along the progression from the 117 to the 711. Also, we see that in this measurement the 711 far surpasses the 731, which is in most respects the most massive of somatotypes. This is due to the fact that the 731 has sufficient musculature to hold in his enormous abdomen, while the abdomen of the 711 protrudes unimpededly.

In *trunk-breadth-three* (Table 35) and *trunk-thickness-three* (Table 36) we see about the same relationship that holds at the middle trunk levels, although at these lowest trunk levels the

TABLE 30

TB$_2$/Ht.

Ratio-index	Somatotypes						
12.2							117
12.6							127
13.0						126, 136	217
13.4					145	216, 226, 236	
13.8				154, 244	225, 235	316, 326	
14.2			163	254, 334, 344	245, 325, 415		
14.6		162, 252	253, 343	424, 434, 514	335, 345, 425		
15.0		262, 352, 442, 522	263, 353, 433, 443	354, 444, 524	435, 515		
15.4	261	172, 362, 452, 532	453, 523, 533	534			
15.8	171, 361	542	543				
16.2	271, 451	612	613				
16.6	371, 541, 621	622	623				
17.0	461, 551, 631	632					
17.4	641						
17.8		712					
18.2	721						
18.6	731						
19.0							
19.4	711						

spreading tendency of endomorphy is not quite so pronounced. The pelvic girdle holds it back a little.

It is as though the trunk were like a football. The first component represents the inflational pressure exerted upon the inner bladder, and the second component is the restrictive and shaping influence exerted by the outer casing, which in the trunk is really the soma. The third component represents counterpressure from the outside. The human trunk as a whole varies from the flat narrowness of ectomorphy, through the wide thick trunks of the mesomorphs, to the barrel-shaped or football-shaped trunk of endomorphy. The six trunk measurements taken as a group constitute a nearly perfect index of this variation in shape, and also an index of the relative predominances of the thoracic and abdominal cavities. Thoracic predominance, where the whole trunk

TABLE 31

ATU/Ht.

Ratio-index	Somatotypes						
4.2							117
4.4							217
4.6						216	127
4.8						126, 136	
5.0					225	316, 226	
5.2					325	236, 326	
5.4				334, 424	145, 235, 335, 415		
5.6				244, 434	245, 345, 425, 515		
5.8			433	154, 344	435		
6.0			253, 343	254, 444			
6.2		442, 252	163, 443, 523	514, 524			
6.4		352	353, 533	354, 534			
6.6	451	162, 522	263, 613				
6.8	261	262, 452, 532	453, 543				
7.0	171, 361, 541	172, 362, 542	623				
7.2	271, 461, 551	612, 622					
7.4	371, 621	632					
7.6	631						
7.8	641						
8.0		712					
8.2	711						
8.4	721						
8.6	731						

is fairly massive, is a clear indication of mesomorphy. Abdominal predominance indicates endomorphy.

An explanatory note on the measurement of the TT_1 is in order. Theoretically this is a somewhat spurious measurement, for it is taken at a level where some of the scapula is necessarily included, and in high ectomorphy the measurement is bound to be more or less influenced by the angle at which the scapula lies. Yet the remarkable thinness of the ectomorphic chest at this level seems to more than compensate for the difficulty, and the distribution of the somatotypes against this measurement

TABLE 32

ATL$_1$/Ht.

Ratio-index	Somatotypes						
4.0							117, 217
4.1							
4.2						216, 316	127
4.3					225, 415, 515	126, 226, 326	
4.4					325, 425	136, 236	
4.5				424, 514, 524	145, 235, 335, 435		
4.6				334, 434, 534	245, 345		
4.7			523	244, 344, 444			
4.8			433, 533	154, 254			
4.9		522	343, 443, 613	354			
5.0		252, 442, 532, 612	253, 353, 543, 623				
5.1		162, 352, 542, 622	163, 453				
5.2	541	262, 362, 452	263				
5.3	451, 621, 631	172, 632					
5.4	261, 361, 551, 641	712					
5.5	171, 271, 461						
5.6	371, 711						
5.7	721						
5.8	731						

(Table 29) is as orderly and useful as that of any of the other trunk measurements. TT$_1$ is a difficult and laborious measurement to take on the living body, but it is easy enough to measure it on film.

TT$_2$ is another measurement which is theoretically unsatisfactory, but practically of considerable value. This measurement is influenced both by respiration and by the degree to which the individual compresses the abdomen by contraction of the abdominal muscles. To meet these difficulties, the profile picture is always taken with the subject in what we call relaxed expiration, i.e., unforced expiration. Also, the assistant photographer tries, in each case, to induce the subject to relax the abdomen. This latter endeavor is not always highly successful, however,

TABLE 33

ATL$_2$/Ht.

Ratio-index	Somatotypes						
3.1							
3.2							117, 217
3.3						216, 316	127
3.4					225, 325, 415, 515	126, 226, 326	
3.5				514	235, 335, 425, 435	136, 236	
3.6				334, 424, 524	145, 245, 345		
3.7			523, 613	244, 344, 434, 444, 534			
3.8		522	433, 533, 623	154, 254, 354			
3.9		612, 532	253, 343, 353, 443, 543				
4.0	621	252, 352, 442, 542, 622	163, 263, 453				
4.1	541, 631	162, 262, 452, 632, 712					
4.2	261, 451, 641	172, 362					
4.3	171, 361, 551, 711						
4.4	271, 461						
4.5	371, 721						
4.6	731						

and we have found it necessary to make peace with a constant source of potential error in the TT$_2$ measurement. There are always a few cases in a series of new pictures where the abdomen is obviously contracted. But the unrelaxable individuals are almost invariably ectomorphs who have an extremely low TT$_2$ anyhow. In these instances we either omit the TT$_2$ measurement or mark it with a question mark to indicate its possibly spurious character. The technique of arriving at the somatotype (see chapter IV) is such as to tolerate a fairly high degree of elasticity in the individual anthropometric measurements of the trunk.

The three arm measurements are to be considered as a group, for together they constitute a reliable index of the three components in the third region. All three of these show a high negative correlation with ectomorphy. *Arm-thickness-upper* (Table

TABLE 34

TT$_2$/Ht.

Ratio-index	Somatotypes						
8.8							117
9.2						126	127
9.6					145	136, 216, 226	217
10.0				154, 244	225, 235, 245	236, 316, 326	
10.4			163, 253	254, 334, 344, 424	325, 335, 345		
10.8		162, 252	263, 343, 353, 433, 443	354, 434, 444	415, 425, 435		
11.2		172, 262, 352, 442	453, 523, 533	514, 524, 534	515		
11.6	261, 171	362, 452, 522	543				
12.0	271, 361, 451	532, 542	623				
12.4	371, 541	632	613				
12.8	461, 551, 621	622					
13.2	631	612					
13.6							
14.0	641						
14.4							
14.8	731	712					
15.2	721						
15.6							
16.0							
16.4							
16.8	711						

31) increases so markedly with endomorphy that when the first component is maximal this measurement exceeds, by more than a factor of two, the diameter found in extreme ectomorphy. The "hamming," or inverted-pyramid enlargement, of the upper arm is one of the most consistent and striking features associated with strength in the first component. This characteristic is entirely absent in mesomorphy, although when the second component is high the arm is enlarged throughout its entire length. Thus, when mesomorphy predominates, the measurements *arm-thickness-lower-one* and *arm-thickness-lower-two* (Tables 32 and 33) increase and tend to keep pace with *arm-*

TABLE 35

TB$_3$/Ht.

Ratio-Index	Somatotypes						
16.6							117, 127
17.0							
17.4						126, 136	217
17.8					145, 225, 235	216, 226, 236	
18.2				154, 244, 334	245, 325, 335, 345	316, 326	
18.6			163, 253, 343	254, 344, 354, 424	415, 425		
19.0		162, 172, 252, 262	263, 353, 433, 443	434, 444, 514	435, 515		
19.4	261, 171	352, 362, 442	453, 523, 533	524, 534			
19.8	271, 361, 451	452, 522, 532	543, 623				
20.2	371, 461	542, 612	613				
20.6	541, 621	622, 632					
21.0	551, 631						
21.4	641	712					
21.8	721						
22.2	731						
23.0	711						

thickness-upper. When endomorphy predominates, ATU tends to exceed both ATL$_1$ and ATL$_2$, especially the latter.

The four leg measurements serve so accurately to bracket the fifth regional somatotype that either of the two lower leg measurements could be dropped and the remaining three would be sufficient for most practical purposes. (Until very recently, we took a fourth arm measurement on all pictures—ATL$_3$, or the minimum transverse wrist measurement—but for purposes of standardization we dropped it because it is not needed for an adequate bracketing of the third regional somatotype.)

The correlation between LTL$_1$ (Table 39) and the third component in the fifth region, is about 0.85. When the first component is high, we see in the thigh the same "ham" formation that characterizes the upper arm. LTU$_1$ (Table 37) is a sensitive index of this phenomenon, and this measurement picks up even

TABLE 36

$TT_3/Ht.$

Ratio-index	Somatotypes						
10.4							117
10.8							127
11.2						126	217
11.6					145	136, 216, 226	
12.0				154, 244	225, 235, 245	236, 316, 326	
12.4			163	334, 424	325, 335, 415		
12.8		162, 252	253, 343	254, 344, 434	345, 425, 435		
13.2		172, 262, 352, 442	263, 353, 433, 443	354, 444, 514	515		
13.6	171, 261	362, 452	453, 523, 533	524, 534			
14.0	271, 361, 451	522, 532	543, 623				
14.4	371, 541	542	613				
14.8	621, 631	612					
15.2	461, 551	622, 632					
15.6	641						
16.0		712					
16.4	721						
16.8	731						
17.2	711						

the earliest beginnings of endomorphy. The first component is likely to make its first localized appearance in a body around the subgluteal folds and about the groins. Even endomorphy 2 may be fairly conspicuous in these regions, if not concealed by a high mesomorphy. A fairly high LTU_1 measurement, unaccompanied by proportionately high diameters lower in the legs, is a certain indication of endomorphic predominance. Conversely, fairly high measurements LTU_2 (Table 38) and LTL_1, unaccompanied by a disproportionately high LTU_1, are indicators of predominant mesomorphy. The level at which LTL_1 is taken on the leg is itself a fairly good index of the relative strengths of the first two components. This measurement is simply the maximum transverse diameter of the calf of the leg. When mesomorphy predominates over endomorphy the maximum thickness is low on the leg, resulting from the "bellying" of the

TABLE 37·

LTU₁/Ht.

Ratio-index	Somatotypes						
8.0							117, 127
8.4							
8.8						126, 226	217
9.2					145, 225, 235	136, 216, 236	
9.6				154, 244	245, 325, 335	326, 316	
10.0			163, 253, 343	254, 334, 344, 424	345, 415, 425		
10.4		162, 252, 442	263, 353, 433	354, 434, 444	435		
10.8	261	262, 352, 522	443, 523	514, 524, 534	515		
11.2	171, 361, 451	172, 362, 452, 532	453, 533				
11.6	271, 461	542, 612	543				
12.0	371, 541	622	613, 623				
12.4	551, 621	632					
12.8	631						
13.2	641	712					
13.6	721						
14.0	711						
14.4	731						

lower part of the gastrocnemius muscle. As endomorphy increases, and comes to dominate in the leg, the gastrocnemius loses its shapeliness and tends to maintain its diameter only in the proximal segment. The lower legs then take on a spindling appearance or, in cases of high endomorphy, a "piano-leg" formation. This relationship between the first and second components in the leg, and also to a less conspicuous degree in the arm, is maintained almost independently of the strength of the third component. It holds at both high and low levels of ectomorphy. When the first component predominates in the lower leg, the calf shows the "feminine" outer curve, and the inner curve tends to be lost.

Leg-thickness-lower-two (Table 40) also yields a high correlation with the third component. Kretschmer, in his original description of the "pyknic" type, characterized it as having slender ankles and wrists. This we have not found to be the case, except where endomorphy occurs in combination with high ectomorphy

Table 38

LTU₂/Ht.

Ratio-index	Somatotypes						
6.0							117
6.2							217, 127
6.4						126, 216	
6.6					225	136, 226, 316	
6.8				334	145, 235, 325, 415	236, 326	
7.0				154, 244, 344, 424	245, 335, 425, 515		
7.2			163, 253, 343	254, 434, 514	345, 435		
7.4		162, 252	433, 523	444, 524			
7.6		352, 442	263, 353, 443	354, 534			
7.8	261	172, 262, 452, 522	453, 533				
8.0	361, 451	362, 532, 612	543, 613				
8.2	171, 461, 541	542, 622	623				
8.4	271, 551, 621	632, 712					
8.6	371, 631						
8.8	641, 711						
9.0	721						
9.2	731						

and a locally low mesomorphy. Endomorphs often look as though they had slender ankles, because of the "hamming" above. Relative to their enormous thighs, their ankles are actually small, but anthropometrically, when 4,000 cases are considered, there is no statistical contradiction of the positive correlation between ankle thickness and endomorphy. There is perhaps, however, a racial justification for the persistence of this idea of Kretschmer's. We have made no statistical study of Jewish women, but have observed many individual cases of high endomorphy combined with small extremities. It may be that there has long been a selective factor at work in this highly urban stock, until a local ectomorphic dysplasia of the distal extremities of both arms and legs has become established as a congenitally determined characteristic. It is probable, however, that if such a characteristic is present, it will be found to occur in a rather

TABLE 39

LTL₁/Ht.

Ratio-index	Somatotypes						
5.0							117, 217
5.2							
5.4						216, 316	127
5.6						126, 226, 326	
5.8					225, 325, 415	136, 236	
6.0					235, 335, 425		
6.2				244, 334, 424	145, 245, 435, 515		
6.4			433	154, 344, 434, 514	345		
6.6		252	253, 343, 443, 523	254, 444, 524, 534			
6.8		162, 352, 442, 522	163, 263, 353, 453, 533	354			
7.0	261	172, 262, 532, 612	543, 613, 623				
7.2	171, 361, 541, 621	362, 452, 542, 622					
7.4	271, 451, 551, 631	632, 712					
7.6	371, 461, 641, 711						
7.8	721						
8.0	731						

small group when a statistical analysis of the matter is made. Possibly it is only aristocratic Jewish women who have these small extremities. In any case, it should be remembered that endomorphic bones are relatively small.

In a number of isolated instances we have found a sharply localized ectomorphic dysplasia in the distal segments of the arms and legs of the college population studied. But this trait has not been confined to any racial group, and it is no more common than a half dozen other recurrent dysplasias which we have studied. A dysplasia actually more common, in our material, is one which involves a mesomorphic increment in the legs, producing the sturdy lower extremities which some anthropologists have called "New England legs." Such legs are supposed to be especially common on the campuses of New

TABLE 40

LTL$_2$/Ht.

Ratio-index	Somatotypes				
3.0					117
3.1				126, 216	127, 217
3.2			225	226, 316, 326	
3.3			154, 244	145, 235, 325, 415	136, 236
3.4		163	254, 334, 424, 514	245, 335, 425, 515	
3.5	162		253, 263, 343, 433, 523	344, 354, 434, 524	345, 435
3.6		172, 252, 522, 532	353, 443, 533, 543, 613	444, 534	
3.7	261, 541	262, 352, 442, 542	453, 623		
3.8	171, 361, 451	362, 452, 612, 622			
3.9	271, 551, 621	632			
4.0	461, 631	712			
4.1	371, 641				
4.2	711, 721				
4.3	731				

England women's colleges. Perhaps this impression results from the fact that the female leg is more closely observed than the male leg.

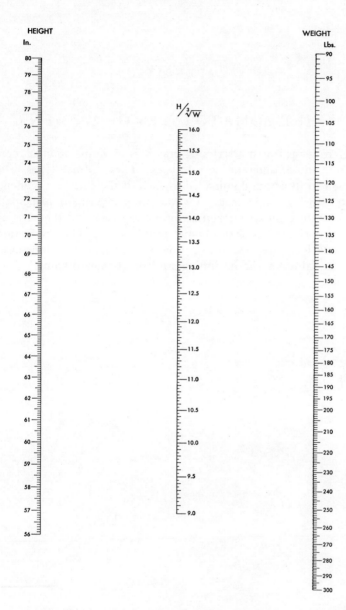

Fig. 90. Nomograph for determining height over cube root of weight when height and weight are known.

NINE SOMATOTYPES OF WOMEN

Here is presented a series of drawings of young women representing nine different somatotypes. These somatotypes were chosen to illustrate dominance in each of the three components. The drawings were made (by Maxine Sunderman) principally from posture pictures taken on bromide paper and they are not to be considered as anthropometrically correct. The proportions are sufficiently representative, however, to lend the drawings a certain value for the beginning student of somatotyping.

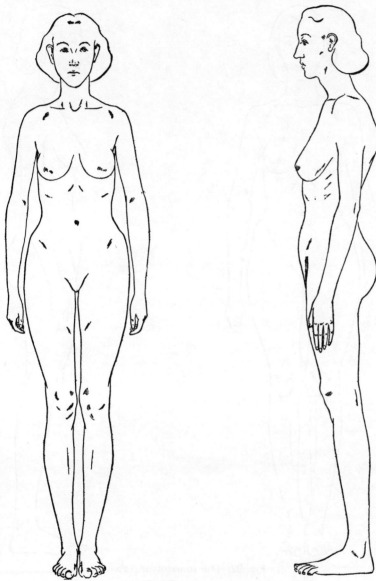

FIG. 91. The somatotype 117.

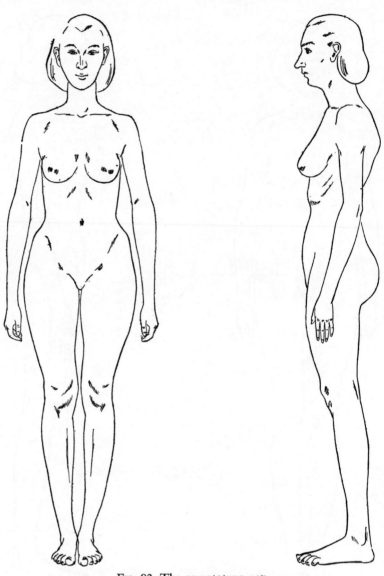

FIG. 92. The somatotype 127.

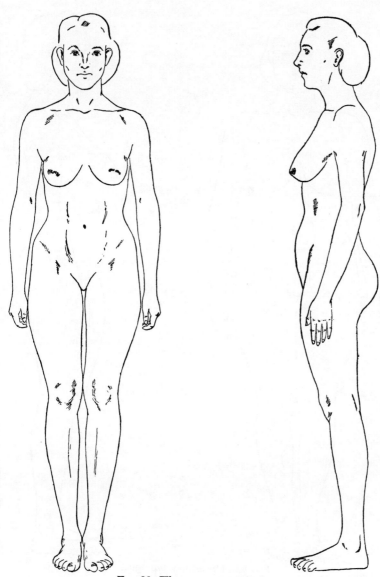

FIG. 93. The somatotype 136.

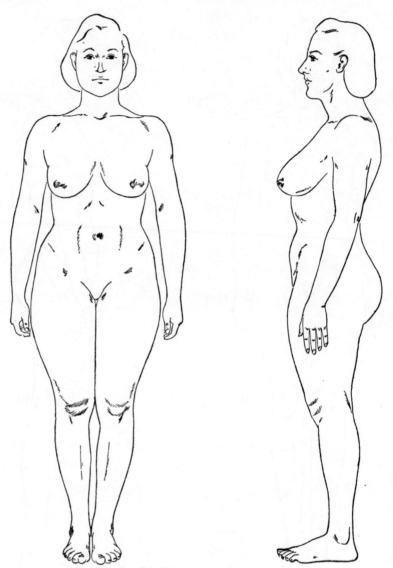

FIG. 94. The somatotype 362.

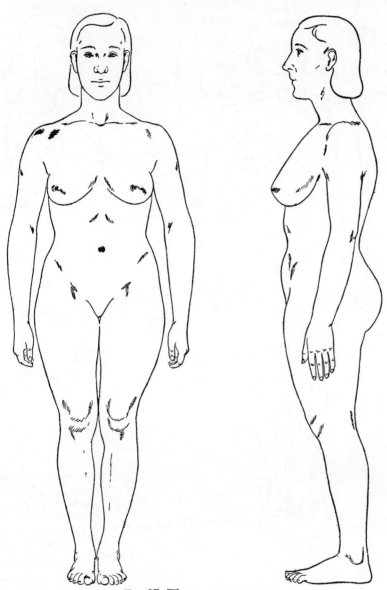

Fig. 95. The somatotype 172.

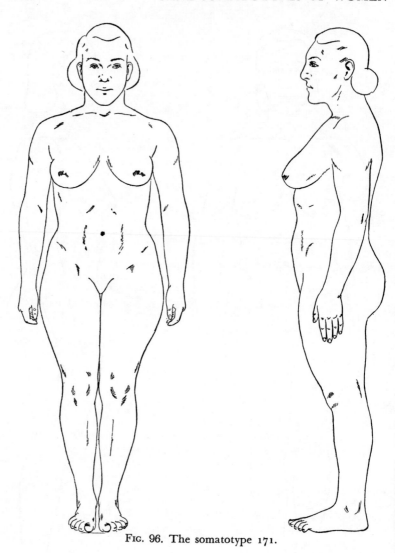

FIG. 96. The somatotype 171.

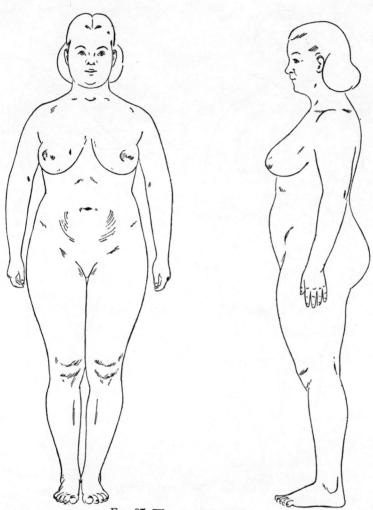

FIG. 97. The somatotype 632.

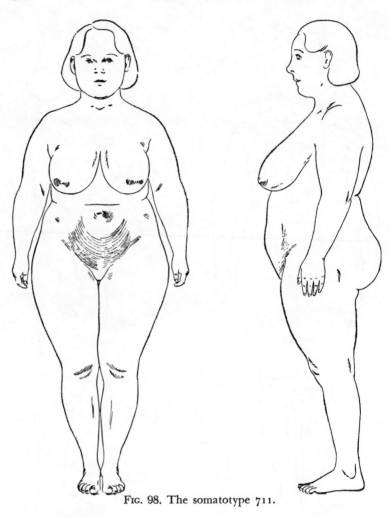

Fig. 98. The somatotype 711.

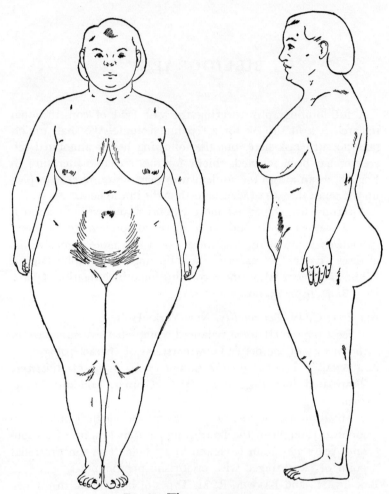

FIG. 99. The somatotype 731.

BIBLIOGRAPHY

A full bibliography covering the vast field of constitutional research is a fit subject for a separate volume. We shall undertake no such task here, but the following list of annotated references has been selected, chiefly for the available literature in English, as an aid to the student who may desire quickly to pick up the main threads of work and thought in the field.

A second list, somewhat more extensive and without annotation, is added as an aid to a more comprehensive or more specialized study of the literature. For a still more extensive list of titles we refer the reader to the following monograph: Tucker, W. B., and Lessa, W., Man: A constitutional investigation. *Quart. Rev. Biol.*, 1940, 15, nos. 3 and 4.

ALLPORT, G. W. *Personality*. New York: Holt, 1937.
See Chapter III for a balanced, comprehensive summary of the history of the better known systems of characterology.

AVICENNA. *A Treatise on the Canon of Medicine of Avicenna*. Translated into English by O. C. Gruner. London: Luzac, 1930.
An illuminating treatise portraying the medical and philosophical thought of the flourishing Saracen Empire of a thousand years ago. Man is viewed as a whole. The constitutional point of view, tinged with mysticism, predominates.

BAKWIN, H., and BAKWIN, R. M. Types of body build in infants. *Amer. J. Dis. Child.*, 1929, 37, 461-472.
In this important paper the authors have shown that the variant morphology of newly born infants is quite as sharply manifest, when precise measurements are taken, as is the case with adult morphology. The authors do not, however, carry out any classification beyond the conventional conceptions of "linear" and "lateral" types. The paper is effectively illustrated.

BARDEEN, C. R. The height, weight index of build in relation to

linear and volumetric proportion, etc. *Carnegie Inst. of Wash,
Contrib. to Embryology*, 1920, no. 46, 483-552.

This is a careful and classic study of the changes in height-weight ratio during various periods of life. Dr. Bardeen has included an excellent summary of the experimental literature on bodily build available in 1920.

BEAN, R. B. The two European types. *Amer. J. Anat.*, 1923, 31, 359.

Bean uses the terms "meso-onto-morph" and "hyper-onto-morph" to refer, respectively, to the massive, strong physiques and the light, linear physiques. He bases the differentiation mainly on the structure of the ear, but secondarily upon the nose, cranium, viscera, and other parts. A third type, the "hypo-onto-morphs," have long trunks and short extremities and retain infantile physiognomy.

BEAN, R. B. Morbidity and morphology. *Johns Hopk. Hosp. Bull.*, 1912, 23, 363.

In this paper Bean discusses the measurements of internal organs made in 100 autopsies of Filipinos. He found that "hyper-onto-morphs" had a short intestine (12 to 15 feet) while "meso-onto-morphs" had a long intestine (20 to 25 feet). He states that he has been able, from the bodily build, to predict the length of the intestine with great accuracy.

BENEKE, F. W. *Die anatomische Grundlagen der Konstitutionsanomalien des Menschen*. Marburg, 1878.

To Beneke belongs much of the credit for whatever may have been accomplished by modern constitutional studies. As a pathologist he made many patient and precise measurements both of internal organs and of external anatomy. His work paved the way directly for that of di Giovanni and Kretschmer, and possibly for the whole series of later constitutional studies.

BRYANT, J. The carnivorous and herbivorous types of man. *Boston Med. & Surg. J.*, 1914, 170, 795; 1915, 172, 321; 1915, 173, 384.

Bryant carried out extensive constitutional observations, using as his frame of reference a twofold classification. Following Goldthwait, he called his two types "herbivorous" and "carnivorous." The second of the three contributions listed contains a valuable table giving anatomical, physiological, chemical, and clinical characteristics of the two opposed types. The third contribution contains a highly suggestive anatomical explanation of the relative inconsequentiality of appendicitis (and other acute infections) in the carnivorous type.

BURCHARD, E. M. L. Physique and psychosis—an analysis of the postulated relationship between bodily constitution and mental disease syndrome. *Comp. Psychol. Monogr.*, 1936, 13, no. 61.

This is one of the best summaries of the constitutional problems raised by Kretschmer's work. Burchard discusses the pertinent literature and presents an unusually well-selected bibliography. He approaches Kretschmer's thesis both sympathetically and critically, applies the Kretschmerian technique to a series of 407 patients, and emerges with results roughly comparable to those of Kretschmer. His discussion of the strengths and weaknesses in the method and his suggestions for further research in the field are well to the point.

CABOT, P. S. deQ. The relationship between characteristics of personality and physique in adolescents. *Genetic Psychol. Monogr.*, 1938, vol. 20, no. 1.

This is a precise analysis of the relation of Kretschmer's criteria of bodily build to various psychological and temperamental traits, in a small group of school children. Cabot's results are on the whole negative. The criteria for bodily build were teachers' ratings in terms of Kretschmer's types.

CIOCCO, A. The historical background of the modern study of constitution. Johns Hopkins University: *Bull. Inst. Hist. Med.*, 1936, 4, 23-38.

Probably the most compact and carefully written modern summary of the constitutional field in general. This paper contains an excellently selected bibliography.

CONNOLLY, C. J. Physique in relation to psychosis. *Stud. Psychol. & Psychiat. Cathol. Univ. Amer.*, Washington. Monograph serial no. 5, vol. 4, 1939.

Father Connolly found that the so-called paranoid dementia praecox patients physically resemble manic-depressive patients more closely than they resemble patients suffering from other types of dementia praecox. This agrees with our own observations (see p. 240).

DAVENPORT, C. B. Body build, its development and inheritance. *Carnegie Institute of Washington,* Publication 329, 1923.

This is a report of what is probably the most extensive study of the heredity of physical pattern yet undertaken. Davenport considers bodily build in terms of a modified dichotomy of "fleshy" and "slender" types. He demonstrates, among other findings, that the offspring of fleshy parents are about twice as variable in bodily build as offspring of slender parents. The offspring of two slender parents show a fairly uniform tendency toward slenderness, those of fleshy parents are highly variable. Davenport concludes from his study that at least three independent hereditary factors influence bodily build.

DI GIOVANNI, A. *Clinical Commentaries Deduced from the Morphology of the Human Body.* Translated into English from the 2nd Italian edition by J. J. Eyre. London and New York, 1919.

Di Giovanni is sometimes called the father of modern constitutional research. His book contains many insights into the relation between physical traits and disease tendencies, but unfortunately there is no systematic classification of physical constitution. The work is centered chiefly around a loose dichotomy of types.

DRAPER, G. *Human Constitution: a Consideration of its Relationship to Disease.* Philadelphia and London: Saunders, 1924.

Draper and his associates carried out extensive anthropometric measurements on patients at the Presbyterian Hospital in New York, and found consistent differences between several specific disease groups. The most conspicuous of these differences were those between the peptic ulcer patients and the gallbladder patients. Through a period of more than twenty years, Draper has published numerous contributions bearing on relationships between physical constitution and immunity. His clinic has exerted a strong influence toward keeping constitutional work alive.

FEIGENBAUM, J., and HOWAT, D. The relation between physical constitution and the incidence of disease: the disease groups include peptic ulcer, cholecystitis and diabetes mellitus. *J. Clin. Invest.,* 1934, 13, 121-138.

These investigators attempted to verify Draper's observations concerning morphology within various disease groups. Their results were, on the whole, negative.

FREEMAN, W. Human constitution: a study of the correlations between physical aspects of the body and susceptibility to certain diseases. *Ann. Int. Med.*, 1934, 7, 805-811.

Dr. Freeman presents 1,260 autopsied cases classified according to the predominant pathology and according to (by subjective judgment) Kretschmer's scheme. The tables which are included suggest many leads and hypotheses as to the relation between disease susceptibility and bodily constitution.

GOLDTHWAIT, J. E. An anatomic and mechanistic conception of disease. *Boston Med. & Surg. J.*, 1915, 172, 881.

In the Shattuck lecture, delivered before the Massachusetts Medical Society at Boston in June, 1915, Dr. Goldthwait described two extreme human types which he and Dr. Bryant (see above) called the herbivorous and carnivorous types. The herbivorous type appears to be our extreme endomorph. The carnivorous type is less satisfactory as a type, and appears to be a mixture of ectomorphy with a greater or less increment of either endomorphy or mesomorphy, or both. Some interesting illustrations are included in this paper.

GORING, C. *The English Convict*. London: H. M. Stationery Office, 1913 (abridged edition, 1919).

In this famous study Goring took precise anthropometric measurements on a vast population of English convicts and demonstrated what he avowedly set out to demonstrate, namely, the statistical untenability of most of Lombroso's observations (see below). Goring dealt not with constitutional patterns but with isolated and for the most part unrelated anthropometric measurements. Yet this vast undertaking was carried out with such precision, and with such careful attention to detail, that it stands as a classic. Undoubtedly this study dealt a lethal blow to the advance of constitutional thought during the generation which has followed Goring, for it greatly discouraged the hope of using physical anthropology in social research.

GRAVES, W. W. The relations of scapular types to problems of human heredity, longevity, morbidity and adaptability in general. *Arch. Int. Med.*, 1924, 34, 1-26.

This is one of a series of papers by Dr. Graves on the interesting thesis that variation in the form of the scapula may be related both to general longevity and to certain characteristics of clinical immunity and temperament. He classified scapulae into three general types, convex, straight, and concave. The paper includes a good bibliography on the anatomy and function of the entire shoulder girdle.

HIPPOCRATES. *On Ancient Medicine: The Genuine Works of Hippocrates.* Translated into English by F. Adams. New York: Wm. Wood.

Recommended as an antidote to the supposition that all knowledge of the human constitution is new.

HOOTON, E. A. *Up from the Ape.* New York: Macmillan, 1931.

A standard text in physical anthropology, with emphasis upon techniques for differentiation among "racially" varying groups.

HOOTON, E. A. *Crime and the Man.* Cambridge: Harvard University Press, 1939.

A summary of the findings in a recent extensive study of the physical anthropology of American convicts. The fundamental difference between the Goring study and the Hooton study lies in the handling of the data. Hooton, using only height-and-weight criteria, and without photographs, broke up his material into subgroups which correspond in a rough way with somatotypes. Handled in this manner, his data show statistically valid relations between criminal tendency and bodily make-up.

HOSKINS, R. G. *The Tides of Life.* New York: Norton, 1933.

Probably the completest available summary of what is actually known about the endocrine glands. The problem of the relation of the endocrine secretions to constitution presents difficult complications.

KLINEBERG, O., ASCH, S. E., and BLOCK, H. An experimental study of constitutional types. *Genetic Psychol. Monogr.,* 1934, 16, 145-221.

These investigators, working at Columbia University, attempted to correlate Kretschmerian ratings of type with various mental tests and tests of temperament. Their results are on the whole negative. Only extremely low correlations were found. The report contains a critical evaluation of the work

of the "modern Kretschmerian school" in Germany, and a good
selected bibliography of this German research.

KRETSCHMER, E. *Körperbau und Charakter.* Berlin: Springer,
1921. Translated from the second German edition into English as *Physique and Character*, by W. J. H. Sprott. London:
Kegan Paul, Trench, Trubner, 1925.

The best known and most widely quoted contribution, during the present generation, in the entire field of constitutional
thought. Kretschmer revived the earlier French emphasis (Rostan) upon the necessity of approaching constitution from the
point of view of at least three, rather than two, basic types.
These three types (pyknic, athletic, and asthenic) are brilliantly
described, but the objective data for discrimination between
the types are perfunctory and inadequate.

LAYCOCK, T. Physiognomical diagnosis. *Med. Times & Gazette,*
1862, 1, 1.

A pleasing and instructive treatment of this fascinating subject. The nineteenth century physiognomists employed a
system of observation which, had it been supported by an objective method of physical classification, might have opened the
way to a vast treasure house of medical knowledge. This is a
treasure house which we still have not stormed.

LOMBROSO, CÉSARE. *Crime, Its Causes and Remedies.* Translated
by Horton. Boston, 1911.

Lombroso stands as a man of great genius in the field of
constitutional inquiry. He never developed an objective system
of physical classification, but, considering that he worked
without such a system, the scope and penetration of his insights were gigantic. It is not a good plan to *begin* the study
of this field with the works of Lombroso, for Lombroso presents a confusingly rich welter of fact, speculation, and intuition. He collected a vast hoard of the suppositions and
observations dominant in the best minds of his own and past
generations. To this he added many nuggets from his own
extremely active and gifted mind. From youth he trained himself to watch and to study men. His work will perhaps provide
leads and hypotheses for many generations of investigators
yet to be born. The principal theoretical conception for which
he is known is perhaps a somewhat unfortunate one. Having

noted certain anatomical abnormalities or "stigmata" in criminals—abnormalities normally found in various genera of the lower animals—Lombroso felt that criminality was to be explained in terms of "throwbacks" in the evolutionary cycle.

LUCAS, W. P., and PRYOR, H. B. The body build factor in the basal metabolism of children. *Amer. J. Dis. Child.*, part 1, 1933, 46, 941-948.

This paper presents a study of the relations of basal metabolism to physical constitution. In a sufficient series of normal children (573 cases) these investigators found a marked statistical relation between high basal metabolic rate and linearity of bodily build. The "lateral" or wide and heavy children showed, as a group, low metabolic rates.

McCLOY, C. H. Appraising physical status and the selection of measurements. *Univ. Ia. Stud. Child Welf.*, 1936, vol. 12, no. 2.

A comprehensive treatment of the general problem of physical constitution, mainly from the point of view of anthropometry done on the living subject. McCloy and his associates have attempted to establish a purely anthropometric technique for the measurement and prediction of bodily build. This is possibly the most careful and complete series of studies of its kind.

MANOUVRIER, L. Etude sur les rapports anthropométriques en général et sur les principales proportions du corps. *Mém. de la Soc. d'Anth. de Paris*, Ser. 3, T. 2, 1902.

Manouvrier classified mankind physically into two broad types: the *Brachyskèles*, or broad skeletons, and the *Macroskèles*, or long (large) skeletons.

MILLER, E. *Types of Mind and Body.* New York: Norton, 1927.

A popularly written little book presenting the principal generalizations and suppositions drawn by Kretschmer and his followers. An excellent introduction for a nonacademic reader.

MOHR, G. J., and GUNDLACH, R. H. The relation between physique and performance. *J. exp. Psychol.*, 1927, 10, 117-157.

These investigators studied a group of 89 Illinois convicts in an attempt to evaluate the Kretschmerian hypothesis. They found fairly clear-cut relations between physical type and performance on several mental tests and tests of temperament.

NACCARATI, S. The morphologic aspect of intelligence. *Arch. Psychol.*, 1921, no. 45.

Naccarati was a brilliant exponent of the Italian school of clinical anthropology (see di Giovanni, Viola, Pende). In this monograph, Naccarati sets forth the principal postulates of his school of thought, with a good summary of the argument. He approached the problem of constitution in terms of a dichotomy of types, with "microsplanchny" and "macrosplanchny" as the two polar opposites. He here reports a product-moment correlation of $+0.36$ between microsplanchny and intelligence test scores, using as subjects a group of 75 Columbia University students.

PATERSON, D. G. *Physique and Intellect.* Century Psychology Series. New York: Century, 1930.

This is a careful, critical summary of the scientific literature available in 1929 on the general problem of relationship between physical and mental traits. Paterson arrives at a pessimistic conclusion concerning the fruitfulness of most of the work done in the field.

PEARL, R. *Constitution and Health.* London: Kegan Paul, Trench, Trubner, 1933.

A trenchant, cautiously written survey of some of the facts and operations pertaining particularly to the medical side of the constitutional problem. Pearl has long been a leader among the American investigators in this field.

PEARSON, K. Relationship of intelligence to size and shape of the head and other mental and physical characters. *Biometrika,* 1906, 5, 105-146.

Pearson is the man who contributed most directly to establishing the coefficient of correlation as a common tool in psychological research. In the study reported here he did not find any significantly positive correlations. This study provides a classic example of the fruitlessness of using isolated anthropometric measurements as physical criteria.

PENDE, N. *Constitutional Inadequacies.* Translated into English from the Italian by S. Naccarati. Philadelphia: Lea & Febiger, 1928.

Pende's work should be read in connection with that of di Giovanni, Viola, and Naccarati. These four men together are known to American students as "the Italian school" of clinical anthropology. As a group they have played a great role in keeping constitutional research alive. Pende's book contains a clear and highly readable exposition of the point of view.

PETERSEN, W. F. Constitution and disease. *Physiol. Rev.,* 1932, 12, 283-308.

A theoretical discussion of the problem of constitution with particular reference to such obscure matters as physiological chemistry and heredity. This little treatise provides a good antidote for oversimplification in a highly perplexing field.

SCHULTZ, A. Fetal growth of man and other primates. *Quart. Rev. Biol.,* 1926, 1, 465.

Schultz, in a compactly presented study, shows that many of the individualizing characteristics of the human body appear early in fetal life. Individuality of the facial features, variations of shape of the head, and bodily asymmetries are in some cases even more marked in the fetus than in adults.

SHELDON, W. H. Morphological types and mental ability. *J. Person. Res.,* 1927, 5, 447-451. Social traits and morphological types. *Person. J.,* 1927, vol. 6, no. 1. Ability and facial measurements. *Person. J.,* 1927, vol. 6, no. 2.

Viola's morphological index was calculated for each of 450 college students. These indices were correlated with various criteria of mental ability and temperament. Many low correlations, but no high ones, were found. A method was developed for taking precise facial measurements from photographs. These measurements likewise showed low correlations, but no high ones, with tests of mental ability and of temperament.

SOMMERVILLE, R. C. Physical, motor and sensory traits. *Arch. Psychol.,* 1924, 12, 1-108.

An exhaustive summary of much of the literature available in 1924 on the problem of the interrelationships between physical traits and other characteristics.

STEVENSON, P. H., SUNG, S. M., PAI, T., and LYMAN, R. S. Chinese constitutional differentiation and Kretschmerian typology. *Hum. Biol.,* 1937, 9, 451-481.

This is the report of an unusually well-planned effort to apply the Kretschmerian classification to an extensive series of Chinese patients. The authors find, among other things, that Chinese men are more "leptosomic" than are Kretschmer's

Swabians, and that the problem of defining "pyknic" is an extremely difficult one.

STOCKARD, C. R. *The Physical Basis of Personality.* New York: Norton, 1931.

Stockard discusses the interesting question of physical resemblances between different types of human beings and other forms of animal life. His comparisons of men with different representatives of the dog tribe have been widely quoted.

STOCKARD, C. R. Human types and growth relations. *Amer. J. Anat.*, 1923, 31, 261.

This paper contains a highly suggestive speculative discussion as to *why* people of the "linear" type have a higher rate of metabolism than do people of the "lateral" type. (See Lucas and Pryor, above.)

VOLLMER, H. The shape of the ear in relation to body constitution. *Arch. Pediat.*, 1937, 54, 574-590.

A highly stimulating and well-illustrated paper describing variations of the form of the external ear in growing children. This subject is one of considerable interest to the student of constitutional problems, for the ear, constructed as it is in large part of a relatively stable tissue (cartilage), is perhaps less modified by the individual's life experience than many of the other external bodily features.

WERTHEIMER, F. I., and HESKETH, F. E. The significance of the physical constitution in mental disease. *Med. Monogr.*, vol. 10. Baltimore: Williams & Wilkins, 1926.

This brilliant monograph contains one of the best known and most complete of the available summaries of the constitutional problem. We recommend to the student who is seriously interested that he read this monograph early in his studies.

Wertheimer and Hesketh devised a somewhat shortened method of calculating what is really Viola's morphological index. They used this index in an attempt to objectify Kretschmer's types. Even with so crude a tool they found fairly good substantiation of the general thesis that schizoid patients tend to be asthenic (microsplanchnic), while manic-depressive patients tend to have more massive physiques.

FURTHER REFERENCES

ADDISON, T. *Collection of the Published Writings.* London, 1868.

ARISTOTLE (?). *Physiognomonica.* Translated into English by T. Loveday and E. L. Forster: *The Works of Aristotle.* Oxford: Clarendon Press, 1913. Chapter I.

BARTELS, V. Gymnastics and dietary regime for the pyknic type. *Fortschr. Med.,* 1934, 52, 963-964.

BAUER, J. *Vorlesungen über allegemeine Konstitutions-Vererbungslehre.* Berlin: Springer, 1923.

BENEDETTI, P. Das Problem der Disposition zur Krebskrankheit. *Z. Konstitutionslehre,* 1931, 16, 261-291.

BENEKE, F. W. *Konstitution und konstitutionelles Kranksein des Menschen.* Marburg, 1881.

BLEULER, E. Körperliche und geistige Konstitutionen. *Naturwissenschaften,* 1921, 9, 753.

BLUNT, K., NELSON, A., and OLESON, H. C. The basal metabolism of underweight children. *J. Biol. Chem.,* 1921, 49, 247.

BORCHARDT, L. *Klinische Konstitutionslehre.* Berlin u. Wien: Urban and Schwarzenberg, 1924.

BORCHARDT, L. Funktionelle und trophische Momente als Ursachen des gegensatzlichen Verhältens von Pyknikern und Asthenikern. *Z. Konstitutionslehre,* 1931, 16, 1.

BRANDT, W. Die biologischen Unterschiede des Pyknikers und des Leptosomen. *Dtsch. med. Wschr.,* 1936, 62, 501-502.

BRUGSCH, T. Die Morphologie der Person. *In* BRUGSCH, T., and LEWY, F. H., *Die Biologie der Person.* Berlin u. Wien: Urban und Schwarzenberg, 1926-1931, 1931, 2, 1-114.

BRYANT, J. Stasis and human efficiency. *Int. Abstr. Surgery,* May, 1914, 449.

CAMPBELL, J. K. The relation of the types of physique to the types of mental diseases. *J. abnorm. (soc.) Psychol.,* 1932, 27, 147-151.

CAROLI, J., and CORMAN, L. La constitution morphologique des ulcéreux. *Arch. d. mal. de l'app. digestif*, 1935, 25, 26-56.

CELSUS, A. C. *On Medicine*. London: E. Cox, 1831. Vol. 1.

CIOCCO, A. Hearing acuity and middle ear infections in constitutional types. *Acta oto-laryng.*, 1933, 18, 365-380.

DAVENPORT, C. B. The height-weight index of build. *Amer. J. phys. Anthrop.*, 1920, 3, 467-475.

DAVENPORT, C. B., and LOVE, A. G. *Army Anthropology*. Medical Department of the United States Army in the World War. Washington, 1921.

DRAPER, G. *Disease and the Man*. London: Kegan Paul, Trench, Trubner, 1930.

DRAPER, G. Man as a complete organism, in health and disease. *New York State J. Med.*, 1934, 34, 1052-1063.

DRAPER, G., BRUENN, H. G., and DUPERTUIS, C. W. Changes in the electrocardiogram as criteria of individual constitution as derived from its physiological panel. *Amer. J. Med. Sci.*, 1937, 194, 514-523.

ENKE, W. The affectivity of Kretschmer's constitutional types as revealed in psycho-galvanic experiments. *Character & Pers.*, 1933, 1, 225-233.

FARR, C. B. Bodily structure, personality and reaction types. *Amer. J. Psychiat.*, 1927-1928, 7, 231-244.

FEIGENBAUM, J., and HOWAT, D. Physical constitution and disease: II. Absence of correlation between the anatomic constitution and predisposition to diabetes mellitus, cholecystitis and peptic ulcer. *Arch. Int. Med.*, 1935, 55, 445-456.

FLEMMING, G. B., and HUTCHINSON, H. S. A study of metabolism in the undernourished infant. *Quart. J. Med.*, 1921, 14, 171.

FREEMAN, W. Psychological panel in diagnosis and prognosis; correlation of personality type with susceptibility to disease, based on 1400 necropsies. *Ann. Int. Med.*, 1930, IV, pp. 29-38.

GALENUS. *De Temperamentis*. Reproduced in facsimile. Cambridge, Macmillan and Bowers, 1881.

GALL, F. J., and SPURZHEIM, J. G. *Recherches sur le Système nerveux*. Paris, 1809.

GARRETT, H. E., and KELLOGG, W. N. The relation of physical constitution to general intelligence, social intelligence and emotional stability. *J. exp. Psychol.*, 1928, 11, 113-129.

GARROD, A. E. *The Inborn Factors in Disease*. Oxford: Clarendon Press, 1931.

GILDEA, E. F., KAHN, E., and MAN, E. B. The relationship between body build and serum lipoids and a discussion of these qualities as pyknophilic and leptophilic factors in the structure of the personality. *Amer. J. Psychiat.*, 1936, 92, 1247-1260.

GRAVES, W. W. The clinical recognition of the scaphoid type of scapula and some of its correlations. *J. Amer. Med. Asso.*, July 2, 1910, p. 12.

GRAVES, W. W. The age-incidence principle of investigation in evaluating the biological significance of inherited variations in the problems of human constitution. *Amer. J. Psychiat.*, 1937, 93, 1109-1117.

GREULICH, W. W., and THOMS, H. Pelvic type and its relationship to body build in white women. *J. Amer. Med. Asso.*, 1939, 112, 485-493.

HACKEL, W. Pathologisch-anatomische und anthropometrische Studien über Konstitution. *Z. Konstitutionslehre*, 1932, 16, 63-80.

HÄCKER, V. Neuere wege der menschlichen Erblichkeitsforschung. *Med. Klinik*, 1922, 18, 1218.

HARRIS, J. A. The measurement of man in the mass. In HARRIS, J. A., JACKSON, C. M., PATERSON, D. G., and SCAMMON, R. E. *The Measurement of Man*. Minneapolis: University of Minnesota Press, 1930.

HAUCHMANN, S. Indices als Bestimmer des Konstitutionstypus. *Z. Konstitutionslehre*, 1929, 14, 679-693.

HEIDBREDER, E. Intelligence and the height-weight ratio. *J. appl. Psychol.*, 1926, 10, 52-62.

HENCKEL, K. O. Konstitutionstypen und europäische Rassen. *Klin. Wschr.*, 1925, 4, 2145.

HESS, A. F., and BLACKBERG, S. N. Constitutional factors in the etiology of rickets. *Amer. J. Physiol.*, 1932, 102, 8.

HIRSCH, I. S., and SHAPIRO, L. L. The morphology of the heart in relation to habitus, and a new method of estimating morphological changes. *Amer. J. Med. Sci.*, 1921, 162, 892.

HOOTON, E. A. *Apes, Men, and Morons*. New York: Putnam, 1937.

HOUGHTON, H. A. The hyposthenic constitution as a hazard of anesthesia. *Anesth. & Analg.*, 1936, 15, 47-52.

HRDLICKA, A. Physiological and medical observations among Indians of southwestern United States and northern Mexico. *Bur. Amer. Ethnol. Bull.*, 34, 1908.

HUNTER, J. *The Works of John Hunter, with Notes.* Edited by J. F. Palmer. London: 1835. Vol. 1.

HUTCHINSON, J. *The Pedigree of Disease.* London: Churchill, 1884.

JACKSON, C. M. Normal and abnormal types. *In* HARRIS, J. A., JACKSON, C. M., PATERSON, D. G., and SCAMMON, R. E. *The Measurement of Man.* Minneapolis: University of Minnesota Press, 1930.

JAENSCH, E. *Eidetic Imagery and Typological Methods of Investigation.* Translated by Oscar Oeser. London: Kegan Paul, 1930.

JAENSCH, WALTHER. *Grundzüge einer Physiologie und Klinik der psychophysischen Persönlichkeit.* Berlin: Springer, 1926.

KAHN, E. *Psychopathic Personalities.* New Haven: Yale University Press, 1932.

KRASUSKY, W. S. Kretschmer's konstitutionelle Typen unter den Kindern im Schulalter. *Arch. Kind.*, 1927, 82-83, 22-32.

KRETSCHMER, E., and ENKE, W. *Die Persönlichkeit der Athletiker.* Leipzig: Georg Thieme, 1936.

KROGMAN, W. M. The inheritance of non-pathological physical traits in man. *Eugen. News*, 1936, 21, 139-146.

KROH, O. Experimentelle Beitrage zur Typen. *Z. Psychol.*, 1929, 14, 1-300.

LAVATER, J. C. *Essays on Physiognomy: for the Promotion of the Knowledge and the Love of Mankind.* Translated into English by Thomas Holcroft. (2 ed., 4 vols.) London: Whittingham, 1804.

LAZAROWITZ, L. Die Rolle der Konstitution bei der Entwicklung der spätleutischen Veränderungen, in erster Reihe der Aortitis. *Wien. Klin. Wschr.*, 1932, 45, 1583-1589.

LEDERER, R. Konstitutionspathologie in den medizinischen Spezialwissenschaften. Berlin: Springer, 1924. Vol. I.

LEWIS, N. D. C. The constitutional factors in dementia praecox. *Nerv. ment. Dis. Monogr.*, 1924, 39.

LITTLE, C. C. *Civilization Against Cancer.* New York: Farrar & Rinehart, 1939.

LOEB, L. Heredity and Internal Secretion in the Etiology of

Cancer. *Communication to the International Cancer Conference in London,* July, 1928.

LOMBROSO, C. *L'Uomo Deliquente.* (4th ed.) Torina: Flli. Bocca, 1889.

LOMBROSO, C. *The Man of Genius.* New York: Scribner's, 1891.

LOMBROSO, G. (daughter of Césare Lombroso) *Criminal Man According to the Classification of Césare Lombroso.* New York, 1911.

LUCAS, W. P., and PRYOR, HELEN B. Physical measurements and physiological processes in young children. *J. Amer. Med. Ass.,* 1931, 97, 1127.

MACAULIFFE, L. Les origines de la morphologie humaine. *Bull. Soc. d'Etude des Formes Humaines,* 1925, nos. 2 and 3, 155.

MEYER, A. An attempt at analysis of the neurotic constitution. *Amer. J. Psychol.,* 1903, 14, 90 ff.

MILLS, R. W. The relation of body habitus to visceral form, position, tonus and motility. *Amer. J. Roentgenol.,* 1917, 4, 155.

MONTESSORI, MARIA. *Pedagogical Anthropology.* Translated from the Italian by Cooper. New York: Stokes, 1913.

MUNZ, E. Die Reaktion des Pyknikers im Rohrschach'schen psychodiagnostichen Versuch. *Z. ges. Neurol. Psychiat.,* 1924, 91, 26-92.

NACCARATI, S. The morphologic basis of the psychoneuroses. *Amer. J. Psychiat.,* 1924, 3, 527-545.

NACCARATI, S., and GARRETT, H. E. The relation of morphology to temperament. *J. abnorm. (soc.) Psychol.,* 1924, 19, no. 3.

NEWMAN, H. H., and OTHERS. *Twins: a Study of Heredity and Environment.* Chicago: University of Chicago Press, 1937.

PATERSON, D. G. Personality and physique. *In* HARRIS, J. A., JACKSON, C. M., PATERSON, D. G., and SCAMMON, R. E. *The Measurement of Man.* Minneapolis: University of Minnesota Press, 1930.

PEARL, R. The relative influence of the constitutional factor in the etiology of tuberculosis. *Amer. Rev. Tuberc.,* 1920, 4, 688-712.

PEARL, R., and CIOCCO, A. Studies on constitution: II. Somatological differences associated with diseases of the heart in white males. *Hum. Biol.,* 1934, 6, 650-713.

PEARL, R., and PEARL, R. D. Studies on human longevity: VI. The distribution and correlation of variation in the total immediate ancestral longevity of nonagenarians and centenarians in relation to the inheritance factor in duration of life. *Hum. Biol.*, 1934, 6, 98-222.

PEARL, R., SUTTON, A. C., HOWARD, W. T., JR., and RIOCH, M. Studies on constitution: I. *Hum. Biol.*, 1929, 1, 10-56.

PIGNET. Du coefficient de robusticité. *Bull. médicale*, 1901, 15 ann., 373-376.

PLATTNER, W. Metrische Körperbaudiagnostik. *Z. ges. Neurol. Psychiat.*, 1934, 151, 374-404.

RIPPY, E. L. Physical types and their relation to disease. *Dallas Med. J.*, 1936, 22, 112-115.

ROSTAN, L. *Cours élémentaire d'hygiène.* (2nd ed., 2 vols.) Paris, 1828.

RUHMANN, W. *Der Ulcuskranke: Studien zur Konstitution und Symptomatik am gesamten Status bei chronischen Ulcus pepticum mit besonderer Berücksichtigung des vegetativen Nervensystems.* Berlin: S. Karger, 1926.

SALTYKOW, S. Tuberkulose und Konstitution. *Verhandl. dtsch. path. Gesellsch.*, 1929, 24, 133.

SCAMMON, R. E. The measurement of the body in childhood. *In* HARRIS, J. A., JACKSON, C. M., PATERSON, D. G., and SCAMMON, R. E. *The Measurement of Man.* Minneapolis: University of Minnesota Press, 1930.

SHAW, F. C. A morphologic study of the functional psychoses. *State Hosp. Quart.*, 1924-25, 10, 413-421.

SIGAUD, C. *La Forme Humaine.* Paris: A. Maloine, 1914.

SLYE, M. Cancer and heredity. *Ann. Int. Med.*, 1927, 1, 951.

SNYDER, L. H. Human blood groups: their inheritance and racial significance. *Amer. J. phys. Anthrop.*, 1926, 9, 233-263, no. 2.

SPIGELIUS, ADRIANUS. *Opera—Omnia Quae Extant.* Amsterdam, 1645.

SPURZHEIM, J. G. *Phrenology in Connexion with the Study of Physiognomy.* Boston: March, Capen & Lyon, 1833.

STERN-PIPER, L. Kretschmer's psycho-physische Typen und die Rassenformen in Deutschland. *Arch. Psychiat.*, 1923, 67, 569.

STERN-PIPER, L. Konstitution und Rasse. *Z. ges. Neurol. Psychiat.*, 1923, 86-265.

STILLER, B. *Die asthenische Konstitutionskrankheit.* Stuttgart: F. Enke, 1907.

SWAIM, L. T. Thirty-nine cases as regards intestinal length and nutrition. *Boston Med. and Surg. J.,* Aug. 22, 1912.

TODD, T. W. *Behaviour Patterns of the Alimentary Tract.* Beaumont Foundation Lectures, Series no. 9. Baltimore: Williams & Wilkins Co., 1930.

TOPPER, A., and MULIER, H. Basal metabolism of children of abnormal weight: underweight children. *Amer. J. Dis. Child.,* 1929, 38, 299.

TOURAINE, G. A., and DRAPER, G. The migrainous patient—a constitutional study. *J. nerv. ment. Dis.,* 1934, 80, 1 (July), 183 (August).

VIOLA, G. L'habitus phthisicus et l'habitus apoplecticus comme conséquence d'une loi qui déforme normalement le type moyen de la race en ces deux types antithétiques. *Comptes rendus de l'Assoc. des anatomistes.* Vingtième réunion (Turin 6-8 avril, 1925). Pp. (of reprint) 33, 1925.

VIOLA, G. *La costituzione individuale.* Bologna: L. Cappelli, 1933.

VIOLA, G. Il mio metodo di valutazione della costituzione individuale. *Riforma med.,* 1935 (Oct. 26), 51, 1635-1638 (no. 43).

VON ROHDEN, F. Konstitutionelle Körperbau-Untersuchungen an Gesunden und Kranken. *Arch. Psychiat.,* 1927, 79, 786-815.

WARSTADT, A., and COLLIER, W. A. Ueber den angeblichen Zusammenhang von Schizophrenie und Tuberkulose. *Allg. Z. Psychiat.,* 1935, 103, 355-365.

WEIDENREICH, F. *Rasse und Körperbau.* Berlin: Springer, 1926.

WEISMAN, S. A. *Your Chest Should Be Flat.* With a foreword by R. E. Scammon, Philadelphia: Lippincott, 1938.

WELLS, S. R. *How to Read Character.* New York: Fowler and Wells, 1869.

WERTHEIMER, F. I., and HESKETH, F. E. A historical review. *Medicine,* 1926, 5, 375-461.

WERTHEIMER, F. I., and HESKETH, F. E. A minimum scheme for the study of the morphologic constitution in psychiatry, with remarks on anthropometric technique. *Arch. Neurol. Psychiat.,* 1925, 17, 93-98.

WERTHEM, F. Progress in psychiatry: IV. Experimental type psychology. *Arch. Neurol. Psychiat.*, 1930, 24, 605-611.

WESTPHAL, K. The use of indices as an auxiliary method in the establishment of physical types. *Hum. Biol.*, 1931, 3, 420-428.

WHEELER, W. M. Physiognomy of insects. *Quart. Rev. Biol.*, 1927, 2, 1.

ZWEIG, H. Habitus und lebensalter. *Z. ges. Anatomie*, 1919, 4, 255.

INDEX

Adaptability, as criterion of intelligence, 229; to conflict, 233.
Adult influence on development of child, 253.
Advertising, use of somatotypre in, 158.
Age levels, standards for, 209.
Age of parent, effect on child, 221.
Alexander, Franz, 246.
Allport, Gordon W., 3.
Aristotle, 110.
Aschner, 22.
Attraction of opposites, in mating, 244.
Bauer, Julius, 22.
Bean, R. B., 22, 33, 34.
Beneke, F. W., 13.
Brugsch, 22.
Bryant, J., 22, 33, 294.
Calvin, 144.
Cancer, 238-239.
Cerebrotonic temperament, described, 228.
Components. The primary morphological components, endomorphy-mesomorphy-ectomorphy, defined, 5.
Concave man, 225.
Constitution, defined, 1.
Constitutional factors in mating, 252.
Continuous distribution of the primary components, 25.
Convex man, 226.
Dangers in typological concepts, 24.
Darwin, 12.
Davenport, Charles, 22, 219.
Davis, H. 124.
Di Giovanni, A., 12, 22.
Draper, G., 22, 237.
Dress requirements, related to constitution, 241.

Dupertuis, C. W., 71, 78, 238.
Dysplasia, defined, 7.
Ectomorphy, defined, 5.
Embryonic layers, related to the primary components, 5-6, 34-35.
Endomorphy, defined, 5.
Eunuchoid types of Kretschmer, 231.
Food, differential requirements, 240.
Freud, 232-233.
Furniture preferences, related to constitution, 241-244.
Gall, F. J. 11.
Genetic factors in the determination of body build, 219.
Goldthwait, J. E., 22, 33, 291.
Goring, C., 294-295.
Gynandromorphy, defined, 7.
Gynandropsychic incompatibility, 234.
Herbivorous constitution, 33-34, 291.
Hercules, 199.
Hesketh, F. E., 27.
Hippocrates, 10, 21, 140.
Hoskins, R. G., 223.
Huter, 22.
Huxley, J., 12.
Intestinal length and weight, constitutional variation in, 32-34.
Jung, Carl, 233, 242, 249.
Jung's theory of regression, 233.
Kraepelin, 20.
Kretschmer, E., 11, 20-27, 51, 79, 230-235, 275-276, 296.
Li'l Abner, 182.
Lombroso, 294.
Longevity, 149, 294-295.
MacAuliffe, 22.
McCloy, C. H., 258.
Machine for somatotyping, 104.
Manouvrier, 22.
Mating, constitutional factors in, 244.
Mesomorphy, defined, 5.
Mills, 22.
Morphology and temperament, 229; and character, 109; as related to medicine, 211; in relation to personality, 2-3, 227, 234.

Naccarati, S., 14-23, 28, 235, 297.
Näcke, 239.
Nicotine, reaction to, 190.
Nomograph, for height-weight relationship, 279.
Opposites, attraction of, in mating, 244.
Osler, Sir William, 235.
Paterson, D. G., 20, 24.
Pende, N., 22, 23, 298.
Permanence of the somatotype, 213-218.
Personality, defined, 2; relationship to the physical constitution, 226-230, 244.
Photographic technique, standardization of, 30.
Phthisic habitus, 10, 13, 22.
Poliomyelitis, susceptibility to, 212, 237.
PPJ (pyknic practical joke), defined, 191.
Primary racial variation, 210.
Psychological and morphological attributes, scales for measurement of, 113-126.
Psychoses and morphology, 20-27.
Psychotic temperament, 27.
Pyknic, meaning of, 191.
Racial classification, problems of, 211.
Rokitansky, 22.
Rostan, L., 22.
Scales, basic types of, 114-116.
Schizophrenia and the overt physical constitution, 25-27.
Second order variables, 7, 67-79.
Sigaud, 22-23.
Smoking, 190.
Somatotonic temperament described, 8, 228.
Spencer, Herbert, 12.
Spurzheim, J. G., 11.
Stevens, S. S., 113-114, 124.
Stockard, Charles R., 22.
Stratz, 22.
"Superman", 182.
Swaim, L. T., 33-34.
Tables for somatotyping, 257-278.
Tarzan, 182.

Temperament, correlated with morphology, 229.
Texture, defined 7.
t-Index, 76-77.
Tucker, W. B., 10, 101-102, 290.
Types, concept of, 27-28.
Types of scales, basic, 114-116.
Viola, G., 13-27, 223, 229.
Virenius, 22.
Viscerotonic temperament described, 32-35, 228.
Volkmann, J., 114.
Walker, 22.
Weidenreich, 22-23.
Wells, S. R., 11-12, 22.
Wertheimer, F. I., 27.
Women, somatotyping of, 66-67, 280-289.